Rev of 1st printing by Leblanc
in JSL XIX 282-4
Rev G.B Keene   Mind Vol LXIV No 254 (1955)
pp 275-6

KT-583-836

GBBHunter

AIR 198

SYMBOLIC LOGIC

THE MACMILLAN COMPANY
NEW YORK · CHICAGO
DALLAS · ATLANTA · SAN FRANCISCO
LONDON · MANILA

IN CANADA
BRETT-MACMILLAN LTD.
GALT, ONTARIO

SYMBOLIC LOGIC

IRVING M. COPI

Professor of Philosophy
University of Michigan

THE MACMILLAN COMPANY, New York

For Amelia

Preface

This book has been written to serve as a first textbook of symbolic logic for undergraduate and graduate students. It presupposes no earlier training in either classical or modern logic. The topics covered in this book are those studied in the author's two-semester course in symbolic logic at the University of Michigan. In this book, as in my teaching, I have attempted to combine two distinct approaches to the subject.

Logic was discussed by its ancient founder, Aristotle, from two quite different points of view. On the one hand, he regarded logic as an instrument or organon for appraising the correctness of reasoning; and on the other, he saw the principles and methods of logic as interesting and important topics to be themselves investigated more or less systematically. Modern symbolic logic can also be viewed from the same two perspectives. Through the development of its special symbols logic has become an immeasurably more powerful instrument for analysis and deduction. And the principles and methods of symbolic logic can be very fruitfully investigated in their own right through the construction and examination of *logistic systems*. The present book combines these two approaches to the study of symbolic logic.

The first half of the book, comprising Chapters One through Five, presents the standard notations, methods, and principles of symbolic logic for *use* in determining the validity or invalidity of arguments. It takes up successively more complex modes of argumentation: beginning with those which involve truth-functionally compound statements, it goes on to arguments containing singly general and then multiply general propositions, and finally relational arguments. The standard methods of truth tables, of Boolean Expansions, and the method of deduction are introduced, the latter including both conditional and *reductio ad absurdum* proofs. Next propositional functions and quantifiers are introduced, with 'natural deduction' rules for working with them. The logic of relations is developed in a separate chapter, which includes a discussion of identity theory and definite descriptions. A great many exercises are provided to help the student acquire a practical mastery of the material.

The second half of the book contains a more systematic treatment of the logical principles *used* in the first half. After a brief discussion of deductive systems in general, a propositional calculus is developed according to the highest modern standards of rigor, and proved to be consistent and complete. Alternative notations and axiom systems for the propositional calculus are discussed, and then a first order function calculus is developed. The latter is shown to be equivalent to the 'natural deduction' methods presented in the first half of the book, and is proved to be consistent and complete.

There are two appendices, the first dealing with the algebra of classes, the second with the ramified theory of logical types.

In the first part of the book an attempt is made to achieve maximum clarity by introducing the special symbols in as natural and intuitive a way as possible. Thus the discussion of the horseshoe symbol ($\supset$) for material implication is intended to minimize the arbitrariness and artificiality which too often surround that notion. No novelties are introduced for their own sakes; on the contrary, every effort has been made to conform to standard notations and usages. Although not pretending to be in any sense a 'handbook,' the present volume explains a number of alternative notations, including the stroke and dagger functions, the use of dots as brackets, and the parenthesis-free Polish notation due to Lukasiewicz. Both the simple and the ramified theories of logical types are explained, and the latter is compared with the object language metalanguage distinction as an alternative method of avoiding the so-called semantical paradoxes. Enough material has been included to enable the student who masters it to go on to read more advanced treatises and even some of the journal articles which report current research in symbolic logic.

The present book is suitable for either a one- or two-semester course in symbolic logic. It is adaptable to courses which stress the informal development of notations and methods for their *use* in appraising arguments, and is equally adaptable to courses whose main emphasis is on the development of systems of symbolic logic. To this end, the chapters are so written as to permit some variation in the order in which they can be read or assigned. Thus Chapters Six, Seven, and Eight can be read before Chapters Four and Five, if it is desired to study the propositional calculus as a logistic system before taking up quantification theory.

Controversial philosophical questions are not allowed to intrude. The entire book is written from what is sincerely intended to be a philosophically neutral point of view.

Some of the material in Chapters Three, Four, Seven, and Nine was first communicated to me by my friend and former colleague Professor Atwell R. Turquette of the University of Illinois, and I am happy to acknowledge my indebtedness to him. The logistic systems R.S. and RS_1, which are set forth in Chapters Seven and Nine, respectively, are early versions of calculi which appear in revised form in Professor J. Barkley Rosser's *Symbolic Logic for Mathematicians*, and I am very grateful to Professor Rosser for his permission to include them here. The proof of completeness for the first-order function calculus presented in Chapter Nine is an adaptation to RS_1 of the completeness proof for an alternative first-order function calculus due to Professor Leon Henkin, of the University of California, whose generous permission to reproduce it here is deeply appreciated. I wish to thank Professor J. Barkley Rosser of Cornell

University and Professor Gustav Bergmann of the State University of Iowa, who read early versions of the manuscript and made a number of very helpful suggestions. And I am grateful to Professor Martin E. Lean of Brooklyn College for his valuable criticism not only of the manuscript of *Symbolic Logic* but also of the manuscript of my earlier *Introduction to Logic*. My thanks to him for the latter are belated only because his identity was not revealed to me by the publisher until the manuscript of the present book was ready for the press. Professor Paul Henle and Dr. Robert McNaughton of the University of Michigan, Professor Nakhnikian of Wayne University, and Dr. Ziff of Harvard University read parts of the manuscript, and I am grateful to them also for helpful suggestions. And I wish to express my gratitude to Mr. Rollin Workman for his expert assistance in the tedious task of proofreading. I also wish to thank Professor Marvin Farber of the University of Buffalo for permission to include in Appendix B some passages which appeared earlier in the journal of *Philosophy and Phenomenological Research*.

I am particularly indebted to my colleague Professor Arthur W. Burks both for his constant encouragement and for his valuable criticisms of my manuscript, of which he read each chapter as it was written. And I wish to acknowledge the help given me by Mr. David M. Copi in preparing the manuscript for publication.

Finally I wish to thank the many students who have participated actively and enthusiastically in the logic classes from which this book developed. I owe a debt to them as well as to the great teachers under whom I studied logic: Rudolf Carnap, C. H. Langford, and Bertrand Russell. I hope this book will not be found too unworthy of the help they have given me.

IRVING M. COPI

Ann Arbor, 1953

Contents

SYMBOLIC LOGIC

CHAPTER ONE

Introduction: Logic
and Language

I. WHAT IS LOGIC?

It is easy to find answers to the question 'What is Logic?'
According to Charles Peirce, 'Nearly a hundred definitions of it
have been given'.* But Peirce goes on to write: 'It will, however,
generally be conceded that its central problem is the classification of arguments, so that all those that are bad are thrown into
one division, and those which are good into another . . . '.

The study of logic, then, is the study of the methods and principles used in distinguishing correct (good) from incorrect (bad)
arguments. This definition is not intended to imply, of course,
that one can make the distinction only if he has studied logic.
But the study of logic will *help* one to distinguish between correct
and incorrect arguments, and it will do so in several ways. First
of all, the proper study of logic will approach it as an art as well
as a science, and the student will do exercises in all parts of the
theory being learned. Here, as anywhere else, practice will help

* 'Logic', in *Dictionary of Philosophy and Psychology*, edited by James Mark Baldwin.
The Macmillan Company, 1925.

1

to make perfect. In the second place, the study of logic, especially symbolic logic, like the study of any other exact science, will tend to increase one's proficiency in reasoning. And finally, the study of logic will give the student certain techniques for testing the validity of all arguments, including his own. This is of value because, when mistakes are easily detected, they are less likely to be made.

Logic has frequently been defined as the science of reasoning. That definition, although it gives a clue to the nature of logic, is not quite accurate. Reasoning is that special kind of thinking called inferring, in which conclusions are drawn from premises. As thinking, however, it is not the special province of logic, but part of the psychologist's subject matter. Psychologists who examine the reasoning process find it to be extremely complex and highly emotional, consisting of awkward trial and error procedures illuminated by sudden—and sometimes apparently irrelevant—flashes of insight. These factors are all of importance to psychology. But the logician is not interested in the actual process of reasoning. He is concerned with the correctness of the completed process. His question is always: does the conclusion reached *follow* from the premises used or assumed? If the premises constitute grounds or good evidence for the conclusion, so that asserting the premises to be true warrants asserting the conclusion to be true also, then the reasoning is correct. Otherwise it is incorrect. The logician's methods and techniques have been developed primarily for the purpose of making this distinction clear. The logician is interested in all reasoning, regardless of its subject matter, but only from this special point of view.

II. THE NATURE OF ARGUMENT

Inferring is an activity in which one proposition is arrived at and affirmed on the basis of one or more other propositions, which were accepted as the starting point of the process. The logician is not concerned with the *process* of inference, but with the propositions which constitute the initial and end points of that process, and the relationships between them.

Propositions are either true or false, and in this they differ from questions, commands, and exclamations. Grammarians classify the linguistic formulations of propositions, questions, commands, and exclamations as declarative, interrogative, imperative, and exclamatory sentences, respectively. These are familiar notions. It is customary to distinguish between declarative sentences and their meanings, using the word 'proposition' to denote the *meaning* of a declarative sentence. The distinction is brought out most clearly by remarking that a declarative sentence is always part of a language, the language in which it is enunciated, while propositions are not peculiar to any of the languages in which they may be formulated. The three statements, 'It is raining', 'Il pleut', and 'Es regnet', are certainly different, for they are in different languages. Yet they have the same meaning, and this common meaning is the *proposition* of which each of them is a different formulation. The logician has traditionally been interested in propositions rather than in the sentences which formulate them.

Corresponding to every possible inference is an *argument*, and it is with these arguments that logic is chiefly concerned. An argument may be defined as any group of propositions of which one is claimed to follow from the others, which are regarded as supplying evidence for the truth of that one. In ordinary usage the word 'argument' also has other meanings, but in logic it has the technical sense explained. In the following chapters the word 'argument' will be used in a derivative sense to refer to any collection of statements in which an argument is formulated or expressed. Every argument has a structure, in the analysis of which the terms 'premiss' and 'conclusion' are usually employed. The *conclusion* of an argument is that proposition which is affirmed on the basis of the other propositions of the argument, and these other propositions which are affirmed as supplying evidence or reasons for accepting the conclusion are the *premisses* of that argument.

We note that 'premiss' and 'conclusion' are relative terms, in the sense that the same proposition can be a premiss in one argument and conclusion in another. Thus the proposition *All men are mortal* is premiss in the argument

> All men are mortal.
> Socrates is a man.
> Therefore Socrates is mortal.

and conclusion in the argument

> All animals are mortal.
> All men are animals.
> Therefore all men are mortal.

Any proposition can be either a premiss or a conclusion, depend‧ing upon its context. It is a premiss when it occurs in an argument which assumes it for the sake of showing that some other proposition is thereby justified. And it is a conclusion when it occurs in an argument which purports to prove it on the basis of other propositions which are assumed.

It is customary to distinguish between *deductive* and *inductive* arguments. All arguments involve the claim that their premisses provide evidence for the truth of their conclusions, but only a *deductive* argument claims that its premisses provide *absolutely conclusive* evidence. The technical terms 'valid' and 'invalid' are used in place of 'correct' and 'incorrect' in characterizing deductive arguments. A deductive argument is *valid* when its premisses and conclusion are so related that it is absolutely impossible for the premisses to be true unless the conclusion is true also. The task of deductive logic is to clarify the nature of the relationship which holds between premisses and conclusion in a valid argument, and to provide techniques for discriminating the valid from the invalid.

Inductive arguments involve only the claim that their premisses constitute *some* evidence for their conclusions. Neither the term 'valid' nor its opposite 'invalid' is properly applied to inductive arguments. Inductive arguments differ among themselves in the degree of likelihood or probability which their premisses confer upon their conclusions, and are studied in inductive logic. But in this book we shall be concerned with deductive arguments alone, and shall use the word 'argument' to refer to deductive arguments exclusively.

III. TRUTH AND VALIDITY

Truth and falsehood are properties of propositions, and may derivatively be said to characterize the declarative sentences or statements in which propositions are formulated. But arguments are not properly characterized as being either true or false. On the other hand, validity and invalidity are properties of arguments rather than of propositions or statements.* There is a connection between the validity or invalidity of an argument and the truth or falsehood of its premises and conclusion, but the connection is by no means a simple one.

Some valid arguments contain true propositions only, as, for example,

> All bats are mammals.
> All mammals have lungs.
> Therefore all bats have lungs.

But an argument may contain false propositions exclusively, and be valid nevertheless, as, for example,

> All trout are mammals.
> All mammals have wings.
> Therefore all trout have wings.

This argument is valid because *if* its premises were true its conclusion would have to be true also, even though in fact they are all false. These two examples show that although some valid arguments have true conclusions, not all of them do. The validity of an argument does not guarantee the truth of its conclusion.

When we consider the argument

> If I were the President then I would be famous.
> I am not the President.
> Therefore I am not famous.

* Some logicians use the term 'valid' to characterize statements which are *logically true*, as will be explained in Chapter Nine, Section VI. For the present, however, we shall apply the terms 'valid' and 'invalid' to arguments exclusively.

we can see that although both premisses and conclusion are true, it is invalid. Its invalidity is made obvious by comparing it with another argument of the same form:

> If Einstein were the President then he would be famous.
> Einstein is not the President.
> Therefore Einstein is not famous.

This argument is clearly invalid, since its premisses are true but its conclusion false. The two latter examples show that although some invalid arguments have false conclusions, not all of them do. The falsehood of its conclusion does not guarantee the invalidity of an argument. But the falsehood of its conclusion does guarantee that *either* the argument is invalid *or* at least one of its premisses is false.

There are two conditions which an argument must satisfy to establish the truth of its conclusion. It must be valid, and all of its premisses must be true. The logician is concerned with only one of those conditions. To determine the truth or falsehood of premisses is the task of scientific inquiry in general, since premisses may deal with any subject matter at all. But determining the validity or invalidity of arguments is the special province of deductive logic. The logician is interested in the question of validity even for arguments whose premisses might happen to be false.

A question might be raised about the legitimacy of that interest. It might be suggested that we ought to confine our attention to arguments having true premisses only. But it is often necessary to depend upon the validity of arguments whose premisses are not known to be true. Modern scientists investigate their theories by deducing conclusions from them which predict the behavior of observable phenomena in the laboratory or observatory. The conclusion is then tested directly by observation, and if it is true, this tends to confirm the theory from which it was deduced, while if it is false, this disconfirms or refutes the theory. In either case, the scientist is vitally interested in the validity of the argument by which the testable conclusion is deduced from the theory being investigated; for if that argument is invalid his whole procedure is without point. The foregoing is an oversimplified account of scientific method, but it serves to illustrate the fact that questions of validity are important even for arguments whose premisses are not true.

IV. SYMBOLIC LOGIC

It has been explained that logic is concerned with arguments, and that these contain propositions as their premisses and conclusions. The latter are not linguistic entities, such as declarative sentences or statements, but rather the *meanings* of statements. However, the communication of propositions and arguments requires the use of language, and this complicates our problem. Arguments formulated in English or in any other natural language are often difficult to appraise because of the vague and equivocal nature of the words in which they are expressed, the ambiguity of their construction, the misleading idioms they may contain, and their pleasing but deceptive metaphorical style. The resolution of these difficulties is not the central problem for the logician, however, for even when they are resolved, the problem of deciding the validity or invalidity of the argument remains.

To avoid the peripheral difficulties connected with ordinary language, workers in the various sciences have developed specialized technical vocabularies. The scientist economizes the space and time required for writing his reports and theories by adopting special symbols to express ideas which would otherwise require a long sequence of familiar words to formulate. This has the further advantage of reducing the amount of attention needed, for when a sentence or equation grows too long its meaning is more difficult to grasp. The introduction of the exponent symbol in mathematics permits the expression of the equation

$$A \times A \times A \times A \times A \times A \times A \times A \times A \times A \times A \times A = B \times B \times B \times B \times B \times B \times B$$

more briefly and intelligibly as

$$A^{12} = B^7.$$

A like advantage has been obtained by the use of graphic formulas in organic chemistry. And the language of every advanced science has been enriched by similar symbolic innovations.

Logic, too, has had a special technical notation developed for it. Aristotle made use of certain abbreviations to facilitate his own investigations, and modern symbolic logic has grown by the introduction of many more special symbols. The difference between the old and the new logic is one of degree rather than of kind, but the difference in degree is tremendous. Modern symbolic logic has become immeasurably more powerful a tool for analysis and deduction through the development of its own technical language. The special symbols of modern logic permit us to exhibit with greater clarity the logical structures of propositions and arguments which may be obscured by their formulation in ordinary language. It is an easier task to divide arguments into the valid and the invalid when they are expressed in a special symbolic language, for in it the peripheral problems of vagueness, ambiguity, idiom, metaphor, and amphiboly do not arise. The introduction and use of special symbols serve not only to facilitate the appraisal of arguments, but also to clarify the nature of deductive inference.

The logician's special symbols are much better adapted than ordinary language to the actual drawing of inferences. Their superiority in this respect is comparable to that enjoyed by Arabic numerals over the older Roman kind for purposes of computation. It is easy to multiply 148 by 47, but very difficult to compute the product of CXLVIII and XLVII. Similarly, the drawing of inferences and the evaluation of arguments is greatly facilitated by the adoption of a special logical notation. To quote

Alfred North Whitehead, one of the great contributors to the advance of symbolic logic:

. . . by the aid of symbolism, we can make transitions in reasoning almost mechanically by the eye, which otherwise would call into play the higher faculties of the brain.*

In view of the importance of the symbols used to formulate arguments, we shall develop our theory in terms of statements rather than propositions, although we are primarily interested in propositions.

* *An Introduction to Mathematics* by A. N. Whitehead. Oxford University Press, 1911.

CHAPTER TWO

Arguments Containing
Compound Statements

I. SIMPLE AND COMPOUND STATEMENTS

All statements can be divided into two kinds, simple and compound. A *simple* statement is one which does not contain any other statement as a constituent part, while every *compound* statement does contain some other statement as a constituent. For example, 'The United Nations Organization will be strengthened or there will be a third world war' is a compound statement which contains as its constituent parts the two simple statements 'The United Nations Organization will be strengthened' and 'there will be a third world war'. The constituent parts of a compound statement may themselves be compound, of course. We turn now to some of the different ways in which statements can be combined into compound statements.

The statement 'Roses are red and violets are blue' is a *conjunction*, a compound statement formed by inserting the word 'and' between two statements. Two statements so combined are called *conjuncts*. The word 'and' has other uses, however, as in the statement 'Castor and Pollux were twins', which is not compound, but a simple statement asserting a relationship. We introduce the dot '·' as a special symbol for combining statements conjunctively. Using it, the preceding conjunction is written 'Roses are red·violets are blue'. Where *p* and *q* are any two statements whatever, their conjunction is written *p·q*.

Every statement is either true or false, so we can speak of the *truth value* of a statement, where the truth value of a true statement is *true* and the truth value of a false statement is *false*. There are two broad categories into which compound statements can be divided, according to whether or not there is any necessary connection between the truth value of the compound statement and the truth values of its constituent statements. The truth value of the compound statement 'Smith believes that lead is heavier than zinc' is completely independent of the truth value of its constituent simple statement 'lead is heavier than zinc', for people have mistaken as well as correct beliefs. On the other hand, there is a necessary connection between the truth value of a conjunction and the truth values of its conjuncts. A conjunction is true if both its conjuncts are true, but false otherwise. Any compound statement whose truth value is completely determined by the truth values of its constituent statements, regardless of whether they are true or false, is a *truth-functionally* compound statement. The only compound statements we shall consider here will be truth-functionally compound statements.

Since conjunctions are truth-functionally compound statements, our dot symbol is a truth-functional connective. Given any two statements *p* and *q* there are just four possible sets of truth values they can have, and in every case the truth value of their conjunction *p·q* is uniquely determined. The four possible cases can be exhibited as follows:

> in case *p* is true and *q* is true, *p·q* is true;
> in case *p* is true and *q* is false, *p·q* is false;
> in case *p* is false and *q* is true, *p·q* is false;
> in case *p* is false and *q* is false, *p·q* is false.

Representing the truth values true and false by the capital letters
'**T**' and '**F**', respectively, the way in which the truth value of a
conjunction is determined by the truth values of its conjuncts can
be displayed more briefly by means of a *truth table* as follows:

p	q	$p{\cdot}q$
T	T	T
T	F	F
F	T	F
F	F	F

Since it specifies the truth value of $p{\cdot}q$ in every possible case, this
truth table can be taken as *defining* the dot symbol. Other English words such as 'moreover', 'furthermore', 'but', 'yet', 'still',
'however', etc., are also used to conjoin two statements into a
single compound one, and all of them can be indifferently translated into the dot symbol so far as truth values are concerned.

The statement 'It is not the case that lead is heavier than gold'
is also compound, being the *denial* (or *negation* or *contradictory*)
of its single constituent statement 'lead is heavier than gold'. We
introduce the symbol '$\sim$', called a *curl* (or a *tilde*) to symbolize
denial. There are often alternative formulations in English of
the denial of a given statement. Thus where L symbolizes the
statement 'lead is heavier than gold', the different statements
'it is not the case that lead is heavier than gold', 'it is false that
lead is heavier than gold', 'lead is not heavier than gold' are all
indifferently symbolized as $\sim L$. More generally, where p is any
statement whatever, its denial is written $\sim p$. Since the denial of
a true statement is false and the denial of a false statement is true,
we can take the following truth table as defining the curl symbol:

p	$\sim p$
T	F
F	T

When two statements are combined disjunctively by inserting
the word 'or' between them, the resulting compound statement
is a *disjunction* (or *alternation*), and the two statements so combined are called *disjuncts* (or *alternatives*). The word 'or' has two

different senses, one of which is clearly intended in the statement 'Premiums will be waived in the event of sickness or unemployment'. The intention here is obviously that premiums are waived not only for sick persons and for unemployed persons, but also for persons who are both sick *and* unemployed. This sense of the word 'or' is called *weak* or *inclusive*. A different sense of 'or' is intended when a restaurant lists 'tea or coffee' on its table d'hôte menu, meaning that for the stated price of the meal the customer can have one or the other, but *not both*. This second sense of 'or' is called *strong* or *exclusive*. A disjunction which uses the inclusive 'or' asserts that *at least one disjunct is true*, while one which uses the exclusive 'or' asserts that *at least one disjunct is true and at least one disjunct is false*. The *partial common meaning*, that at least one disjunct is true, is the whole meaning of an inclusive disjunction, and a part of the meaning of an exclusive disjunction.

In Latin, the word 'vel' expresses the inclusive sense of the word 'or', and the word 'aut' expresses the exclusive sense. It is customary to use the first letter of 'vel' to symbolize 'or' in its inclusive sense. Where p and q are any two statements whatever, their weak or inclusive disjunction is written $p \vee q$. The symbol 'v', called a *wedge* (or a *vee*), is a truth-functional connective, and is defined by the following truth table:

p	q	$p \vee q$
T	T	T
T	F	T
F	T	T
F	F	F

An obviously valid argument containing a disjunction is the following Disjunctive Syllogism:

> The United Nations Organization will be strengthened or there will be a third world war.
> The United Nations Organization will not be strengthened.
> Therefore there will be a third world war.

It is evident that a Disjunctive Syllogism is valid on *either* interpretation of the word 'or', that is, regardless of whether its first premiss asserts an inclusive or exclusive disjunction. It is usually difficult, and sometimes impossible, to discover which sense of the word 'or' is intended in a disjunction. But the typical valid argument that has a disjunction for a premiss is, like the Disjunctive Syllogism, valid on either interpretation of the word 'or'. Hence we effect a simplification by translating any occurrence of the word 'or' into the logical symbol 'v'—*regardless of which sense of 'or' is intended*. Of course where it is explicitly stated that the disjunction is exclusive, by use of the added phrase 'but not both', for example, we do have the symbolic apparatus for symbolizing that sense, as will be explained below.

The use of parentheses, brackets, and braces for punctuating mathematical expressions is familiar. No number is uniquely denoted by the expression '6 + 9 ÷ 3', although when punctuation makes clear how its constituents are to be grouped, it denotes either 5 or 9. Punctuation is needed to resolve ambiguity in the language of symbolic logic too, since compound statements may themselves be combined to yield more complicated compounds. Ambiguity is present in $p \cdot q$ v r, which could be either the conjunction of p with q v r, or else the disjunction of $p \cdot q$ with r. These two different senses are unambiguously given by different punctuations: $p \cdot (q$ v $r)$ and $(p \cdot q)$ v r. In case p and q are both false and r is true, the first punctuated expression is false (since its first conjunct is false) but the second punctuated expression is true (since its second disjunct is true). Hence a difference in punctuation can mean all the difference between truth and falsehood. In symbolic logic, as in mathematics, we use parentheses, brackets, and braces for punctuation. To cut down on the number of punctuation marks required, however, we establish the symbolic convention that in any expression the curl will apply to the smallest statement which the punctuation permits. Thus the ambiguity of $\sim p$ v q, which might mean either $(\sim p)$ v q or $\sim(p$ v $q)$, is resolved by our convention to mean the first of these, for the curl can (and therefore by our convention *does*) apply to the first constituent p rather than to the larger expression $p \lor q$.

Since an exclusive disjunction asserts that at least one of its disjuncts is true and at least one of them is false, we can symbolize the exclusive disjunction of any two statements p and q quite simply as $(p \lor q) \cdot (\sim p \lor \sim q)$. Thus we are able to symbolize conjunctions, denials, and both inclusive and exclusive disjunctions. Any compound statement which is built up out of simple statements by repeated use of truth-functional connectives will have its truth value completely determined by the truth values of those simple statements. For example, if A and B are true statements and X and Y are false, the truth value of the compound statement $\sim[(\sim A \lor X) \lor \sim(B \cdot Y)]$ can be discovered as follows. Since A is true, $\sim A$ is false, and since X is false also, the disjunction $(\sim A \lor X)$ is false. Since Y is false, the conjunction $(B \cdot Y)$ is false, and so its denial $\sim(B \cdot Y)$ is true. Hence the disjunction $(\sim A \lor X) \lor \sim(B \cdot Y)$ is true, and its denial, which is the original statement, is false. Such a stepwise procedure, beginning with the inmost constituents, always permits us to determine the truth value of a truth-functionally compound statement from the truth values of its constituent simple statements.

EXERCISES

If A and B are true statements and X and Y are false statements, which of the following compound statements are true?

1. $\sim(A \cdot X)$
2. $\sim A \cdot \sim X$
3. $\sim A \lor \sim X$
4. $\sim(A \lor X)$
5. $\sim(A \cdot B)$
6. $\sim A \lor \sim B$
7. $\sim A \cdot \sim B$
8. $\sim(A \lor B)$
9. $\sim(A \cdot \sim B)$
10. $\sim(A \cdot \sim X)$
11. $(A \lor B) \cdot (X \lor Y)$
12. $(A \cdot B) \lor (X \cdot Y)$
13. $(A \lor X) \cdot (B \lor Y)$
14. $(A \cdot X) \lor (B \cdot Y)$
15. $[A \cdot (B \lor X)] \lor \sim[(A \cdot B) \lor (A \cdot X)]$
16. $[X \lor (B \cdot Y)] \lor \sim[(X \lor B) \lor (X \lor Y)]$
17. $\sim\{\sim[\sim(A \cdot \sim B) \cdot \sim A] \cdot \sim A\}$
18. $\sim\{\sim[\sim(A \cdot \sim X) \cdot \sim A] \cdot \sim A\}$
19. $\sim\{\sim[\sim(A \cdot \sim X) \cdot \sim A] \cdot \sim X\}$
20. $\sim\{\sim[\sim(X \cdot \sim A) \cdot \sim X] \cdot \sim X\}$

II. IMPLICATION

The compound statement 'If the train is late then we shall miss our connection' is a *conditional* (or a *hypothetical*, an *implication*, or an *implicative statement*). The constituent between the 'if' and the 'then' is called the *antecedent* (or the *implicans* or *protasis*), and the constituent which follows the 'then' is the *consequent* (or the *implicate* or *apodosis*). A conditional does not assert either that its antecedent is true or that its consequent is true; it asserts only that *if* its antecedent is true then its consequent is true also, that is, that its antecedent *implies* its consequent. The key to the meaning of a conditional is the relation of *implication* asserted to hold between its antecedent and consequent, in that order.

If we examine a number of different conditionals we can see that there are different kinds of implications which they may assert. In the conditional 'If all cats like liver and Dinah is a cat then Dinah likes liver', the consequent follows *logically* from its antecedent. On the other hand, in the conditional 'If the figure is a triangle then it has three sides', the consequent follows from the antecedent by the very *definition* of the word 'triangle'. But the truth of the conditional 'If gold is placed in *aqua regia* then the gold dissolves' is not a matter of either logic or definition. The connection asserted here is *causal*, and must be discovered empirically. These examples show that there are different kinds of implications which constitute different senses of the 'if-then' phrase. Having noted these differences, we now seek to find some identifiable common meaning, some partial meaning that is common to these admittedly different types of conditionals.

Our discussion of 'if-then' will parallel our previous discussion of the word 'or'. First, we pointed out two different senses of that word. Second, we noted that there was a common partial meaning: that *at least one disjunct is true* was seen to be involved in both the inclusive and the exclusive 'or'. Third, we introduced the special symbol 'v' to represent this common partial meaning (which was the whole meaning of 'or' in its inclusive sense). Fourth, we observed that since arguments like the Disjunctive

Syllogism are valid on either interpretation of the word 'or', symbolizing *any* occurrence of the word 'or' by the wedge symbol preserves the validity of all such arguments. And since we are interested in arguments from the point of view of determining their validity, this translation of the word 'or' into 'v', which may abstract from or ignore part of its meaning in some cases, is wholly adequate for our present purposes.

A common partial meaning of these different kinds of conditional statements emerges when we ask what circumstances would suffice to establish the *falsehood* of a conditional. Under what circumstances would we agree that the conditional 'If gold is placed in this solution then the gold dissolves' is false? Clearly the statement is false in case gold is actually placed in this solution and *does not dissolve*. Any conditional with a true antecedent and a false consequent must be false. Hence any conditional *if p then q* is known to be false in case the conjunction $p \cdot \sim q$ is known to be true, that is, in case its antecedent is true and its consequent false. For the conditional to be true, the indicated conjunction must be false, which means that its denial must be true. In other words, for any conditional *if p then q* to be true, $\sim(p \cdot \sim q)$, the denial of the conjunction of its antecedent with the denial of its consequent, must be true also. We may, then, regard the latter as a *part* of the meaning of the former.

We introduce the new symbol '$\supset$', called a *horseshoe*, to represent the partial meaning common to all conditional statements, defining '$p \supset q$' as an abbreviation for '$\sim(p \cdot \sim q)$'. The horseshoe is a truth-functional connective, whose exact significance is indicated by the following truth table:

p	q	$\sim q$	$p \cdot \sim q$	$\sim(p \cdot \sim q)$	$p \supset q$
T	T	F	F	T	T
T	F	T	T	F	F
F	T	F	F	T	T
F	F	T	F	T	T

Here the first two columns represent all possible truth values for the constituent statements p and q, and the third, fourth, and fifth represent successive stages in determining the truth value of the compound statement $\sim(p\cdot\sim q)$ in each case. The sixth column is identically the same as the fifth since the statements which head them are defined to express the same proposition. The horseshoe symbol must not be thought of as representing *the* meaning of 'if-then', or *the* relation of implication, but rather a common partial factor of the various different kinds of implications which may be signified by the 'if-then' phrase.

We can regard the horseshoe as symbolizing a special, extremely weak kind of implication, and it is expedient for us to do so, since convenient ways to read '$p \supset q$' are 'if p then q', 'p implies q', or 'p only if q'. The weak implication symbolized by '$\supset$' is called *material implication*, and its special name indicates that it is a special notion, not to be confused with the other more usual kinds of implication. Some conditional statements in English do assert merely material implications, as for example 'If Communist Russia is a peace-loving nation then I'm a Dutchman'. It is clear that the implication asserted here is neither logical, definitional, nor causal. No 'real connection' is alleged to hold between what the antecedent asserts and what is asserted by the consequent. This sort of conditional is ordinarily intended as an emphatic or humorous method of denying the truth of its antecedent, for it always contains a notoriously or ridiculously false statement as consequent. Any such assertion about truth values is adequately symbolized using the truth functional connective '$\supset$'.

Although most conditional statements assert more than a merely material implication between antecedent and consequent, we now propose to symbolize *any* occurrence of 'if-then' by the truth-functional connective '$\supset$'. It must be admitted that such symbolization abstracts from or ignores part of the meaning of most conditional statements. But the proposal can be justified on the grounds that the validity of all valid arguments involving conditionals is preserved when the conditionals are regarded as asserting material implications only, as will be established in the following sections.

EXERCISES

If A and B are true statements and X and Y are false statements, which of the following compound statements are true?

1. $A \supset (B \supset A)$
2. $X \supset (B \supset X)$
3. $(X \supset B) \supset X$
4. $(A \supset B) \supset A$
5. $(X \supset Y) \supset X$
6. $(X \supset Y) \supset Y$
7. $(X \supset Y) \supset (Y \supset X)$
8. $(X \supset A) \supset (A \supset X)$
9. $(A \supset X) \supset (X \supset A)$

10. $(X \supset A) \supset (\sim A \supset \sim X)$
11. $(X \supset A) \supset (\sim X \supset \sim A)$
12. $[(A \supset B) \supset A] \supset A$
13. $[(A \supset Y) \supset A] \supset A$
14. $[(X \supset Y) \supset X] \supset X$
15. $[(X \supset B) \supset X] \supset X$
16. $[(A \supset X) \supset X] \supset X$
17. $\sim(A \cdot B) \supset (\sim A \vee \sim B)$
18. $\sim(A \cdot X) \supset (\sim A \cdot \sim X)$

19. $[(A \cdot B) \supset X] \supset [A \supset (B \supset X)]$
20. $[X \supset (A \supset Y)] \supset [(X \supset A) \supset Y]$

III. ARGUMENT FORMS AND TRUTH TABLES

In this section we shall develop a purely mechanical method for testing the validity of arguments containing truth-functionally compound statements. That method is closely related to the familiar technique of *refutation by logical analogy* which was used in the first chapter to show the invalidity of the argument

> If I were the President then I would be famous.
> I am not the President.
> Therefore I am not famous.

That argument was shown to be invalid by constructing another argument of the same form:

> If Einstein were the President then he would be famous.
> Einstein is not the President.
> Therefore Einstein is not famous.

which is obviously invalid since its premises are true and its conclusion false. Any argument is proved invalid if another argument *of the same form* can be constructed with true premises and a false conclusion. This reflects the fact that validity and invalidity are purely *formal* characteristics of arguments: any two arguments having the same form are either both valid or both invalid, regardless of any differences in their subject matter. The notion of two arguments having *the same form* is one which deserves further examination.

It is convenient in discussing forms of arguments to use small letters from the middle part of the alphabet, '*p*', '*q*', '*r*', '*s*', . . . as *statement variables*, which are defined simply to be letters for which, or in place of which, statements may be substituted. Now we define an *argument form* to be any sequence of symbols which contains statement variables, such that when statements are substituted for the statement variables—the same statement replacing the same statement variable throughout—the result is an argument. Any argument which results from the substitution of statements for the statement variables of an argument form is said to *have* that form, or to be a *substitution instance* of that argument form. If we symbolize the simple statement 'The United Nations Organization will be strengthened' as *O*, and the simple statement 'There will be a third world war' as *W*, then the Disjunctive Syllogism presented earlier can be symbolized as

$$O \text{ v } W$$
$$\sim O$$
$$\therefore W$$

It has the form *p* v *q*, ∼*p* ∴ *q*, from which it results by replacing the statement variables *p* and *q* by the statements *O* and *W*, respectively. But that is not the only form of which it is a substitution instance. The same argument is obtained by replacing the statement variables *p*, *q*, and *r* in the argument form *p*, *q* ∴ *r* by the statements *O* v *W*, ∼*O*, and *W*, respectively. We define *the* form of a given argument as that argument form from which the argument results by replacing each distinct statement variable by a different *simple* statement. Thus *the* form of the argument *O* v *W*, ∼*O* ∴ *W* is the argument form *p* v *q*, ∼*p* ∴ *q*. Although *p*, *q* ∴ *r* is *a* form of that argument, it is not *the* form of

X This def. admits the paradoxes

it. The technique of refutation by logical analogy can now be described more precisely. If *the* form of a given argument can be shown to have any substitution instance with true premisses and false conclusion, then the given argument is invalid.

The terms 'valid' and 'invalid' can be extended to apply to argument forms as well as arguments. An *invalid* argument form is one which has at least one substitution instance with true premisses and a false conclusion. The technique of refutation by logical analogy presupposes that any argument of which *the* form is an invalid argument form is an invalid argument. Any argument form is *valid* which is not invalid; a *valid* argument form is one which has no substitution instance with true premisses and false conclusion. Any given argument can be proved valid if it can be shown that *the* form of the given argument is a valid argument form.

To determine the validity or invalidity of an argument form we must examine all possible substitution instances of it to see if any of them have true premisses and false conclusions. The arguments with which we are here concerned contain only simple statements and truth-functional compounds of them, and we are interested only in the truth values of their premisses and conclusions. We can obtain all possible substitution instances whose premisses and conclusions have different truth values, by considering all possible arrangements of truth values for the statements which can be substituted for the distinct statement variables in the argument form to be tested. These can be set forth most conveniently in the form of a truth table, with an initial or guide column for each distinct statement variable appearing in the argument form. Thus to prove the validity of the Disjunctive Syllogism form $p \vee q$, $\sim p$ $\therefore$ q we construct the following truth table:

p	q	$p \vee q$	$\sim p$
T	T	T	F
T	F	T	F
F	T	T	T
F	F	F	T

Each row of this table represents a whole class of substitution instances. The **T**'s and **F**'s in the two initial columns represent the truth values of statements which can be substituted for the variables *p* and *q* in the argument form. These determine the truth values in the other columns, the third of which is headed by the first 'premiss' of the argument form and the fourth by the second 'premiss'. The second column's heading is the 'conclusion' of the argument form. An examination of this truth table reveals that whatever statements are substituted for the variables *p* and *q*, the resulting argument cannot have true premisses and a false conclusion, for the third row represents the only possible case in which both premisses are true, and there the conclusion is true also.

Since truth tables provide a purely mechanical or *effective* method of deciding the validity or invalidity of any argument of the general type here considered, we can now justify our proposal to symbolize all conditional statements by means of the truth-functional connective '⊃'. The justification for treating all implications as though they were mere material implications is that all valid arguments containing conditional statements remain valid when those conditionals are interpreted as asserting material implications only. The three simplest and most intuitively valid forms of argument involving conditional statements are *modus ponens* (if *p* then *q*, *p* ∴ *q*), *modus tollens* (if *p* then *q*, ~*q* ∴ ~*p*), and the Hypothetical Syllogism (if *p* then *q*, if *q* then *r* ∴ if *p* then *r*). That they all remain valid when their conditionals are interpreted as asserting material implications is easily established by truth tables. The validity of *modus ponens* is shown by the same truth table which defines the horseshoe symbol:

p	*q*	*p* ⊃ *q*
T	T	T
T	F	F
F	T	T
F	F	T

Here the two premisses are represented by the third and first columns, and the conclusion by the second. Only the first row represents substitution instances in which both premisses are true, and in that row the conclusion is true also. The validity of *modus tollens* is shown by the truth table:

p	q	$p \supset q$	$\sim q$	$\sim p$
T	T	T	F	F
T	F	F	T	F
F	T	T	F	T
F	F	T	T	T

Here only the fourth row represents substitution instances in which both premisses (the third and fourth columns) are true, and there the conclusion (the fifth column) is true also. Since the Hypothetical Syllogism form contains three distinct statement variables, the truth table for it must have three initial columns and will require eight rows for listing all possible substitution instances:

p	q	r	$p \supset q$	$q \supset r$	$p \supset r$
T	T	T	T	T	T
T	T	F	T	F	F
T	F	T	F	T	T
T	F	F	F	T	F
F	T	T	T	T	T
F	T	F	T	F	T
F	F	T	T	T	T
F	F	F	T	T	T

In constructing it, the three initial columns represent all possible arrangements of truth values for the statements which can be substituted for the statement variables p, q, and r, the fourth column is filled in by reference to the first and second, the fifth by reference to the second and third, and the sixth by reference to the first and third. The premisses are both true only in the first, fifth, seventh, and eighth rows, and in these rows the conclusion is true also. This suffices to demonstrate that the Hypothetical Syllogism remains valid when its conditionals are symbolized by means of the horseshoe symbol. Any doubts that remain about the claim that all valid arguments containing conditionals remain valid when their conditionals are interpreted as asserting merely material implication can be allayed by the reader's providing, symbolizing, and testing his own examples by means of truth tables.

To test the validity of an argument form by a truth table requires one with a separate initial or guide column for each different statement variable, and a separate row for every possible assignment of truth values to the statement variables involved. Hence testing an argument form containing n distinct statement variables requires a truth table having 2^n rows. In constructing truth tables it is convenient to fix upon some uniform pattern for inscribing the **T**'s and **F**'s in their initial or guide columns. In this book we shall follow the practice of simply alternating **T**'s and **F**'s down the extreme right hand initial column, alternating pairs of **T**'s with pairs of **F**'s down the column directly to its left, next alternating quadruples of **T**'s with quadruples of **F**'s, . . . , and finally filling in the top half of the extreme left hand initial column with **T**'s and its bottom half with **F**'s.

There are two invalid argument forms which bear a superficial resemblance to the valid argument forms *modus ponens* and *modus tollens*. These are $p \supset q$, $q \therefore p$, and $p \supset q$, $\sim p \therefore \sim q$, and they are known as the Fallacies of Affirming the Consequent and of Denying the Antecedent, respectively. The invalidity of both can be shown by a single truth table:

p	q	$p \supset q$	$\sim p$	$\sim q$
T	T	T	F	F
T	F	F	F	T
F	T	T	T	F
F	F	T	T	T

The two premisses in the Fallacy of Affirming the Consequent head the second and third columns, and are true in both the first and third rows. But the conclusion, which heads the first column, is false in the third row, which shows that the argument form does have a substitution instance with true premisses and a false conclusion, and is therefore invalid. Columns three and

four are headed by the two premisses in the Fallacy of Denying the Antecedent, which are true in both the third and fourth rows. Its conclusion heads the fifth column, and is false in the third row, which shows that the second argument form is invalid also.

EXERCISES

I. Use truth tables to decide the validity or invalidity of the following argument forms:

1. $p \ \therefore \ p \vee q$
2. $p \cdot q \ \therefore \ p$
3. $p \supset q \ \therefore \ {\sim}q \supset {\sim}p$
4. $p \supset q, p \supset r \ \therefore \ q \supset r$
5. $(p \supset q) \cdot (p \supset r), {\sim}p \ \therefore \ {\sim}q \vee {\sim}r$
6. $(p \supset q) \cdot (p \supset r), {\sim}q \vee {\sim}r \ \therefore \ {\sim}p$
7. $(p \supset q) \cdot (r \supset s), p \vee r \ \therefore \ q \vee s$
8. $(p \supset q) \cdot (r \supset s), {\sim}q \vee {\sim}s \ \therefore \ {\sim}p \vee {\sim}r$
9. $p \supset (q \vee r), (r \cdot s) \supset t \ \therefore \ p \supset t$
10. $p \supset (q \cdot r), (r \vee s) \supset t \ \therefore \ p \supset t$

II. Use truth tables to decide the validity or invalidity of the following arguments:

1. If I work then I earn money, and if I don't work then I enjoy myself. Therefore if I don't earn money then I enjoy myself.
2. If Jones needs money then either he will reduce prices or he will apply to the bank for a loan. Jones will not apply to the bank for a loan. Therefore if Jones does not reduce prices then he does not need money.
3. If Jones needs money then either he will reduce prices or he will apply to the bank for a loan. Jones will reduce prices. Therefore if Jones needs money then he will not apply to the bank for a loan.
4. If Jones needs money, then he will reduce prices and he will advertise heavily. Jones will not advertise heavily. Therefore Jones does not need money.
5. If Brown invests in real estate then if the market drops then he will lose money. The market will not drop. Therefore either Brown invests in real estate or he will lose money.
6. If Robinson keeps his promise then if the deliveries are made on time then the merchandise will be in good condition. The merchan-

dise will be in good condition. Therefore if Robinson keeps his promise then the deliveries are made on time.

7. If Robinson keeps his promise then if the deliveries are made on time then the merchandise will be in good condition. The merchandise will not be in good condition. Therefore if the deliveries are made on time then Robinson does not keep his promise.

8. If Hansen wants the contract then he will enter a bid, and if he enters a bid then the competition is wide open. Hansen wants the contract or the competition is wide open. Therefore Hansen will not enter a bid.

9. If Andrews wins first place and Baker wins second place, then either the favorite will be shut out or the crowd will be disappointed. It is not true that if Baker wins second place then the crowd will be disappointed. Therefore if the favorite is shut out then Andrews wins first place.

10. If Andrews wins first place and Baker wins second place, then the favorite will be shut out and the crowd will be disappointed. It is not true that if Baker wins second place then the favorite will be shut out. Therefore Andrews does not win first place.

IV. TAUTOLOGIES, CONTRADICTIONS, AND CONTINGENCIES

The introduction of statement variables in the preceding section enabled us to define both argument forms in general and *the* form of a given argument. Now we define a *statement form* to be any sequence of symbols containing statement variables, such that when statements are substituted for the statement variables—the same statement replacing the same statement variable throughout—the result is a statement. And any statement which results from substituting statements for the statement variables of a statement form is said to *have* that form, or to be a *substitution instance* of it. Just as we distinguished *the* form of a given argument, so we distinguish *the* form of a given statement as that statement form from which the given statement results by replacing each distinct statement variable by a different simple statement. For example, where A, B, and C are different simple statements, the compound statement $A \supset (B \text{ v } C)$ is a substitution instance of the statement form $p \supset q$, and also of the statement form $p \supset (q \vee r)$, but only the latter is *the* form of the given statement.

Although the statements 'Balboa discovered the Pacific Ocean' (B) and 'Balboa discovered the Pacific Ocean or else he didn't' $(B \vee \sim B)$ are both true, we discover their truth in quite different ways. The truth of B is a matter of history, and must be learned through empirical investigation. Moreover, events might possibly have been such as to make B false; there is nothing *necessary* about the truth of B. But the truth of the statement $B \vee \sim B$ *can* be known independently of empirical investigation, and no events could possibly have sufficed to make it false, for it is a necessary truth. The statement $B \vee \sim B$ is a formal truth, a substitution instance of a statement form *all* substitution instances of which are true. A statement form which has only true substitution instances is said to be *tautologous*, or a *tautology*. The form of $B \vee \sim B$ is $p \vee \sim p$, and it is proved a tautology by the following truth table:

p	$\sim p$	$p \vee \sim p$
T	F	T
F	T	T

That there are only **T**'s in the column headed by the statement form in question shows that all of its substitution instances are true. Any statement which is a substitution instance of a tautologous statement form is formally true, and is itself said to be tautologous, or a tautology.

Similarly, although the statements 'Cortez discovered the Pacific' (C) and 'Cortez discovered the Pacific and Cortez did not discover the Pacific' $(C \cdot \sim C)$ are both false, we discover their falsehood in quite different ways. The first simply *happens* to be false, and that must be learned empirically; whereas the second is necessarily false, and that can be known independently of empirical investigation. The statement $C \cdot \sim C$ is formally false, a substitution instance of a statement form *all* of whose substitution instances are false. One statement is said to contradict, or to be a contradiction of, another statement when it is logically impossible for them both to be true. In this sense, *contradiction* is a relation between statements. But there is another, related sense of that term. When it is logically impossible for a particular statement to be true, that statement itself is said to be self-contradictory, or a self-contradiction. Such statements are also said more simply to be contradictory, or contradictions, and we shall follow the latter usage here. A statement form which has only false substitution instances is said to be *contradictory*, or a *contradiction*, and the same terms are applied to its substitution instances. The statement form $p \cdot \sim p$ is proved a contradiction by the fact that in its truth table only **F**'s occur in the column which it heads.

Statements and statement forms which are neither tautologous nor contradictory are said to be *contingent*, or *contingencies*. For example, p, $\sim p$, p v q, $p \cdot q$, and $p \supset q$ are contingent statement forms; and B, C, $\sim B$, $\sim C$, $B \cdot C$, B v C are contingent statements. The term is appropriate, since their truth values are not formally determined but are dependent or contingent upon what happens to be the case.

It is easily proved that $p \supset (q \supset p)$ and $\sim p \supset (p \supset q)$ are tautologies. When expressed in English as 'A true statement is implied by any statement whatever', and as 'A false statement implies any statement whatever', they seem rather strange. They have been called by some writers the *paradoxes of material implication*. But when it is kept in mind that the horseshoe symbol is a truth-functional connective which stands for *material* implication rather than either 'implication in general' or more usual kinds such as logical or causal, then the tautologous statement forms in question are not at all surprising. And when the misleading English formulations are corrected by inserting the word 'materially' before 'implied' and 'implies', then the air of paradox vanishes. Material implication is a special, technical notion, and the logician's motivation for introducing and using it is the tremendous extent to which it simplifies his task of distinguishing between valid and invalid arguments.

Two statements are said to be *materially equivalent* when they

(handwritten margin note: If note on p. 16 above)

have the same truth value, and we symbolize the statement *that* they are materially equivalent by inserting the symbol ' $\equiv$ ' between them. Being a truth-functional connective, the three bar symbol is defined by the following truth table:

p	q	$p \equiv q$
T	T	T
T	F	F
F	T	F
F	F	T

To say that two statements are materially equivalent is to say that they materially imply each other, as is easily verified by a truth table. Hence the three bar symbol may be read either 'is materially equivalent to' or 'if and only if'. Two statements are said to be *logically equivalent* when the statement of their material equivalence is a tautology. The 'principle of Double Negation', expressed as $p \equiv \sim\sim p$ is proved to be tautologous by a truth table.

There are two logical equivalences which express an important relationship concerning conjunctions, disjunctions, and denials. Since a conjunction asserts that both its conjuncts are true, its denial need only assert that at least one is false. Thus denying the conjunction $p \cdot q$ amounts to asserting the disjunction of the denials of p and q. This statement of equivalence is symbolized as $\sim(p \cdot q) \equiv (\sim p \vee \sim q)$, and proved to be a tautology by the following truth table:

p	q	$p \cdot q$	$\sim(p \cdot q)$	$\sim p$	$\sim q$	$\sim p \vee \sim q$	$\sim(p \cdot q) \equiv (\sim p \vee \sim q)$
T	T	T	F	F	F	F	T
T	F	F	T	F	T	T	T
F	T	F	T	T	F	T	T
F	F	F	T	T	T	T	T

Similarly, since a disjunction asserts merely that at least one disjunct is true, to deny it is to assert that both are false. Denying the disjunction $p \vee q$ amounts to asserting the conjunction of the denials of p and q. It is symbolized as $\sim(p \vee q) \equiv (\sim p \cdot \sim q)$, and is easily proved tautologous by a truth table. These two equivalences are known as De Morgan's Theorems, after the English mathematician-logician Augustus De Morgan (1806–1871), and can be stated compendiously in English as: The denial of the $\begin{cases}\text{conjunction}\\\text{disjunction}\end{cases}$ of two statements is logically equivalent to the $\begin{cases}\text{disjunction}\\\text{conjunction}\end{cases}$ of their denials.

Two statement forms are said to be logically equivalent if no matter what statements are substituted for their statement variables—the same statement replacing the same statement variable in both statement forms—the resulting pairs of statements are equivalent. Thus De Morgan's Theorem asserts that $\sim(p \vee q)$ and $\sim p \cdot \sim q$ are logically equivalent statement forms. Since $\sim(p \cdot \sim q)$ and $\sim p \vee q$ are logically equivalent, either can be taken as defining $p \supset q$; and the second is the more usual choice.

To every argument corresponds a conditional statement whose antecedent is the conjunction of the argument's premises and whose consequent is the argument's conclusion. That corresponding conditional is a tautology if and only if the argument is valid. Thus to the valid argument form $p \vee q$, $\sim p$ $\therefore$ q corresponds the tautologous statement form $[(p \vee q) \cdot \sim p] \supset q$; and to the invalid argument form $p \supset q$, q $\therefore$ p corresponds the non-tautologous statement form $[(p \supset q) \cdot q] \supset p$. An argument form ⟨*Paradoxes*⟩ is valid if and only if its truth table has a **T** under its conclusion in every row in which there are **T**'s under all of its premises. Since an **F** can occur in the column headed by its corresponding conditional only where there are **T**'s under all of those premises and an **F** under the conclusion, it is clear that there can be only **T**'s under a conditional which corresponds to a valid argument form. If an argument is valid, the statement that the conjunction of its premises implies its conclusion is a tautology.

EXERCISES

I. Use truth tables to characterize the following statement forms as tautologous, contradictory, or contingent:

1. $p \supset p$
2. $p \supset \sim p$
3. $(p \supset \sim p) \cdot (\sim p \supset p)$
4. $(\sim p \cdot q) \cdot (q \supset p)$
5. $p \supset (q \supset p)$

6. $p \supset [q \equiv (p \supset q)]$
7. $p \supset [p \equiv (p \supset q)]$
8. $p \supset (\sim p \supset q)$
9. $[(p \supset q) \supset q] \supset q$
10. $[(p \supset q) \supset p] \supset p$

II. Use truth tables to decide which of the following pairs of statement forms are logically equivalent:

1. p and $p \cdot (q \vee \sim q)$
2. p and $p \vee (q \cdot \sim q)$
3. p and $p \cdot (q \supset p)$
4. p and $p \vee (p \cdot q)$
5. p and $q \vee (p \cdot q)$
6. p and $p \cdot (p \vee q)$
7. $p \supset q$ and $\sim q \supset \sim p$
8. $p \supset q$ and $\sim p \supset \sim q$
9. $p \vee q$ and $p \supset \sim q$
10. $p \vee q$ and $\sim p \supset q$
11. $p \supset (q \supset r)$ and $(p \supset q) \supset r$
12. $p \supset (q \supset r)$ and $(p \cdot q) \supset r$
13. $p \vee (q \cdot r)$ and $(p \vee q) \cdot (p \vee r)$
14. $p \vee q$ and $(p \cdot \sim q) \vee q$
15. $p \vee (q \cdot r)$ and $(p \vee q) \cdot r$
16. $p \cdot q$ and $(p \vee \sim q) \cdot q$
17. p and $q \equiv (p \supset q)$
18. $p \supset q$ and $(p \vee q) \equiv q$
19. $p \cdot (q \vee r)$ and $(p \vee q) \cdot (p \vee r)$
20. $p \cdot (q \vee r)$ and $(p \cdot q) \vee (p \cdot r)$

V. NORMAL FORMS AND BOOLEAN EXPANSIONS

In this section we shall develop an alternative method for distinguishing between valid and invalid arguments by distinguishing between tautologous, contradictory, and contingent statement forms. First we observe that given a complicated statement form it is frequently possible to find a simpler one logically equivalent to it, to which the original form may be 'reduced' by means of certain algebraic operations. In treating the logic of compound statements and statement forms from the algebraic point of view, it is convenient to use a different notation for denial or negation. In the present section the negation of any expression will be symbolized by drawing a bar above it. In this notation, the familiar truths of De Morgan are symbolized as $\overline{p \cdot q} \equiv (\bar{p} \vee \bar{q})$ and $\overline{p \vee q} \equiv (\bar{p} \cdot \bar{q})$. All of the statement forms treated here are truth-functional, so that their status as tautologous, contradictory, or contingent remains unchanged when any part is replaced by a logically equivalent expression. Thus $p \vee \bar{p}$ is a tautology and remains one when p is replaced in it by $\bar{\bar{p}}$, since p and $\bar{\bar{p}}$ are logically equivalent by the principle of Double Negation.

Since $p \cdot (q \cdot r)$ and $(p \cdot q) \cdot r$ are logically equivalent, they may be indifferently written as $p \cdot q \cdot r$. Similarly, both $p \vee (q \vee r)$ and $(p \vee q) \vee r$ may be written as $p \vee q \vee r$. The logical equivalences involved are often referred to as principles of Association. The convention of dropping these unnecessary parentheses permits us to enunciate generalized statements of De Morgan's Theorems as $\overline{p_1 \cdot p_2 \cdot p_3 \cdot \ldots \cdot p_n} \equiv (\bar{p}_1 \vee \bar{p}_2 \vee \bar{p}_3 \vee \ldots \vee \bar{p}_n)$ and $\overline{p_1 \vee p_2 \vee p_3 \vee \ldots \vee p_n} \equiv (\bar{p}_1 \cdot \bar{p}_2 \cdot \bar{p}_3 \cdot \ldots \cdot \bar{p}_n)$. The two tautologies $[p \cdot (q \vee r)] \equiv [(p \cdot q) \vee (p \cdot r)]$ and $[p \vee (q \cdot r)] \equiv [(p \vee q) \cdot (p \vee r)]$ are often referred to as principles of Distribution. Generalized principles of Distribution may be expressed as

$$[p \cdot (q_1 \vee q_2 \vee \ldots \vee q_n)] \equiv [(p \cdot q_1) \vee (p \cdot q_2) \vee \ldots \vee (p \cdot q_n)]$$

and

$$[p \vee (q_1 \cdot q_2 \cdot \ldots \cdot q_n)] \equiv [(p \vee q_1) \cdot (p \vee q_2) \cdot \ldots \cdot (p \vee q_n)].$$

It is convenient to have four other principles of logical equivalence available for purposes of algebraic manipulation and transformation. First, the principles of Commutation, expressed as

$$(p \cdot q) \equiv (q \cdot p) \qquad \text{and} \qquad (p \vee q) \equiv (q \vee p).$$

Second, the principles of Tautology, which, stated as

$$p \equiv (p \vee p) \qquad \text{and} \qquad p \equiv (p \cdot p)$$

assure us that any statement, wherever it may occur, is replaceable by the disjunction (conjunction) both of whose disjuncts (conjuncts) are the same as the given statement, and vice versa. Third is the principle that any statement p is logically equivalent to the conjunction of itself with any tautology of the form $q \vee \bar{q}$, that is

$$p \equiv [p \cdot (q \vee \bar{q})].$$

Our fourth and final principle is the logical equivalence

$$p \equiv [p \vee (q \cdot \bar{q})]$$

which permits us to interchange p and $p \vee (q \cdot \bar{q})$ wherever either of them occurs.

It is clear that by invoking the defining equivalences

$$(p \supset q) \equiv (\bar{p} \vee q) \qquad \text{and} \qquad (p \equiv q) \equiv [(p \cdot q) \vee (\bar{p} \cdot \bar{q})]$$

material implications and equivalences can always be eliminated in favor of, or expressed in terms of, conjunctions, disjunctions, and negations. Moreover, by repeated uses of De Morgan's Theorems and Double Negation, any form can be replaced by a logically equivalent one in which no negation symbol applies to a compound part. Thus

$$\overline{\bar{p} \cdot [(\bar{q} \vee r) \cdot (s \cdot \bar{t})]}$$

is transformed by repeated applications of De Morgan's principles and Double Negation as follows:

$$\bar{\bar{p}} \vee \overline{[(\bar{q} \vee r) \cdot (s \cdot \bar{t})]}$$
$$p \vee [\overline{(\bar{q} \vee r)} \vee \overline{(s \cdot \bar{t})}]$$
$$p \vee [(\bar{q} \vee r) \vee (\bar{s} \vee \bar{\bar{t}})]$$
$$p \vee [(\bar{q} \vee r) \vee (\bar{s} \vee t)]$$

which becomes, by the principle of Association,

$$p \vee \bar{q} \vee r \vee \bar{s} \vee t$$

in which the negation symbol is applied only to the single variables q and s.

By the principle of Distribution we can easily change any given form into an equivalent one in which conjunction symbols

occur—if at all—only between single variables or their negations, or else into a different equivalent form in which disjunction
symbols occur—if at all—only between single variables or their
negations. Thus the expression

(1) $(p \lor q) \cdot (r \lor s)$

in which the conjunction symbol occurs between disjunctions,
reduces by repeated applications of the principles of Distribution
and Association into

(2) $(p \cdot r) \lor (q \cdot r) \lor (p \cdot s) \lor (q \cdot s)$

in which conjunction symbols connect single variables only.
And the expression

(3) $(p \cdot q) \lor (r \cdot s)$

in which the disjunction symbol occurs between conjunctions,
reduces by repeated applications of the other parts of the principles of Distribution and Association into

(4) $(p \lor r) \cdot (q \lor r) \cdot (p \lor s) \cdot (q \lor s)$

in which disjunction symbols connect single variables only.

Two 'normal forms' can be defined. A statement form is in
conjunctive normal form when in addition to statement variables it
contains no symbols other than those for conjunction, disjunction, and negation; negation symbols apply only to single
variables; and no disjunct is a conjunction, i.e., disjunction
symbols occur only between single variables or their negations.
Thus (1) and (4) above are in *conjunctive normal form*. A statement
form is in *disjunctive normal form* when in addition to statement
variables it contains no symbols other than those for conjunction,
disjunction, and negation; negation symbols apply only to
single variables; and no conjunct is a disjunction, i.e., conjunction
symbols occur only between single variables or their negations.
Thus (2) and (3) above are in *disjunctive normal form*.

Let us examine the moderately complicated form $(p \supset \bar{q}) \supset$
$(p \equiv \bar{q})$ to see what gain in perspicuity is achieved by reducing

it to disjunctive normal form. By replacing the material implication symbols by their definitions, the initial expression is reduced first to

$$(\bar{p} \vee \bar{q}) \supset (p \equiv \bar{q})$$

and then to

$$\overline{(\bar{p} \vee \bar{q})} \vee (p \equiv \bar{q}).$$

Replacing the material equivalence symbol by its definition, we obtain

$$\overline{(\bar{p} \vee \bar{q})} \vee [(p \cdot \bar{q}) \vee (\bar{p} \cdot \bar{\bar{q}})].$$

Applying De Morgan's principle we obtain

$$(\bar{\bar{p}} \cdot \bar{\bar{q}}) \vee [(p \cdot \bar{q}) \vee (\bar{p} \cdot \bar{\bar{q}})]$$

which by the principles of Double Negation and Association becomes

$$(p \cdot q) \vee (p \cdot \bar{q}) \vee (\bar{p} \cdot q).$$

Although it is already in disjunctive normal form, it can be further simplified by the following transformations. First we apply the principle of Tautology to replace the first disjunct by its 'double', obtaining

$$(p \cdot q) \vee (p \cdot q) \vee (p \cdot \bar{q}) \vee (\bar{p} \cdot q).$$

Then we rearrange the terms by simply commuting or interchanging the second and third disjuncts, to get

$$(p \cdot q) \vee (p \cdot \bar{q}) \vee (p \cdot q) \vee (\bar{p} \cdot q).$$

Using the principle of Distribution on the first pair of disjuncts (taking the first equivalence expressed in the principle *in reverse order*) we obtain

$$[p \cdot (q \vee \bar{q})] \vee (p \cdot q) \vee (\bar{p} \cdot q)$$

and using it again on the two right hand disjuncts we get

$$[p \cdot (q \vee \bar{q})] \vee [(p \vee \bar{p}) \cdot q].$$

Now by the principle that the conjunction of any statement p with a tautology of the form $q \vee \bar{q}$ is logically equivalent to the statement itself, we obtain first

$$p \vee [(p \vee \bar{p}) \cdot q]$$

and finally

$$p \vee q$$

which is logically equivalent to, but much simpler than the form with which we began.*

The term 'normal form' is sometimes reserved for more specific types of expressions. These more specific types are also called *Boolean Expansions* or *Boolean normal forms*, after the British logician George Boole (1815–1864). A statement form containing the variables p, q, r, . . . is said to be in disjunctive Boolean normal form, or a disjunctive Boolean Expansion, provided that it is in disjunctive normal form, every disjunct contains exactly one occurrence of every variable (either the variable or its negation), the variables occur in alphabetical order in each disjunct, and no two disjuncts are the same. The disjunctive Boolean Expansion of $p \vee q$ is formed by first replacing p by $p \cdot (q \vee \bar{q})$ and q by $(p \vee \bar{p}) \cdot q$ to obtain the equivalent expression $p \cdot (q \vee \bar{q}) \vee (p \vee \bar{p}) \cdot q$, then using the Distribution and Association rules to obtain $(p \cdot q) \vee (p \cdot \bar{q}) \vee (p \cdot q) \vee (\bar{p} \cdot q)$, and finally cancelling out any repetitions of the same disjunct by the rules of Commutation and Tautology, which results in $(p \cdot q) \vee (p \cdot \bar{q}) \vee (\bar{p} \cdot q)$. The disjunctive Boolean Expansion of any non-contradictory statement form can be obtained by the same general method.

A statement form containing the variables p, q, r, . . . is said to be in conjunctive Boolean normal form, or a conjunctive Boolean Expansion, provided that it is in conjunctive normal form, every conjunct contains exactly one occurrence of every variable (either the variable or its negation), the variables occur in alphabetical order in each conjunct, and no two conjuncts are the same. The conjunctive Boolean Expansion of $p \cdot q$ is formed by first replacing p by $p \vee (q \cdot \bar{q})$ and q by $(p \cdot \bar{p}) \vee q$ to

---

* An application of normal forms to electrical circuits (parallel connections being representable by 'v' and series connections being representable by '·') has been made by Claude E. Shannon, "A Symbolic Analysis of Relay and Switching Circuits", *Transactions of the American Institute of Electrical Engineers*, vol. 57 (1938), pp. 713–723.

An informal account of the above and several other interesting applications can be found in John E. Pfeiffer's article "Symbolic Logic", in *Scientific American*, Vol. 183, No. 6, December 1950. Cf. also "Logic Machines" by Martin Gardner, *Ibid.*, Vol. 186, No. 3, March 1952.

Mendelson 21-23
Brown & Stuermann 251-7

obtain $[p \vee (q \cdot \bar{q})] \cdot [(p \cdot \bar{p}) \vee q]$, then using the Distribution and Association rules to obtain $(p \vee q) \cdot (p \vee \bar{q}) \cdot (p \vee q) \cdot (\bar{p} \vee q)$, and finally cancelling out any repetition of the same conjunct by the rules of Commutation and Tautology, which results in $(p \vee q) \cdot (p \vee \bar{q}) \cdot (\bar{p} \vee q)$. The conjunctive Boolean Expansion of any non-tautologous statement form is easily obtained by the same general method, and can be used for deciding whether the original form is contradictory. Any conjunctive Boolean Expansion containing n variables and 2^n conjuncts is reducible to an explicit contradiction. Thus the conjunctive Boolean Expansion $(p \vee q) \cdot (p \vee \bar{q}) \cdot (\bar{p} \vee q) \cdot (\bar{p} \vee \bar{q})$ is equivalent by the rule of Distribution to $[p \vee (q \cdot \bar{q})] \cdot [\bar{p} \vee (q \cdot \bar{q})]$, which is equivalent to the explicit contradiction $p \cdot \bar{p}$. It is equally obvious that the conjunctive Boolean Expansion of any contradiction will contain 2^n conjuncts if it involves n variables. Hence the general rule is that a statement form containing n variables is contradictory if and only if it has a conjunctive Boolean Expansion which contains 2^n conjuncts.

The negation of a conjunctive Boolean Expansion is reducible by repeated applications of De Morgan's Theorem and Double Negation to a logically equivalent disjunctive Boolean Expansion which contains the same variables and has the same number of disjuncts as the original conjunctive Boolean Expansion has conjuncts. Thus the conjunctive Boolean Expansion $(p \vee q \vee r) \cdot (p \vee q \vee \bar{r}) \cdot (\bar{p} \vee \bar{q} \vee r)$ has its negation $\overline{(p \vee q \vee r) \cdot (p \vee q \vee \bar{r}) \cdot (\bar{p} \vee \bar{q} \vee r)}$ logically equivalent to the disjunctive Boolean Expansion $(\bar{p} \cdot \bar{q} \cdot \bar{r}) \vee (\bar{p} \cdot \bar{q} \cdot r) \vee (p \cdot q \cdot \bar{r})$. Since the negation of a contradiction is a tautology, and a conjunctive Boolean Expansion containing n variables is a contradiction if and only if it contains 2^n conjuncts, it follows that a disjunctive Boolean Expansion containing n variables is a tautology if and only if it contains 2^n disjuncts.

That such a disjunctive Boolean Expansion must be tautologous can perhaps be seen more clearly by the following considerations. In the first place, since we are concerned with truth-functional compounds only, to speak of substituting statements for the statement variables of a form is equivalent to speaking of an assignment of truth values to the variables of that form. Now just as each row of a truth table with n initial or guide columns represents a different assignment of truth values to the n statement variables involved, so each disjunct of the Boolean Expansion represents a different assignment of truth values to the variables they contain. And just as the 2^n rows of a truth table having n initial or guide columns represent all possible assignments of truth values to its variables, so the 2^n disjuncts of a disjunctive Boolean Expansion represent all possible assignments of truth values to its variables. Since the 2^n disjuncts represent all possible assignments of truth values to its variables, at least one of them must be true. And since it asserts only that at least one of its disjuncts is true, any disjunctive Boolean Expansion containing n variables and 2^n disjuncts is tautologous.

It was pointed out in the preceding section that an argument is valid if and only if its corresponding conditional statement (whose antecedent is the conjunction of the argument's premises and whose consequent is the argument's conclusion) is a tautology. Since counting the number of disjuncts of its disjunctive Boolean Expansion permits us to decide whether or not a given form is a tautology, this provides us with an alternative method of deciding the validity of arguments. Thus the argument form $p \vee q$, $\sim p$ $\therefore$ q is proved valid by constructing the disjunctive Boolean Expansion of its corresponding conditional $[(p \vee q) \cdot \bar{p}]$ $\supset q$, and observing that the number of its disjuncts is 2^2.

Since the negation of a tautology is a contradiction, an argument is valid if and only if the negation of its corresponding conditional is a contradiction. Hence another method of deciding the validity of an argument is to form the conjunctive Boolean Expansion of the negation of its corresponding conditional and count the number of its conjuncts. If it contains n distinct variables and has 2^n conjuncts, then the argument is valid; otherwise it is invalid.

EXERCISES

I. For each of the following find as simple an equivalent normal form as you can:

1. $p \vee (q \cdot \bar{p})$

2. $q \cdot (p \vee \bar{q})$

3. $(p \vee q) \cdot (q \vee r) \cdot (p \vee r) \cdot r$

4. $(p \cdot q) \vee (q \cdot r) \vee (p \cdot r) \vee r$

5. $p \cdot \{p \supset [q \cdot (q \supset r)]\}$

6. $p \vee \{\bar{p} \supset [q \vee (\bar{q} \supset r)]\}$

7. $(p \vee q) \supset [(p \supset q) \supset \overline{(q \vee \bar{q})}]$

8. $(p \cdot \bar{q}) \supset [(p \supset q) \supset \overline{(p \cdot \bar{q})}]$

9. $\{p \cdot [(q \cdot r) \vee \bar{p}]\} \vee \{(p \cdot q) \cdot [r \supset (\bar{p} \cdot \bar{r})]\} \vee \{p \cdot [\bar{p} \supset (\bar{p} \cdot q \cdot \bar{r})]\}$

10. $(p \cdot q) \vee (\bar{p} \cdot \bar{q} \cdot r) \vee (\bar{p} \cdot q) \vee (p \cdot \bar{q} \cdot r) \vee (p \cdot \bar{q}) \vee (p \cdot q \cdot r) \vee (\bar{p} \cdot q \cdot r)$

II. Characterize the statement forms of Exercise I on page 31 as tautologous, contradictory, or contingent by counting the terms of their Boolean Expansions.

III. Decide the validity or invalidity of the arguments in Exercise II on page 25 by counting the number of disjuncts in the disjunctive Boolean Expansions of their corresponding conditionals.

CHAPTER THREE

The Method of Deduction

I. FORMAL PROOF OF VALIDITY

When we consider arguments which contain more than two or three different simple statements as constituents, it becomes cumbersome and tedious to use truth tables or Boolean Expansions to test their validity. A more convenient method of establishing the validity of some arguments is to *deduce* their conclusions from their premises by a sequence of shorter, more elementary arguments already known to be valid. Consider, for example, the following argument, in which six different simple statements occur:

> Andrews was at his office or else had gone to Bridge-port, and either Andrews was at his office or he missed the call from Charleston.
> If Andrews was at his office then Davis saw him.
> If Davis saw him then the extradition papers were signed.

If Andrews went to Bridgeport and missed the call
from Charleston, then if a felony was involved the
extradition papers were signed.
The extradition papers were not signed.
Therefore no felony was involved.

It may be translated into our symbolism as

$$(A \text{ v } B) \cdot (A \text{ v } C)$$
$$A \supset D$$
$$D \supset E$$
$$(B \cdot C) \supset (F \supset E)$$
$$\sim E$$
$$\overline{\therefore \sim F}$$

To prove this argument valid by the methods of the preceding
chapter would require a truth table of sixty-four rows, or a
Boolean Expansion with sixty-four conjuncts or disjuncts. But
its conclusion can validly be deduced from its premises in just
half a dozen steps. From the second and third premises, $A \supset D$
and $D \supset E$, we validly infer $A \supset E$ by a Hypothetical Syllogism.
From $A \supset E$ and the fifth premiss, $\sim E$, we validly infer $\sim A$ by
modus tollens. By the principle of Distribution the first premiss,
$(A \text{ v } B) \cdot (A \text{ v } C)$, is logically equivalent to $A \text{ v } (B \cdot C)$, which may
therefore be validly inferred from it. From these last two results,
$A \text{ v } (B \cdot C)$ and $\sim A$, we validly infer $B \cdot C$ by a Disjunctive Syllogism. From that and the fourth premiss, $(B \cdot C) \supset (F \supset E)$,
we validly infer $F \supset E$ by *modus ponens*. Finally, from $F \supset E$ and
the fifth premiss, $\sim E$, by *modus tollens* we validly infer $\sim F$, the
conclusion of the original argument. That its conclusion follows
from its premises by six elementary valid arguments *proves*
the original argument to be valid.

A more concise way of writing out this proof of validity is to
list the premises and the statements which follow from them
in one column, with the latter's justifications written beside
them. It is convenient to put the conclusion to the right of the
last premiss, separated from it by a slanting line, which auto-
matically labels all of the statements above it as premises. The

formal proof of validity can be written as

1. $(A \vee B) \cdot (A \vee C)$
2. $A \supset D$
3. $D \supset E$
4. $(B \cdot C) \supset (F \supset E)$
5. $\sim E$ $/ \therefore \sim F$
6. $A \supset E$ from 2, 3 by a Hypothetical Syllogism
7. $\sim A$ from 6, 5 by *modus tollens*
8. $A \vee (B \cdot C)$ from 1 by Distribution
9. $B \cdot C$ from 8, 7 by a Disjunctive Syllogism
10. $F \supset E$ from 4, 9 by *modus ponens*
11. $\sim F$ from 10, 5 by *modus tollens*

For the sake of definiteness, we must specify what valid arguments can be regarded as sufficiently elementary to be used in the method of deduction. It is convenient to provide a list of elementary valid argument forms, and to permit the use of any argument which is a substitution instance of one of the valid argument forms listed. We begin our list with *modus ponens*: $p \supset q$, $p \therefore q$. It should be observed that step 10 of the preceding proof follows from steps 4 and 9 by *modus ponens*, even though *modus ponens* is not *the* form of the argument: $(B \cdot C) \supset (F \supset E)$, $B \cdot C \therefore F \supset E$.

We define a formal proof of validity for a given argument as a sequence of statements each of which is either a premiss of that argument or follows from preceding statements by an elementary valid argument, and such that the last statement in the sequence is the conclusion of the argument whose validity is being proved. This definition is completed by specifying that an elementary valid argument is a substitution instance of one of the argument forms in the following list:

ELEMENTARY VALID ARGUMENT FORMS

1. *Modus Ponens* (M.P.): $p \supset q, p \therefore q.$
2. *Modus Tollens* (M.T.): $p \supset q, \sim q \therefore \sim p.$
3. Hypothetical Syllogism (H.S.):
$$p \supset q, q \supset r \therefore p \supset r.$$

4. Disjunctive Syllogism (D.S.):
$$p \vee q, \sim p \therefore q.$$

5. Constructive Dilemma (C.D.):
$$(p \supset q) \cdot (r \supset s), p \vee r \therefore q \vee s.$$

6. Destructive Dilemma (D.D.):
$$(p \supset q) \cdot (r \supset s), \sim q \vee \sim s \therefore \sim p \vee \sim r.$$

7. Simplification (Simp.): $p \cdot q \therefore p.$

8. Conjunction (Conj.): $p, q \therefore p \cdot q.$

9. Addition (Add.): $p \therefore p \vee q.$

Logically equivalent expressions may be substituted for each other wherever they occur.

10. De Morgan's Theorems (De M.): $\sim(p \cdot q) \equiv (\sim p \vee \sim q).$
    $\sim(p \vee q) \equiv (\sim p \cdot \sim q).$

11. Commutation (Com.): $(p \vee q) \equiv (q \vee p).$
    $(p \cdot q) \equiv (q \cdot p).$

12. Association (Assoc.): $[p \vee (q \vee r)] \equiv [(p \vee q) \vee r].$
    $[p \cdot (q \cdot r)] \equiv [(p \cdot q) \cdot r].$

13. Distribution (Dist.): $[p \cdot (q \vee r)] \equiv [(p \cdot q) \vee (p \cdot r)].$
    $[p \vee (q \cdot r)] \equiv [(p \vee q) \cdot (p \vee r)].$

14. Double Negation (D.N.): $p \equiv \sim \sim p.$

15. Transposition (Trans.): $(p \supset q) \equiv (\sim q \supset \sim p).$

16. Definition of Material Implication (Impl.):
    $(p \supset q) \equiv (\sim p \vee q).$

17. Definitions of Material Equivalence (Equiv.):
    $(p \equiv q) \equiv [(p \supset q) \cdot (q \supset p)].$
    $(p \equiv q) \equiv [(p \cdot q) \vee (\sim p \cdot \sim q)].$

18. Exportation (Exp.): $[(p \cdot q) \supset r] \equiv [p \supset (q \supset r)].$

19. Tautology (Taut.): $p \equiv (p \vee p).$
    $p \equiv (p \cdot p).$

The first nine argument forms listed are easily validated by the method of truth tables. Since we are dealing with truth-functionally compound statements exclusively, if any part of a statement is replaced by an expression which is logically equivalent to that part, the truth value of the resulting statement is the same as that of the original statement. This is sometimes called the principle of Substitution, sometimes the principle of Extensionality.* The remainder of the list contains all those logical equivalences which are certified as intersubstitutable. The names listed are all standard: some of them have been borrowed from corresponding identities in mathematics proper. Formal proofs of validity can be written more concisely by using the abbreviations suggested.

Some simple argument forms, although perfectly valid, are not included in the preceding list of nineteen elementary valid argument forms. Although the argument $A \cdot B \therefore B$ is obviously valid, its form $p \cdot q \therefore q$ is not included in the list. Hence B does not follow from $A \cdot B$ by any single elementary valid argument form *as defined by our list*. It can be deduced, however, using two elementary valid arguments, and the formal proof of validity for the given argument can be set down as

1. $A \cdot B / \therefore B$
2. $B \cdot A$ 1, Com.
3. B 2, Simp.

We could add the intuitively valid argument form $p \cdot q \therefore q$ to our list, but if we began to expand our list in this way there would be no stopping, and we should end up with a list which was too long and therefore unmanageable. Nevertheless, the given list does contain some redundancies. For example, *modus tollens* could be dropped from our list without any real weakening of the machinery, for any step deduced by it could be deduced by other forms in the list. Thus in our first proof, step 7, $\sim A$, which was deduced from steps 6 and 5, $A \supset E$ and $\sim E$, by *modus tollens*, could have been deduced without it, since $\sim E \supset \sim A$ follows from $A \supset E$ by the principle of Transposition, and $\sim A$ from $\sim E \supset \sim A$ and $\sim E$ by *modus ponens*. But *modus tollens* is so common and intuitive a principle of inference that it has been included anyway, and others have also been included for convenience despite their logical redundancy.

The test of whether or not a given sequence of statements is a formal proof is *effective*. That is, direct observation will suffice to decide whether or not every step beyond the premises actually

---

* It will be stated more formally, in an appropriate context, and demonstrated, in Chapter Seven.

does follow from preceding steps by an elementary valid argument. No 'thinking' is required: neither thinking about what the statements mean, nor using logical intuition to check the validity of any step's deduction. Even where the 'justification' of a step is not written beside it, there is a finite, mechanical procedure for deciding whether or not the step is legitimate. Each step is preceded by a finite number of other steps, and only a finite number of elementary valid argument forms are admissible. Although time consuming, it can be verified by inspection whether the step in question follows from any single preceding step or any pair of preceding steps by any one of the elementary valid argument forms listed. For example, in the foregoing proof, step 2, $B \cdot A$, is preceded only by step 1, $A \cdot B$. Its legitimacy can be decided by observing that although it does not follow from $A \cdot B$ by *modus ponens*, nor by *modus tollens*, nor by a Hypothetical Syllogism, and so on through number 10, when we come to number 11 we can *see*, simply by observing the forms, that step 2 follows from step 1 by the principle of Commutation. Similarly, the legitimacy of any step can be decided by a finite number of observations, none of which involves anything more than comparing shapes or patterns. To preserve this property of effectiveness we lay down the rule that only one step should be taken at a time. Although the explanatory notation beside each step is not, strictly speaking, part of the proof, it is helpful, and should always be included.

Although the test of whether or not a given sequence of statements is a formal proof is effective, *constructing* such a formal proof is *not* an effective procedure. In this respect the present method differs from the methods of the preceding chapter. The use of truth tables and Boolean Expansions is *completely* mechanical: given any argument of the general sort with which we are now concerned, its validity can always be tested by following the simple rules presented in Chapter Two. But in constructing a formal proof of validity on the basis of the nineteen elementary valid argument forms listed, it is necessary to *think* or 'figure out' where to begin and how to proceed. Although we have no effective or purely mechanical method of procedure, it is usually much easier to construct a formal proof of validity than to write out a truth table or Boolean Expansion involving hundreds or even thousands of rows or terms.

In the absence of mechanical rules for the construction of formal proofs of validity, two hints on procedure may be suggested. One is simply to begin with the premisses and deduce conclusions by elementary valid arguments, for as more and more statements become available, the greater is the likelihood of being able to see a way of arriving at the conclusion of the argument to be proved valid. The other method is to work backward from the conclusion by looking for some statement or pair of statements from which it could be deduced by an elementary valid argument, and then trying to deduce those intermediate statements from still others, and so on, until you come to some which are derivable from the original premisses. A judicious combination of these two methods is often the best way to proceed. Practice, of course, is the best method of acquiring facility in using the method of deduction.

EXERCISES

I. Each of the following is a formal proof of validity for the indicated argument. State the 'justification' for each step which is not a premiss:

1. 1. $A \supset B$
   2. $\sim(B \lor C) / \therefore \sim A$
   3. $\sim B \cdot \sim C$
   4. $\sim B$
   5. $\sim A$

2. 1. $\sim D \lor E$
   2. $\sim F \supset \sim E / \therefore D \supset F$
   3. $D \supset E$
   4. $E \supset F$
   5. $D \supset F$

3. 1. $(G \supset H) \cdot (I \supset H)$
   2. $J \supset (G \lor I)$
   3. J $/ \therefore H$
   4. $G \lor I$
   5. $H \lor H$
   6. H

4. 1. $(K \cdot L) \lor (M \cdot N)$
   2. $K \supset \sim K$ $/ \therefore M$
   3. $\sim K \lor \sim K$
   4. $\sim K$
   5. $\sim K \lor \sim L$
   6. $\sim(K \cdot L)$
   7. $M \cdot N$
   8. M

5.   1. $(O \supset P)\cdot(Q \supset R)$
    2. $(P \supset S)\cdot(R \supset T)$
    3. $S \supset \sim T$
    4. $O \supset Q$ $/\therefore \sim O$
    5. $\sim S \text{ v} \sim T$
    6. $\sim P \text{ v} \sim R$
    7. $\sim O \text{ v} \sim Q$
    8. $O \supset \sim Q$
    9. $\sim Q \supset \sim O$
  10. $O \supset \sim O$
  11. $\sim O \text{ v} \sim O$
  12. $\sim O$

6.   1. $U \supset (V \supset W)$
    2. $(W\cdot X) \supset Y$
    3. $\sim Z \supset (X\cdot\sim Y)/\therefore\ U \supset (V \supset Z)$
    4. $(U\cdot V) \supset W$
    5. $W \supset (X \supset Y)$
    6. $(U\cdot V) \supset (X \supset Y)$
    7. $\sim(X\cdot\sim Y) \supset \sim\sim Z$
    8. $\sim(X\cdot\sim Y) \supset Z$
    9. $(\sim X \text{ v} \sim\sim Y) \supset Z$
  10. $(\sim X \text{ v } Y) \supset Z$
  11. $(X \supset Y) \supset Z$
  12. $(U\cdot V) \supset Z$
  13. $U \supset (V \supset Z)$

7.   1. $(A \text{ v } B) \supset (C\cdot D)$
    2. $(D \text{ v } E) \supset F$ $/\therefore\ A \supset F$
    3. $\sim(A \text{ v } B) \text{ v } (C\cdot D)$
    4. $[\sim(A \text{ v } B) \text{ v } C]\cdot[\sim(A \text{ v } B) \text{ v } D]$
    5. $[\sim(A \text{ v } B) \text{ v } D]\cdot[\sim(A \text{ v } B) \text{ v } C]$
    6. $\sim(A \text{ v } B) \text{ v } D$
    7. $[\sim(A \text{ v } B) \text{ v } D] \text{ v } E$
    8. $\sim(A \text{ v } B) \text{ v } (D \text{ v } E)$
    9. $(A \text{ v } B) \supset (D \text{ v } E)$
  10. $(A \text{ v } B) \supset F$
  11. $\sim F \supset \sim(A \text{ v } B)$
  12. $\sim\sim F \text{ v} \sim(A \text{ v } B)$
  13. $\sim\sim F \text{ v } (\sim A\cdot\sim B)$

   14. $(\sim\sim F \text{ v} \sim A)\cdot(\sim\sim F \text{ v} \sim B)$
   15. $\sim\sim F \text{ v} \sim A$
   16. $\sim F \supset \sim A$
   17. $A \supset F$

8.   1. $[G \supset (H\cdot I)]\cdot[J \supset (H\cdot K)]$
     2. $[(L \supset \sim G)\cdot M] \supset N$
     3. $(M \supset N) \supset (L\cdot J)$ $/\therefore I \text{ v } K$
     4. $(L \supset \sim G) \supset (M \supset N)$
     5. $(L \supset \sim G) \supset (L\cdot J)$
     6. $\sim(L \supset \sim G) \text{ v } (L\cdot J)$
     7. $\sim(\sim L \text{ v} \sim G) \text{ v } (L\cdot J)$
     8. $(\sim\sim L\cdot\sim\sim G) \text{ v } (L\cdot J)$
     9. $(L\cdot\sim\sim G) \text{ v } (L\cdot J)$
   10. $(L\cdot G) \text{ v } (L\cdot J)$
   11. $L\cdot(G \text{ v } J)$
   12. $(G \text{ v } J)\cdot L$
   13. $G \text{ v } J$
   14. $(H\cdot I) \text{ v } (H\cdot K)$
   15. $H\cdot(I \text{ v } K)$
   16. $(I \text{ v } K)\cdot H$
   17. $I \text{ v } K$

9.   1. $O \supset (P \supset Q)$
     2. $(P\cdot Q) \supset (O\cdot R)$
     3. P $/\therefore (\sim O \text{ v} \sim Q) \supset (\sim O\cdot\sim Q)$
     4. $(O\cdot P) \supset Q$
     5. $(P\cdot O) \supset Q$
     6. $P \supset (O \supset Q)$
     7. $O \supset Q$
     8. $P \supset [Q \supset (O\cdot R)]$
     9. $Q \supset (O\cdot R)$
   10. $\sim Q \text{ v } (O\cdot R)$
   11. $(\sim Q \text{ v } O)\cdot(\sim Q \text{ v } R)$
   12. $\sim Q \text{ v } O$
   13. $Q \supset O$
   14. $(O \supset Q)\cdot(Q \supset O)$
   15. $O \equiv Q$
   16. $(O\cdot Q) \text{ v } (\sim O\cdot\sim Q)$
   17. $\sim\sim(O\cdot Q) \text{ v } (\sim O\cdot\sim Q)$

18. $\sim(O \cdot Q) \supset (\sim O \cdot \sim Q)$
19. $(\sim O \text{ v} \sim Q) \supset (\sim O \cdot \sim Q)$

10. 1. $S \supset (T \cdot U)$
   2. $T \supset W$
   3. $(X \supset \sim Y) \supset \sim W$
   4. $T \supset (S \cdot \sim X)$ $/ \therefore T \supset X$
   5. $\sim S \text{ v} (T \cdot U)$
   6. $(\sim S \text{ v} T) \cdot (\sim S \text{ v} U)$
   7. $\sim S \text{ v} T$
   8. $S \supset T$
   9. $S \supset W$
  10. $\sim\sim W \supset \sim(X \supset \sim Y)$
  11. $W \supset \sim(X \supset \sim Y)$
  12. $S \supset \sim(X \supset \sim Y)$
  13. $S \supset \sim(\sim X \text{ v} \sim Y)$
  14. $S \supset (\sim\sim X \cdot \sim\sim Y)$
  15. $\sim S \text{ v} (\sim\sim X \cdot \sim\sim Y)$
  16. $(\sim S \text{ v} \sim\sim X) \cdot (\sim S \text{ v} \sim\sim Y)$
  17. $\sim S \text{ v} \sim\sim X$
  18. $\sim(S \cdot \sim X)$
  19. $\sim T$
  20. $\sim T \text{ v} X$
  21. $T \supset X$

II. Construct a formal proof of validity for each of the following arguments, in each case using the suggested notation:

1. Either the governor did not hear the question or he is reluctant to take a stand. He did hear the question. Therefore he must be reluctant to take a stand. (H,R)

2. My coat is either in the hall or in the bedroom. It is not in the bedroom. Therefore it is in the hall. (H,B)

3. It is not true that Roosevelt carried either Maine or Vermont. Therefore Roosevelt did not carry Maine. (M,V)

4. If I work I make money. If I don't work I enjoy myself. Therefore, either I make money or I enjoy myself. (W,M,E)

5. If the switch is turned the light will go on. Hence if the switch is turned either the light will go on or something is wrong with the wiring. (S,L,W)

6. Military production will be increased only if the supply of consumer goods is curtailed. If the supply of consumer goods is curtailed the standard of living is bound to fall. Military production will be increased. So the standard of living is bound to fall. (*M,C,F*)

7. It was either a wolf or a dog that howled last night. Had it been a wolf the flock would have been disturbed. But the flock was not disturbed. Therefore it must have been a dog. (*W,D,F*)

8. If Brown is late the meeting will be delayed. So if both Adams and Brown are late the meeting will be delayed. (*B,D,A*)

9. If the demand stays constant and prices are lowered then the volume of business will increase. If the lowering of prices will cause the volume of business to increase, then we can control the market. Demand is bound to stay constant. Thus we can control the market. (*D,P,B,C*)

10. If he had a gun then he would have used it if he had seen his assailant. He had a gun although he didn't use it. Therefore he did not see his assailant. (*G,U,S*)

11. If I go to my first class tomorrow I must get up very early, and if I go to the party tonight I will stay up late. If I stay up late and get up very early then I will have to get along on only six hours of sleep. I cannot get along on only six hours of sleep. So I must either miss my first class tomorrow or stay away from the party tonight. (*C,E,P,L,S*)

12. If you accuse him and bring proof then he will be convicted, but if you accuse him and do not bring proof then he will not be convicted. Hence if you accuse him then your bringing proof will be equivalent to his being convicted. (*A,B,C*)

13. Had either the President or the Secretary of Defense been notified, a statement would have been issued and a special cabinet meeting called. Had a statement been issued there would have been a special newscast. There was, however, no special newscast. So the President could not have been notified. (*P,S,I,C,N*)

14. If either Jones or Smith wins the nomination then the campaign will be well financed and victory will be assured. Therefore either Jones will not win the nomination or the campaign will be well financed. (*J,S,C,V*)

15. If you marry a rich girl you will be wealthy, but if you marry a poor girl you will be able to manage your own business. You will marry either a rich girl or a poor girl. However, if you marry a rich girl

you will not be able to manage your own business, while if you marry a poor girl you will not be wealthy. Therefore you will be able to manage your own business if and only if you are not wealthy. (R,W,P,M)

16. Either the dam is out, or the river has overflowed its banks and the fields will be flooded. If the dam is out then the fields will be flooded. Therefore the fields will be flooded. (D,R,F)

17. If he enters the tournament then if he does his best he will win the first round. If he wins the first round and goes on to the finals then he will set a new course record. If he plays his usual game then he will go on to the finals but will not set a new course record. Therefore if he enters the tournament then if he does his best he will not play his usual game. (E,B,W,G,S,U)

18. If I go to the wedding I must spend the week-end in Miami. But if I spend the week-end in Miami then I won't be able to pay both the landlord and the grocer. If I don't pay the landlord I'll have to dodge him all month, and I can't possibly dodge him all month. Furthermore, I do have to pay the grocer. So I won't be able to go to the wedding. (W,M,L,G,D)

19. If he signs the bill the governor will antagonize labor, and if he antagonizes labor he cannot be reelected. But if he vetoes the bill he will break with the majority of his own party. The governor certainly cannot be reelected if he breaks with the majority of his own party. The governor must be reelected or his political career is finished. He must either sign the bill or veto it. So it looks as though the governor's political career is finished. (S,A,R,V,B,F)

20. Had he married a beautiful woman he would have been jealous, and had he married a homely woman he would have been disgusted. Had he been either jealous or disgusted he would have been unhappy. He was not unhappy. Therefore he did not marry either a beautiful woman or a homely one. (B,J,H,D,U)

21. If Robinson went to New York then he took his wife, and if he went on business then he took his secretary. So if Robinson went to New York on business then he took both his wife and his secretary. (N,W,B,S)

22. If you read the *Times* you will be bored, and if you read the *Mirror* you will be disgusted. So if you read either the *Times* or the *Mirror* you will be either bored or disgusted. (T,B,M,D).

23. If Henry goes east then he will visit New England. If Henry goes east then if he visits New England he will tour Massachusetts. If Henry visits New England then if he tours Massachusetts he will stop off in Boston. Therefore if Henry goes east then he will stop off in Boston. (E,N,M,B)

24. If old Henning wants to retire then he will either turn the presidency over to his son or sell the business. If old Henning needs money then he will either sell the business or borrow additional capital. Old Henning will never sell the business. Therefore if he neither turns the presidency over to his son nor borrows additional capital then he neither wants to retire nor needs money. (R,T,S,N,B)

25. If the fugitives head either north or east, then if we go either south or west we shall not meet them and our pursuit will be in vain. If we don't meet them or we fail to recognize them then they will have escaped for good. So if the fugitives head north then if we go south then they will have escaped for good. (N,E,S,W,M,P,R,G)

II. THE RULE OF CONDITIONAL PROOF

In this section we introduce a new rule to use in the method of deduction: the rule of Conditional Proof. This rule can be applied only to arguments whose conclusions are conditional statements. The new rule can best be explained and justified by reference to the principle of Exportation and the correspondence, noted in Chapter Two, between valid argument forms and tautologies.

To every argument there corresponds a conditional statement whose antecedent is the conjunction of the argument's premises and whose consequent is the conclusion of the argument. As has been remarked, an argument is valid if and only if its corresponding conditional is a tautology. If an argument has a conditional statement for its conclusion, which we may symbolize as $A \supset C$, then if we symbolize the conjunction of its premises as P, the argument is valid if and only if the conditional

(1) $$P \supset (A \supset C)$$

is a tautology. If we can deduce the conclusion $A \supset C$ from the premises in P by a sequence of elementary valid arguments, we thereby prove the argument to be valid and the associated conditional (1) to be a tautology. By the principle of Exportation, (1) is logically equivalent to

(2) $(P \cdot A) \supset C.$

But (2) is the conditional associated with a somewhat different argument. This second argument has as its premises all of the premises of the first argument *plus* an additional premiss which is the antecedent of the conclusion of the first argument. And the conclusion of the second argument is the consequent of the conclusion of the first argument. Now if we deduce the conclusion of the second argument, C, from the premises in $P \cdot A$ by a sequence of elementary valid arguments, we thereby prove that its associated conditional statement (2) is a tautology. But since (1) and (2) are logically equivalent, this fact proves that (1) is a tautology also, from which it follows that the original argument, with one less premiss and the conditional conclusion $A \supset C$, is valid also. Now the rule of Conditional Proof permits us to infer the validity of any argument $P \therefore A \supset C$ from a formal proof of validity for the argument $P, A \therefore C$.

Given any argument whose conclusion is a conditional statement, a proof of its validity using the rule of Conditional Proof, that is, a conditional proof of its validity, is constructed by assuming the antecedent of its conclusion as an additional premiss and then deducing the consequent of its conclusion by a sequence of elementary valid arguments. Thus a conditional proof of validity for the argument $(A \lor B) \supset (C \cdot D)$, $(D \lor E) \supset F \therefore A \supset F$ may be written as

1. $(A \lor B) \supset (C \cdot D)$
2. $(D \lor E) \supset F$ $/\therefore A \supset F$
3. A $/\therefore F$ (C.P.)
4. $A \lor B$ 3, Add.
5. $C \cdot D$ 1, 4, M.P.
6. $D \cdot C$ 5, Com.
7. D 6, Simp.
8. $D \lor E$ 7, Add.
9. F 2, 8, M.P.

Here the second slant line and three dot 'therefore' symbol, as well as the parenthesized 'C.P.', indicate that the rule of Conditional Proof is being used. The foregoing proof should be compared with the seventeen-step proof given in Exercise 7 on pages 47–48.

Since the rule of Conditional Proof can be used in dealing with any valid argument having a conditional statement as conclusion, it can be applied more than once in the course of the same deduction. Thus a conditional proof of validity for

$$A \supset (B \supset C), B \supset (C \supset D) \therefore A \supset (B \supset D)$$

will be a proof of validity for

$$A \supset (B \supset C), B \supset (C \supset D), A \therefore B \supset D$$

and since the latter itself has a conditional conclusion, it can be given a conditional proof by proving the validity of

$$A \supset (B \supset C), B \supset (C \supset D), A, B \therefore D.$$

Each use of the conditional method should be signalled by an additional slant line and 'therefore' sign, in addition to the notation '(C.P.)'. The suggested proof would be written:

1. $A \supset (B \supset C)$
2. $B \supset (C \supset D)$ $/\therefore A \supset (B \supset D)$
3. A $/\therefore B \supset D$ (C.P.)
4. B $/\therefore D$ (C.P.)
5. $B \supset C$ 1, 3, M.P.
6. C 5, 4, M.P.
7. $C \supset D$ 2, 4, M.P.
8. D 7, 6, M.P.

The rule of Conditional Proof is a genuine addition to the proof apparatus presented in Section I. Not only does it permit the construction of *shorter* proofs of validity for arguments which could be proved valid by appealing to the original list of nineteen elementary valid arguments alone, but it permits us to establish the validity of valid arguments whose validity could *not* be proved by reference to the original list alone. For example, the obviously valid argument $A \supset B$ $\therefore$ $A \supset (A \cdot B)$ cannot be proved valid using only the original list of nineteen elementary valid argument forms, but it is easily proved valid by using, in addition, the rule of Conditional Proof. Its conditional proof of validity is

1. $A \supset B$ $/ \therefore A \supset (A \cdot B)$
2. A $/ \therefore A \cdot B$ (C.P.)
3. B 1, 2, M.P.
4. $A \cdot B$ 2, 3, Conj.

EXERCISES

Give conditional proofs of validity for the last five arguments in exercise set II on pages 51–52.

III. THE RULE OF INDIRECT PROOF

The method of *indirect proof*, often called the method of proof by *reductio ad absurdum*, is familiar to all who have studied elementary geometry. In deriving his theorems, Euclid often begins by assuming the opposite of what he wants to prove. If that assumption leads to a contradiction, or 'reduces to an absurdity', then that assumption must be false, and so its negation—the theorem to be proved—must be true.

An indirect proof of validity for a given argument is constructed by assuming, as an additional premiss, the negation of its conclusion, and then deriving an explicit contradiction from the augmented set of premisses. Thus an indirect proof of validity for the argument $A \supset (B \cdot C)$, $(B \vee D) \supset E$, $D \vee A$ $\therefore$ E may be set down as follows:

1. $A \supset (B \cdot C)$
2. $(B \vee D) \supset E$
3. $D \vee A$ $/ \therefore E$
4. $\sim E$ I.P. (Indirect Proof)
5. $\sim(B \vee D)$ 2, 4, M.T.
6. $\sim B \cdot \sim D$ 5, De M.
7. $\sim D \cdot \sim B$ 6, Com.

8. $\sim$D   **7**, Simp.
9. A **3, 8**, D.S.
10. $B \cdot C$ **1, 9**, M.P.
11. B **10**, Simp.
12. $\sim$B   **6**, Simp.
13. $B \cdot \sim B$ **11, 12**, Conj.

In the above, step 13 is an explicit contradiction, so the demonstration is complete, for the validity of the original argument
follows by the rule of Indirect Proof.

It is easy to show that from a contradiction *any* conclusion can
validly be deduced. In other words, any argument of the form
p, $\sim p$ $\therefore$ q is valid, no matter what statements be substituted
for the variables p and q. Thus from steps 11 and 12 in the
preceding proof, the conclusion E can be derived in just two
more steps. Such a continuation would proceed:

14. B v E **11**, Add.
15. E **14, 12**, D.S.

Hence it is possible to regard an indirect proof of the validity
of a given argument not as the deduction of its validity *from
the fact that* a contradiction was obtained, but rather as deducing
that argument's conclusion *from the contradiction itself*. Thus
instead of viewing a *reductio ad absurdum* proof as proceeding
only up to the contradiction, we can regard it as *going on through*
the contradiction to the conclusion of the original argument.
If we symbolize the premisses of an argument as P and its conclusion as C, then an indirect proof of the validity of P $\therefore$ C will
be provided by a formal proof of validity for the argument P,
$\sim C$ $\therefore$ C.

What connection is there between the two arguments P $\therefore$ C
and P, $\sim C$ $\therefore$ C so that proving the second valid suffices to
establish the validity of the first? A formal proof of validity for
the latter constitutes a conditional proof of validity for a third
argument P $\therefore$ $\sim C \supset C$. But the conclusion of this third argument is logically equivalent to the conclusion of the first. By
the definition of material implication, $\sim C \supset C$ is logically

equivalent to $\sim\sim C$ v C, which is logically equivalent to C v C by the principle of Double Negation. And C v C and C are logically equivalent by the principle of Tautology. Since the first and third arguments have identical premises and logically equivalent conclusions, any proof of validity for one is a proof of validity for the other also. A proof of validity for the second argument is both a conditional proof of the third and an indirect proof of the first. Thus we see that there is an intimate relationship between the conditional and the indirect methods of proof, that is, between the rule of Conditional Proof and the rule of Indirect Proof.

Adding the rule of Indirect Proof serves to strengthen our proof apparatus still further. Any argument whose conclusion is a tautology can be shown to be valid, regardless of what its premises may be, by the method of truth tables. But if the tautologous conclusion of an argument is not a conditional statement, and the premises are consistent with each other and quite irrelevant to that conclusion, then the argument cannot be proved valid by the method of deduction without use being made of the rule of Indirect Proof. Although the argument $A \therefore B$ v $(B \supset C)$ cannot be proved valid by the means set forth in the two previous sections, its validity is easily established using the rule of Indirect Proof. One proof of its validity is this:

1. A $/ \therefore B$ v $(B \supset C)$
2. $\sim[B$ v $(B \supset C)]$ I.P.
3. $\sim[B$ v $(\sim B$ v $C)]$ 2, Impl.
4. $\sim[(B$ v $\sim B)$ v $C]$ 3, Assoc.
5. $\sim(B$ v $\sim B) \cdot \sim C$ 4, De M.
6. $\sim(B$ v $\sim B)$ 5, Simp.
7. $\sim B \cdot \sim \sim B$ 6, De M.

Having augmented our original list of nineteen elementary valid argument forms by the rules of Conditional and Indirect Proof, our exposition of the method of deduction is now complete. Any argument whose validity can be established by the use of truth tables can be proved valid by the method of deduction as set forth in the first three sections of the present chapter. This will not be proved, however, until the end of Chapter Seven.

EXERCISES

For each of the following arguments construct both a formal proof of validity and an indirect proof, and compare their lengths:

1. $(A \cdot B) \supset (C \cdot D)$, $B \supset \sim D$ $\therefore$ $\sim A$ v $\sim B$
2. $(E \supset F) \cdot (G \supset H)$, $(F \supset I) \cdot (H \supset J)$, $E \cdot G$ $\therefore$ $I \cdot J$
3. $(K$ v $L) \supset (M \cdot N)$, $(M$ v $O) \supset (N \supset \sim K)$ $\therefore$ $\sim K$
4. $P \supset (Q \supset R)$, $P \supset Q$, $\sim S \supset (R$ v $P)$ $\therefore$ S v R
5. $(\sim T$ v $U) \supset (W \cdot X)$, $(W$ v $Y) \supset (X \supset T)$ $\therefore$ T

IV. PROOFS OF TAUTOLOGIES

The conditional and indirect methods of proof can be used not only to establish the validity of arguments, but also to prove that certain statements and statement forms are tautologies. Any conditional statement corresponds, in a sense, to an argument whose single premiss is the antecedent of the conditional, and whose conclusion is the conditional's consequent. The conditional is a tautology if and only if that argument is valid. Hence a conditional is proved tautologous by deducing its consequent from its antecedent by a sequence of elementary valid arguments. Thus the statement $(A \cdot B) \supset A$ is proved tautologous by the same sequence of steps which proves the validity of the argument $A \cdot B$ $\therefore$ A. It has already been noted that the conditional method can be used repeatedly in a single proof. Thus the conditional statement

$$(Q \supset R) \supset [(P \supset Q) \supset (P \supset R)]$$

is proved tautologous by the following sequence of statements:

1. $Q \supset R$ / $\therefore$ $(P \supset Q) \supset (P \supset R)$
2. $P \supset Q$ / $\therefore$ $P \supset R$ (C.P.)
3. $P \supset R$ 2, 1, H.S.

For some more complicated conditional statements, this method of proving them tautologous is shorter and easier than constructing truth tables or Boolean Expansions.

There are many tautologies which are not conditional in form, and to these the preceding method cannot be applied. But any tautology can be established as tautologous by the indirect method. As applied to an *argument*, the indirect method of proving it valid proceeds by adding the negation of its conclusion to the argument's premisses and then deducing a contradiction by a sequence of elementary valid arguments. As applied to a *statement*, the indirect method of proving it tautologous proceeds by taking its negation as premiss and then deducing a contradiction by a sequence of elementary valid arguments. Thus the statement $B \vee \sim B$ is proved to be a tautology by the following:

1. $\sim(B \vee \sim B)$ / $\therefore$ $B \vee \sim B$ (I.P.)
2. $\sim B \cdot \sim \sim B$ 1, De M.

To say that a statement is a tautology is to assert that its truth is unconditional, that is, that it can be established without appealing to any other statements as premisses. Another, perhaps not too misleading, way of saying the same thing is to assert the validity of the 'argument' which has the statement in question as 'conclusion', but has no premisses at all. If the 'conclusion' *is* a tautology, then the method of deduction permits us to prove that the 'argument' is valid even though it has no premisses—using either the rule of Conditional Proof or the rule of Indirect Proof. Any tautology can be established by the method of deduction, although this will not be proved until the end of Chapter Seven.

EXERCISES

I. Use the method of conditional proof to verify that the following are tautologies:

1. $(A \supset B) \supset [(B \supset C) \supset (A \supset C)]$
2. $[(A \supset B) \vee (A \supset C)] \supset [A \supset (B \vee C)]$
3. $[(A \supset B) \cdot (A \supset C)] \supset [A \supset (B \cdot C)]$

4. $(A \supset B) \supset [A \supset (A \cdot B)]$
5. $[A \supset (B \supset C)] \supset [B \supset (A \supset C)]$
6. $(A \supset B) \supset [(\sim A \supset B) \supset B]$
7. $(A \supset B) \supset [(A \cdot C) \supset (B \cdot C)]$
8. $[(A \supset B) \supset B] \supset (A \lor B)$
9. $(B \supset C) \supset [(A \lor B) \supset (C \lor A)]$
10. $[(A \supset C) \lor (B \supset C)] \supset [(A \cdot B) \supset C]$
11. $[(A \supset B) \cdot (C \supset D)] \supset [(A \cdot C) \supset (B \cdot D)]$
12. $[(A \supset B) \supset A] \supset A$
13. $P \supset (P \cdot P)$
14. $(P \cdot Q) \supset P$
15. $(P \supset Q) \supset [\sim(Q \cdot R) \supset \sim(R \cdot P)]$

II. Use the method of indirect proof to verify that the following are tautologies:

1. $A \supset A$
2. $\sim(A \lor B) \supset \sim A$
3. $(A \supset B) \lor (A \supset \sim B)$
4. $(A \supset B) \lor (\sim A \supset B)$
5. $(A \supset B) \lor (B \supset C)$
6. $A \equiv [A \cdot (A \lor B)]$
7. $A \equiv [A \lor (A \cdot B)]$
8. $(A \lor B) \equiv [(A \cdot \sim B) \lor B]$

V. PROVING INVALIDITY

We can establish the invalidity of an argument by using a truth table to show that its form is invalid. The truth table proves invalidity if it contains at least one row in which truth values are assigned to the statement variables in such a way that the premisses are made true and the conclusion false. If we can devise such a truth value assignment without constructing the entire truth table, we shall have a shorter method of proving invalidity.

Consider the invalid argument

> If the Senator votes against this bill then he is op-
> posed to more severe penalties against tax evaders.

> If the Senator were a tax evader himself then he
> would be opposed to more severe penalties against
> tax evaders.
> Therefore if the Senator votes against this bill he
> must be a tax evader himself.

which may be symbolized as

$$V \supset O$$
$$H \supset O$$
$$\therefore V \supset H$$

Instead of constructing a truth table, we can prove its invalidity by making an assignment of truth values to the constituent statements V, O, and H which will make the premises true and the conclusion false. The conclusion is made false by assigning 'true' to V and 'false' to H; and both premises are made true by assigning 'true' to O. This method of proving invalidity is closely related to the truth table method. In effect, making the indicated truth value assignment amounts to describing one row of the relevant truth table—that row which suffices to establish the invalidity of the argument being tested. The relationship appears more clearly, perhaps, when the truth value assignments are written out horizontally, as

V	O	H	$V \supset O$	$H \supset O$	$V \supset H$
true	true	false	true	true	false

This new method of proving invalidity is shorter than writing out a complete truth table, and the amount of time and work saved is proportionally greater for more complicated arguments. In proving the invalidity of more extended arguments, a certain amount of trial and error may be needed to discover a truth value assignment which works. But even so, this method is quicker and easier than writing out the entire truth table. It is obvious that the present method will suffice to prove the invalidity of any argument which can be shown to be invalid by a truth table.

EXERCISES

I. Prove the invalidity of each of the following arguments by the method of assigning truth values:

1. $A \supset B$
   $C \supset D$
   $A \vee D$
   ___
   $\therefore B \vee C$

2. $E \supset F$
   $G \supset H$
   $E \vee G$
   ___
   $\therefore F \cdot H$

3. $I \supset (J \vee K)$
   $J \supset (K \supset L)$
   $\sim L$
   ___
   $\therefore \sim I$

4. $M \supset (N \cdot O)$
   $P \supset (M \vee Q)$
   $Q \supset (O \supset R)$
   $\sim P \vee \sim R$
   ___
   $\therefore P \supset Q$

5. $S \vee T$
   $T \equiv (S \supset U)$
   $U \vee (T \cdot W)$
   $W \equiv (U \supset T)$
   ___
   $\therefore S \equiv T$

6. $X \equiv (Y \vee Z)$
   $Y \equiv (Z \vee X)$
   $Z \equiv (X \vee Y)$
   $\sim X$
   ___
   $\therefore Y \vee Z$

7. $A \supset (B \vee C)$
   $D \supset (E \vee F)$
   $\sim B \supset (F \vee G)$
   $(F \supset D) \cdot (\sim E \supset \sim D)$
   $\sim G$
   ___
   $\therefore A \supset (D \vee F)$

8. $\sim L \supset (K \supset M)$
   $H \supset (I \cdot J)$
   $J \supset (I \supset K)$
   $O \supset (L \supset P)$
   $N \cdot \sim (M \cdot N)$
   ___
   $\therefore H \supset P$

9. $(T \supset U) \cdot (U \supset T)$
   $(Q \cdot U) \vee (\sim U \cdot \sim Q)$
   $(Q \vee S) \vee (T \vee U)$
   $\sim Q \supset (R \cdot W)$
   $(S \supset \sim T) \cdot (\sim S \supset \sim Y)$
   $W \supset (\sim Y \supset \sim W)$
   $(Q \vee T) \cdot (S \vee X)$
   ___
   $\therefore W \cdot X$

10. $A \supset (B \supset \sim C)$
    $D \supset B$
    $(\sim F \supset C) \cdot (\sim A \supset \sim E)$
    $J \supset \sim H$
    $(G \supset J) \cdot (\sim I \supset \sim H)$
    $G \equiv \sim D$
    $(B \supset H) \cdot (\sim D \supset H)$
    ___
    $\therefore E \equiv F$

II. For each of the following, decide whether or not the indicated conclusion follows from the stated premises. If it does, use the method of deduction to prove the argument valid; if not, prove invalidity by the method of assigning truth values to the constituent simple statements:

1. $(A \supset B) \cdot (C \supset D)$
   $(B \supset E) \cdot (D \supset F)$
   $(E \supset G) \cdot (F \supset H)$
   ___
   $\therefore (A \vee C) \supset (G \vee H)$

2. $(I \supset J) \cdot (K \supset L)$
   $(J \supset M) \cdot (N \supset L)$
   $(M \supset O) \cdot (N \supset P)$
   ___
   $\therefore (I \vee K) \supset (O \vee P)$

3. $(Q \supset R) \cdot (Q \supset S)$
$(R \supset T) \cdot (S \supset U)$
$(\sim T \supset \sim W) \cdot (\sim U \supset X)$
∴ $(Q \supset W)$ v $(Q \supset X)$

4. $(Q \supset R) \cdot (Q \supset S)$
$(R \supset T) \, (S \supset U)$
$(\sim Y \supset \sim W) \cdot (\sim U \supset W)$
∴ $(Q \supset W)$ v $(Q \supset \sim W)$

5. $A \supset \sim(B \cdot C)$
$(D$ v $E) \supset F$
$F \supset \sim(G$ v $H)$
$\sim C \cdot (E \cdot G)$
∴ $\sim A$

6. $(I \supset J) \cdot (K \supset L)$
$(J \supset M) \cdot (L \supset N)$
$(M \supset O) \cdot (N \supset P)$
$I \cdot K$
∴ $O \cdot P$

7. $(Q \supset R) \cdot (S \supset T)$
$(R \supset U) \cdot (W \supset T)$
$(U \supset X) \cdot (W \supset Y)$
$Q \cdot S$
∴ $X \cdot Y$

8. $(Q \supset R) \cdot (S \supset T)$
$(R \supset T) \cdot (\sim S \supset Q)$
$(U \supset W) \cdot (W \supset \sim T)$
$\sim U \supset U$
∴ $R \supset Q$

9. $(X \supset \sim Y) \cdot (Y \supset X)$
$\sim Y \supset (\sim X \supset Z)$
$(W \supset \sim Y) \cdot (\sim Z \supset \sim W)$
$\sim Y \supset X$
∴ $X \supset (\sim Y \supset Z)$

10. $(X \supset \sim Y) \cdot (Y \supset X)$
$\sim Y \supset (\sim X \supset Z)$
$(W \supset \sim Y) \cdot (\sim Z \supset \sim W)$
$\sim Y \supset X$
∴ $X \supset (\sim X \supset Z)$

VI. SHORTER TRUTH TABLE TECHNIQUE—REDUCTIO AD ABSURDUM METHOD

There is still another method of testing the validity of arguments, and of classifying statements as tautologous, contradictory, or contingent. In the preceding section it was pointed out that an argument is invalid if and only if it is possible to assign truth values to its simple constituent statements in such a way as to make all its premises true and its conclusion false. It is impossible to make such truth value assignments in the case of a valid argument. Hence to prove the validity of an argument it suffices to prove that no such truth values can be assigned. We do so by showing that its premises can be made true and its conclusion false only by assigning truth values *inconsistently*, so that some constituent statement is assigned both a 'true' and a 'false'. In other words, if the truth value 'true' is assigned to each premiss of a valid argument and the truth value 'false' is assigned to its conclusion, this will necessitate assigning *both* 'true' and 'false' to some constituent statement, which is, of course, a contradiction.

Thus to prove the validity of the argument $(A \lor B) \supset (C \cdot D)$, $(D \lor E) \supset F \therefore A \supset F$ we assign 'true' to each premiss and 'false' to the conclusion. Assigning 'false' to the conclusion requires that 'true' be assigned to A and 'false' be assigned to F. Since 'true' is assigned to A, the antecedent of the first premiss is true, and since the premiss has been assigned 'true', its consequent must be true also, so that 'true' must be assigned to both C and D. Since 'true' is assigned to D, the antecedent of the second premiss is true, and since the premiss has been assigned 'true', its consequent must be true also, so that 'true' must be assigned to F. But we have already been forced to assign 'false' to F to make the conclusion false. Hence the argument is invalid only if the statement F is both true and false, which is impossible. This method of proving the validity of an argument is a version of the *reductio ad absurdum* technique, which uses truth value assignments rather than the method of deduction.

It is easy to extend the use of this method to the classification of statements (and statement forms). Thus to certify that Peirce's Law $[(p \supset q) \supset p] \supset p$ is a tautology, we assign it the truth value 'false', which requires us to assign 'true' to its antecedent $[(p \supset q) \supset p]$ and 'false' to its consequent p. For the conditional $[(p \supset q) \supset p]$ to be true while *its* consequent p is false, its antecedent $(p \supset q)$ must be assigned the truth value 'false' also. But for the conditional $p \supset q$ to be false, its antecedent p must be assigned 'true' and its consequent q assigned 'false'. However, we were previously forced to assign 'false' to p, so that assuming Peirce's Law false leads to a contradiction, which proves it a tautology.

If it *is* possible to assign truth values consistently to its constituents on the assumption that it is false, then the expression in question is not a tautology, but must be either contradictory or contingent. In such a case we attempt to assign truth values so as to make it true. If this attempt leads to a contradiction the expression cannot possibly be true and must be a contradiction. But if truth values can be assigned so as to make it true and (other) truth values assigned so as to make it false, then it is neither a tautology nor a contradiction, but is contingent.

The *reductio ad absurdum* method of assigning truth values is by far the quickest and easiest method of testing arguments and classifying statements. It is, however, more readily applied in some cases than in others. If 'false' is assigned to a disjunction, 'false' must be assigned to both disjuncts, and where 'true' is assigned to a conjunction, 'true' must be assigned to both conjuncts. Here the sequence of assignments is forced. But where 'true' is assigned to a disjunction or 'false' to a conjunction, that assignment by itself does not determine *which* disjunct is true or *which* conjunct is false. Here we should have to experiment and make various 'trial assignments', which will tend to diminish the advantage of the method for such cases. Despite these complications, however, in the vast majority of cases the *reductio ad absurdum* method is superior to any other method known.

EXERCISES

1. Use the *reductio ad absurdum* method of assigning truth values to decide the validity or invalidity of the arguments in Exercise II on pages 62–63.
2. Use the *reductio ad absurdum* method of assigning truth values to establish that the statements in Exercises I and II on pages 59–60 are tautologies.
3. Use the *reductio ad absurdum* method of assigning truth values to classify the statements in Exercise I on page 31 as tautologous, contradictory, or contingent.

CHAPTER FOUR

Propositional Functions
and Quantifiers

I. SINGULAR PROPOSITIONS AND GENERAL PROPOSITIONS

The logical techniques developed thus far apply only to arguments whose validity depends upon the way in which simple statements are truth-functionally combined into compound statements. Those techniques cannot be applied to such arguments as the following categorical syllogism:

> All humans are mortal.
> Socrates is human.
> Therefore Socrates is mortal.

The validity of such an argument depends upon the inner logical structure of the non-compound statements which it contains. In order to appraise such arguments we must develop methods for analyzing non-compound statements and symbolizing their inner structures.

The second premiss of the preceding argument is a *singular proposition*;* it asserts that the individual Socrates has the prop-

---

* In the following chapters we shall follow tradition in using the term 'proposition' as synonymous with 'statement'. It should be observed that this usage deviates from that presented in Chapter One.

erty of being human. We call 'Socrates' the *subject* term and 'human' the *predicate* term. Any (affirmative) singular proposition asserts that the particular individual named by its subject term has the property specified by its predicate term. We regard as individuals not only persons, but any *things*, such as animals, cities, nations, planets, or stars, of which properties can significantly be predicated. Properties can be specified not only by adjectives, but by nouns or even verbs: thus 'Helen is a gossip' and 'Helen gossips' have the same meaning, which can also be expressed as 'Helen is gossipy'.

In symbolizing singular propositions we shall use the small letters '*a*' through '*w*' to denote particular individuals, ordinarily using the first letter of the individual's name to denote it (or him). In any particular context these symbols denote particular individuals, and we therefore call them 'individual constants'. To designate properties we shall use capital letters, being guided by the same principle in their selection. Thus in the context of the preceding argument we should denote Socrates by the small letter '*s*' and symbolize the properties *human* and *mortal* by the capital letters '*H*' and '*M*'. To express a singular proposition in our symbolism we write the symbol for its predicate term to the left of the symbol for its subject term. Thus we symbolize 'Socrates is human' as '*Hs*' and 'Socrates is mortal' as '*Ms*'. *

Examining the symbolic formulations of a number of singular propositions which have the same predicate term, we observe them to have a common pattern. The symbolic formulations of the singular propositions 'Aristotle is human', 'Boston is human', 'California is human', 'Descartes is human', . . . , which are '*Ha*', '*Hb*', '*Hc*', '*Hd*', . . . , all consist of the property symbol '*H*' followed by an individual constant. We shall use the expression '*Hx*' to symbolize the pattern which is common to all those singular propositions which assert particular individuals to have the property *human*. The small letter '*x*'—called an 'individual variable'—is a mere *place marker* which serves to

---

* Some logicians enclose the individual constant in parentheses, symbolizing 'Socrates is human' as '*H(s)*', but we shall not follow that practice here.

indicate where an individual constant may be written for a singular proposition to result. The singular propositions '*Ha*', '*Hb*', '*Hc*', '*Hd*', . . . are either true or false; but '*Hx*' is neither true nor false, not being a proposition. Such expressions as '*Hx*' are called 'propositional functions', which are defined to be expressions which contain individual variables and become propositions when their individual variables are replaced by individual constants.* Any singular proposition can be regarded as a *substitution instance* of the propositional function from which it results by the substitution of an individual constant for the individual variable in the propositional function. The process of obtaining a proposition from a propositional function by sub- stituting a constant for a variable is called 'instantiation'. The negative singular propositions 'Aristotle is not human' and 'Boston is not human', symbolized as '∼*Ha*' and '∼*Hb*', result by *instantiation* from the propositional function '∼*Hx*', of which they are substitution instances. Thus we see that symbols other than property symbols and individual variables can occur in propositional functions.

General propositions such as 'Everything is mortal' and 'Some- thing is mortal' differ from singular propositions in not con- taining the names of any particular individuals. However, they also can be regarded as resulting from propositional functions, not by instantiation, but by the process called 'generalization' or 'quantification'. The first example, 'Everything is mortal', can alternatively be expressed as

> Given any thing in the universe, it is mortal.

Here the relative pronoun 'it' refers back to the indefinite word 'thing' which precedes it in the statement. We can use the individual variable '*x*' in place of the pronoun 'it' and its indefinite antecedent 'thing' to paraphrase the first general proposition as

> Given any *x* in the universe, *x* is mortal.

---

* Some writers have defined 'propositional functions' to be the *meanings* of such expressions; but here we define them to be the expressions themselves.

Then we can use the notation already introduced to rewrite it as

> Given any *x* in the universe, *Mx*.

The phrase 'Given any *x* in the universe' is called a 'universal quantifier', and is symbolized as '(x)'. Using this new symbol we can completely symbolize our first general proposition as

$$(x)Mx.$$

We can similarly paraphrase the second general proposition, 'Something is mortal', successively as

> There exists at least one thing such that it is mortal.
> There exists at least one *x* such that *x* is mortal.

and as

> There exists at least one *x* such that *Mx*.

The phrase 'There exists at least one *x* such that' is called an 'existential quantifier' and is symbolized as '$(\exists x)$'. Using the new symbol we can completely symbolize our second general proposition as

$$(\exists x)Mx.$$

General propositions can be formed from a propositional function by placing either a universal or an existential quantifier before it. It is obvious that the universal quantification of a propositional function is true if and only if all of its substitution instances are true, and that the existential quantification of a propositional function is true if and only if it has at least one true substitution instance. If we grant that there is at least one individual in the universe, so that every propositional function has at least one substitution instance (true or false), then if the universal quantification of a propositional function is true, its existential quantification must be true also.

A further relationship between universal and existential quantification can be shown by considering two additional general propositions, 'Something is not mortal' and 'Nothing is mortal', which are the respective denials of the first two considered. 'Something is not mortal' is symbolized as '$(\exists x) \sim Mx$' and 'Nothing is mortal' is symbolized as '$(x) \sim Mx$'. These show that the negation of the universal (existential) quantification of a propositional function is logically equivalent to the existential (universal) quantification of the new propositional function which results from placing a negation symbol in front of the first propositional function. Where we use the Greek letter *phi* to represent any property symbol whatever, the general connections between universal and existential quantification can be described in terms of the following square array:

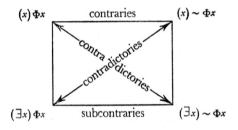

Assuming the existence of at least one individual: we can say that the two top propositions are *contraries*, since they might both be false but cannot both be true; the two bottom propositions are *subcontraries* which can both be true but cannot both be false; propositions which are at opposite ends of the diagonals are *contradictories*, of which one must be true and the other false; and finally, on each side, the truth of the lower proposition is implied by the truth of the proposition which is directly above it.

Traditional logic emphasized four types of subject-predicate propositions illustrated by the following:

> All humans are mortal.
> No humans are mortal.
> Some humans are mortal.
> Some humans are not mortal.

These were classified as 'universal affirmative', 'universal negative', 'particular affirmative', and 'particular negative', respectively, and their types abbreviated as '*A*', '*E*', '*I*', '*O*', again respectively. (The letter names have been presumed to come from the Latin '*AffIrmo*' and '*nEgO*', meaning *I affirm* and *I deny*.) These four special forms of subject-predicate propositions are easily symbolized by means of propositional functions and quantifiers.* The first of them, the *A* proposition, can successively be paraphrased as

> Given any thing in the universe, if it is human then it is mortal.
>
> Given any *x* in the universe, if *x* is human then *x* is mortal.
>
> Given any *x* in the universe, *x* is human ⊃ *x* is mortal.

and finally symbolized as

$$(x)[Hx \supset Mx].$$

Our symbolic formulation of the *A* proposition is the universal quantification of the complex propositional function '*Hx* ⊃ *Mx*', which has as its substitution instances not singular propositions but conditionals whose antecedents and consequents are singular propositions having the same subject terms. Among the substitution instances of the propositional function '*Hx* ⊃ *Mx*' are the conditionals '*Ha* ⊃ *Ma*', '*Hb* ⊃ *Mb*', '*Hc* ⊃ *Mc*', and so on. In the symbolization of the general *A* proposition the square brackets serve as punctuation marks to indicate that the universal quantifier '(*x*)' *applies to* or *has within its scope* the whole of the complex propositional function '*Hx* ⊃ *Mx*'. The notion of the *scope of a quantifier* is very important, for differences in scope correspond to differences in meaning. The expression '(*x*)[*Hx* ⊃ *Mx*]' is a proposition which asserts that all substitution instances of the propositional function '*Hx* ⊃ *Mx*' are true. On the other hand, the expression '(*x*)*Hx* ⊃ *Mx*' is a propositional function whose substitution instances are '(*x*)*Hx* ⊃ *Ma*', '(*x*)*Hx* ⊃ *Mb*', '(*x*)*Hx* ⊃ *Mc*', etc.

---

* An alternative method of symbolizing them is presented in Appendix A.

The **E** proposition 'No humans are mortals' may similarly be paraphrased successively as

> Given anything in the universe, if it is human then it is not mortal.
>
> Given any x in the universe, if x is human then x is not mortal.
>
> Given any x in the universe, x is human $\supset$ x is not mortal.

and then symbolized as

$$(x)[Hx \supset \sim Mx].$$

Similarly, the **I** proposition 'Some humans are mortals', may be paraphrased as

> There exists at least one thing such that it is human and it is mortal.
>
> There exists at least one x such that x is human and x is mortal.
>
> There exists at least one x such that x is human·x is mortal.

and completely symbolized as

$$(\exists x)[Hx \cdot Mx].$$

Finally, the **O** proposition 'Some humans are not mortal', becomes

> There exists at least one thing such that it is human and it is not mortal.
>
> There exists at least one x such that x is human and x is not mortal.

and is completely symbolized as

$$(\exists x)[Hx \cdot \sim Mx].$$

Where the Greek letters *phi* and *psi* are used to represent any property symbols whatever, the four general subject-predicate propositions of traditional logic may be represented in a square array as

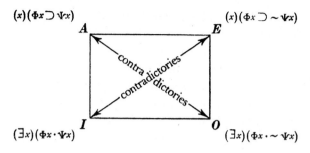

Of these, the *A* and the *O* are contradictories, and the *E* and the *I* are contradictories also. But none of the other relationships discussed in connection with the square array on page 70 hold for the traditional *A*, *E*, *I*, and *O* propositions, even where we assume that there exists at least one individual in the universe. Where 'Φx' is a propositional function which has no true substitution instances, then regardless of what property is symbolized by Ψ, the propositional functions '$\Phi x \supset \Psi x$' and '$\Phi x \supset {\sim}\Psi x$' have only true substitution instances, for all their substitution instances are conditional statements with false antecedents. In such cases the *A* and *E* propositions which are the universal quantifications of these complex propositional functions are true, so that the *A* and *E* propositions are not contraries. Again, where 'Φx' is a propositional function which has no true substitution instances, then regardless of what 'Ψx' might be, the propositional functions '$\Phi x \cdot \Psi x$' and '$\Phi x \cdot {\sim}\Psi x$' have only false substitution instances, for their substitution instances are conjunctions whose first conjuncts are false. In such cases the *I* and *O* propositions which are the existential quantifications of these complex propositional functions are false, so that the *I* and *O* propositions are not subcontraries. In all such cases, then, since the *A* and *E* propositions are true and the *I* and *O* propositions are false, the truth of a universal does *not* imply the truth of its particular; no implication relation holds between them.

If we make the assumption that there exists at least one individual in the universe, then '$(x)[\Phi x \supset \Psi x]$' does imply

'$(\exists x)[\Phi x \supset \Psi x]$'. But the latter is *not* an *I* proposition. An *I* proposition of the form 'Some Φ's are Ψ's' is symbolized as '$(\exists x)[\Phi x \cdot \Psi x]$', which asserts that there is at least one thing having both the property Φ and the property Ψ. But the proposition '$(\exists x)[\Phi x \supset \Psi x]$' asserts only that there is at least one object which has the property Ψ *if* it has the property Φ, which is a very different and much weaker assertion.

The four traditional subject-predicate forms *A*, *E*, *I*, and *O* are not the only forms of general propositions. There are others which involve the quantification of more complicated proposi-tional functions. Thus the general proposition 'All members are either parents or teachers', which does *not* mean the same as 'All members are parents or all members are teachers', is symbolized as '$(x)[Mx \supset (Px \text{ v } Tx)]$'. And the general proposi-tion 'Some Senators are either disloyal or misguided', is sym-bolized as '$(\exists x)[Sx \cdot (Dx \text{ v } Mx)]$'. It should be observed that such a statement as 'Apples and bananas are nourishing' can be symbolized either as the conjunction of two *A* propositions, '$\{(x)[Ax \supset Nx]\} \cdot \{(x)[Bx \supset Nx]\}$', or as a single non-compound general proposition, '$(x)[(Ax \text{ v } Bx) \supset Nx]$'. But it should *not* be symbolized as '$(x)[(Ax \cdot Bx) \supset Nx]$', for to say that apples and bananas are nourishing is to say that anything is nourishing which is *either* an apple *or* a banana, *not* to say that anything is nourishing which is *both* an apple and a banana (whatever that might be). Finally, we observe that an exceptive proposition such as 'All students except freshmen are eligible' is symbolized as '$(x)[Sx \supset (Ex \equiv \sim Fx)]$'. It must be emphasized that there are no mechanical rules for translating statements from English into our logical notation. In every case one must *understand the meaning* of the English sentence, and then *re-express* that meaning in terms of propositional functions and quantifiers.

EXERCISES

Symbolize each of the following statements by means of propositional functions and quantifiers:

 1. Athletes are brawny.
 2. Camels are not all dromedaries.
 3. An elephant never forgets.
 4. Horses are sometimes graceful.
 5. None but the insecure are jealous.
 6. There are large kangaroos.
 7. There are no new monarchs.
 8. Not all philosophers are old.
 9. Whatever is reposeful is also quiet.
10. Nothing is simple which is technical.
11. Some automobiles are both comfortable and economical.
12. All vegetables are both delicious and nutritious.
13. No man who is innocent will be punished.
14. Every student is either a graduate or an undergraduate.
15. Not every man who is a citizen is a patriot.
16. Oysters and clams are delicious.
17. Some roads are passable only if they are dry.
18. No whisky is good unless it has been aged.
19. All acrobats and dancers are strong and graceful.
20. Dogs are expensive if and only if they are pedigreed.

II. PROVING VALIDITY

To construct formal proofs of validity for arguments symbolized by means of quantifiers and propositional functions we must augment our list of elementary valid argument forms. We shall add four rules governing quantification, stating them very simply in this section and giving them a more adequate formulation in Section V.

1. Universal Instantiation.   Since the universal quantification of a propositional function is true if and only if all substitution instances of that propositional function are true, we can add to our list of elementary valid argument forms the principle that any substitution instance of a propositional function can validly be inferred from its universal quantification. We can express this rule symbolically as

$$\frac{(x)\Phi x}{\therefore \ \Phi z}$$ (where 'z' is any individual symbol).

Since this rule permits substitution instances to be inferred from universal quantifications, we shall refer to it as the 'principle of Universal Instantiation', and abbreviate it as '**UI**'.* The addition of **UI** permits us to give a formal proof of validity for the argument: 'All humans are mortal; Socrates is human; therefore Socrates is mortal'.

1. $(x)[Hx \supset Mx]$
2. Hs $/\therefore Ms$
3. $Hs \supset Ms$ 1, **UI**
4. Ms 3, 2, M.P.

2. Universal Generalization. We can explain our next rule by analogy with fairly standard mathematical practice. A geometer may begin a proof by saying, 'Let *ABC* be any arbitrarily selected triangle'. Then he may go on to prove that the triangle *ABC* has some specified property, and concludes that *all* triangles have that property. Now what justifies his final conclusion? Why does it follow from triangle *ABC* having that property that *all* triangles do? The answer is that if no assumption other than its triangularity is made about *ABC*, then the expression '*ABC*' can be taken as denoting any triangle you please. And if the argument has established that *any* triangle must have the property in question, then it follows that *all* triangles do. We now introduce a notation analogous to that of the geometer in his reference to 'any arbitrarily selected triangle'. The hitherto unused small letter '*y*' will be used to denote *any arbitrarily selected individual*. Thus the expression 'Φy' is a substitution instance of the propositional function 'Φx', and it asserts that *any arbitrarily selected individual* has the property Φ. Clearly 'Φy' follows validly from '$(x)\Phi x$' by **UI**, since what is true of all individuals is true of any arbitrarily selected individual. The inference is equally valid in the other direction, since what is true of *any arbitrarily selected individual*

---

* This rule and the three which follow are variants of rules for 'natural deduction' which were devised independently by Gerhard Gentzen and Stanislaw Jaśkowski in 1934.

must be true of *all* individuals. We augment our list of elementary valid argument forms further by adding the principle that the universal quantification of a propositional function can validly be inferred from its substitution instance with respect to the symbol '*y*'. Since this rule permits the inference of general propositions which are universal quantifications, we shall refer to it as the 'principle of Universal Generalization', and abbreviate it as '**UG**'. Our symbolic expression for this second quantification rule is

$$\frac{\Phi y}{\therefore (x)\Phi x}$$ (where '*y*' denotes any arbitrarily selected individual)

We can use the new notation and the additional rule **UG** to construct a formal proof of validity for the argument: 'No mortals are perfect; all humans are mortal; therefore no humans are perfect'.

1. $(x)[Mx \supset \sim Px]$
2. $(x)[Hx \supset Mx]$ / $\therefore (x)[Hx \supset \sim Px]$
3. $Hy \supset My$ 2, **UI**
4. $My \supset \sim Py$ 1, **UI**
5. $Hy \supset \sim Py$ 3, 4, H.S.
6. $(x)[Hx \supset \sim Px]$ 5, **UG**

3. Existential Generalization. Since the existential quantification of a propositional function is true if and only if that propositional function has at least one true substitution instance, we can add to our list of elementary valid argument forms the principle that the existential quantification of a propositional function can validly be inferred from any substitution instance of that propositional function. This rule permits the inference of general propositions which are existentially quantified, so we call it the 'principle of Existential Generalization' and abbreviate it as '**EG**'. Its symbolic formulation is

$$\frac{\Phi z}{\therefore (\exists x)\Phi x}$$ (where '*z*' is any individual symbol)

4. Existential Instantiation. One further quantification rule is required. The existential quantification of a propositional function asserts that there exists at least one individual the substitution of whose name for the variable '*x*' in that propositional function will yield a true substitution instance of it. Of course we may not know anything else about that individual. But we can take any individual constant, say '*w*', which has had no prior occurrence in that context and use it to denote the individual, or one of the individuals, whose existence has been asserted by the existential quantification. Knowing that there is such an individual, and having agreed to denote it by '*w*', we can infer from the existential quantification of a propositional function the substitution instance of that propositional function with respect to the individual symbol '*w*'. We add as our final quantification rule the principle that from the existential quantification of a propositional function we may validly infer the truth of its substitution instance with respect to an individual constant which has no prior occurrence in that context. The new argument form may be written as

$$\frac{(\exists x)\Phi x}{\therefore \ \Phi z}$$ (where '*z*' is an individual constant having no prior occurrence in the context.)

It will be referred to as the 'principle of Existential Instantiation' and abbreviated as '**EI**'.

We make use of the last two quantification rules in constructing a formal proof of validity for the argument: 'All dogs are carnivorous; some animals are dogs; therefore some animals are carnivorous'.

1. $(x)[Dx \supset Cx]$
2. $(\exists x)[Ax \cdot Dx]$ / $\therefore$ $(\exists x)[Ax \cdot Cx]$
3. $Aw \cdot Dw$ 2, **EI**
4. $Dw \supset Cw$ 1, **UI**
5. $Dw \cdot Aw$ 3, Com.
6. Dw 5, Simp.
7. Cw 4, 6, M.P.
8. Aw 3, Simp.

9. *Aw·Cw*   8, 7, Conj.
10. $(\exists x)[Ax·Cx]$ 9, **EG**

We can show the need for the indicated restriction on the use of **EI** by considering the obviously invalid argument: 'Some cats are animals; some dogs are animals; therefore some cats are dogs'. If we ignored the restriction on **EI** that the substitution instance inferred by it can contain only an individual constant which had no prior occurrence in the context, we might be led to construct the following 'proof':

1. $(\exists x)[Cx·Ax]$
2. $(\exists x)[Dx·Ax]/\therefore (\exists x)[Cx·Dx]$
3. *Cw·Aw*   1, **EI**
4. *Dw·Aw*   2, **EI** (erroneous)
5. *Cw*   3, Simp.
6. *Dw*   4, Simp.
7. *Cw·Dw*   5, 6, Conj.
8. $(\exists x)[Cx·Dx]$ 7, **EG**

The mistake here occurs at step 4. The second premiss assures us that there is at least one thing which is both a dog and an animal. But we are not free to use the symbol '*w*' to denote that thing because '*w*' has already been used to denote one of the things asserted by the first premiss to be both a cat and an animal. To avoid errors of this sort we must obey the indicated restriction in using **EI**. It should be clear that whenever we use both **EI** and **UI** in a proof to instantiate with respect to the same individual constant, we must use **EI** first.

5. Strengthened Rule of Conditional Proof.   In the preceding chapter the method of Conditional Proof was applied only to arguments whose conclusions were conditional in form. But now we must consider arguments whose conclusions are non-compound general propositions. To deal with them we shall strengthen our rule of Conditional Proof and thereby give it wider applicability.

To formulate our strengthened rule of Conditional Proof we must adopt a new method of writing out proofs which make use of the Conditional Method. As explained in the preceding chapter, we used the method of Conditional Proof to establish the validity of an argument having a conditional as conclusion by adding the antecedent of that conditional to the argument's premises as an assumption, and then deducing the conditional's consequent. The old notation involved the use of an additional slant line and an extra *therefore* sign, as in proving the validity of the argument '$A \supset B$ ∴ $A \supset (A \cdot B)$' by the following four step proof (as explained in Section II of Chapter Two):

1. $A \supset B$/∴ $A \supset (A \cdot B)$
2. A /∴ $A \cdot B$
3. B 1, 2, M.P.
4. $A \cdot B$ 2, 3, Conj.

A Conditional Proof of validity for that same argument is set down in our new notation as the following sequence of five steps:

1. $A \supset B$ /∴ $A \supset (A \cdot B)$
2. A assumption
3. B 1, 2, M.P.
4. $A \cdot B$ 2, 3, Conj.
5. $A \supset (A \cdot B)$ 2–4, C.P.

Here the fifth step is inferred not from any one or two of the preceding steps but from the *sequence* of steps 2, 3, 4, which constitutes a valid deduction of step 4 from steps 1 and 2. In step 5 we infer the validity of the argument '$A \supset B$ ∴ $A \supset (A \cdot B)$' from the demonstrated validity of the argument '$A \supset B$, A ∴ $A \cdot B$'. That inference is 'justified' by noting the sequence of steps to which appeal is made, and using the letters 'C.P.' to show that the principle of Conditional Proof is being used.

In the second of the preceding proofs, step 2, the assumption, has steps 3 and 4 dependent upon it. Step 5, however, is *not* dependent upon step 2, but only upon step 1. Step 5 is therefore *outside* or *beyond the scope* of the assumption made as step 2. When an assumption is made in a Conditional Proof of validity, its 'scope' is always *limited*, never extending all the way to the last line of the demonstration.

A notation is now introduced which is very helpful in keeping track of assumptions and their *scopes*. A bent arrow is used for this purpose, with its head pointing at the assumption from the left, its shaft bending down to run along all steps within the scope of the assumption, and then bending inward to mark the end of the scope of that assumption. The scope of the assumption in the preceding proof is indicated thus:

1. $A \supset B / \therefore A \supset (A \cdot B)$
2. A assumption
3. B 1, 2, **M.P.**
4. $A \cdot B$ 2, 3, **Conj.**
5. $A \supset (A \cdot B)$ 2–4, **C.P.**

It should be observed that only a line inferred by the principle of Conditional Proof ends the scope of an assumption, and that every use of the rule of Conditional Proof serves to end the scope of an assumption. If the scope of an assumption does *not* extend all the way to the end of a proof, then the final step of the proof does not *depend* on that assumption, but has been proved to follow from the original premises alone. Hence we need not restrict ourselves to using as assumptions only the antecedents of conditional conclusions. *Any* proposition can be taken as an assumption of limited scope, for the final step which is the conclusion will always be beyond its scope and independent of it.

A more complex demonstration which involves making *two* assumptions is the following (incidentally, when our bent arrow notation is used, the word 'assumption' need not be written, since each assumption is sufficiently identified as such by the arrowhead on its left):

1. $(A \lor B) \supset [(C \lor D) \supset E] / \therefore A \supset (C \supset E)$
2. A
3. $A \lor B$ 2, **Add.**
4. $(C \lor D) \supset E$ 1, 3, **M.P.**
5. C
6. $C \lor D$ 5, **Add.**
7. E 4, 6, **M.P.**
8. $C \supset E$ 5–7, **C.P.**
9. $A \supset (C \supset E)$ 2–8, **C.P.**

In this proof, lines 2 through 8 lie within the scope of the first assumption, while lines 5, 6, and 7 lie within the scope of the second assumption. From these examples it is clear that the scope of an assumption in a proof contains all lines from itself down *to* the line which is inferred by C.P. from the sequence of steps beginning with that assumption. In the preceding proof, the second assumption lies within the scope of the first because it lies between the first assumption and step 9 which is inferred by C.P. from the sequence of steps 2 through 8.

When we use this new method of writing out a Conditional Proof of validity the scope of every original premiss extends all the way to the end of the proof. The original premisses may be supplemented by additional assumptions provided that the latter's scopes are limited and do not extend to the end of the proof. Each step of a formal proof of validity must be either a premiss, or an assumption of limited scope, or must follow validly from one or two preceding steps by an elementary valid argument form, or must follow from a *sequence* of preceding steps by the principle of Conditional Proof.

It should be remarked that the strengthened principle of Conditional Proof includes the method of Indirect Proof as a special case. Since any assumption of limited scope may be made in a Conditional Proof of validity, we can take as our assumption the negation of the argument's conclusion. Once a contradiction is obtained, we can *continue on through* the contradiction to obtain the desired conclusion by Addition and the Disjunctive Syllogism.* Once that is done, we can use the rule of Conditional Proof to end the scope of that assumption and obtain a conditional whose consequent is the argument's conclusion and whose antecedent is the negation of that conclusion. And from such a conditional the argument's conclusion will follow by Implication, Double Negation, and Tautology.

Any assumption of limited scope may be made in a Conditional Proof of validity, and in particular we are free to make an assumption of the form 'Φy'. Thus the argument 'All fresh-

* As explained on page 56.

men and sophomores are invited and will be welcome; therefore all freshmen are invited' may be proved valid by the following Conditional Proof:

1. $(x)[(Fx \lor Sx) \supset (Ix \cdot Wx)]/ \therefore (x)[Fx \supset Ix]$
$\rightarrow$2. Fy
3. $(Fy \lor Sy) \supset (Iy \cdot Wy)$		1, **UI**
4. $Fy \lor Sy$		2, Add.
5. $Iy \cdot Wy$		3, 4, M.P.
6. Iy		5, Simp.
7. $Fy \supset Iy$		2–6. C.P.
8. $(x)[Fx \supset Ix]$		7, **UG**

More than one assumption of limited scope can be made in proving the validity of arguments involving quantifiers, as in the following Conditional Proof:

1. $(x)[(Ax \lor Bx) \supset (Cx \cdot Dx)]$
2. $(x)\{(Cx \lor Ex) \supset [(Fx \lor Gx) \supset Hx\}/ \therefore (x)[Ax \supset (Fx \supset Hx)]$
3. $(Ay \lor By) \supset (Cy \cdot Dy)$ 1, **UI**
4. $(Cy \lor Ey) \supset [(Fy \lor Gy) \supset Hy]$ 2, **UI**
$\rightarrow$5. Ay
6. $Ay \lor By$		5, Add.
7. $Cy \cdot Dy$		3, 6, M.P.
8. Cy		7, Simp.
9. $Cy \lor Ey$		8, Add.
10. $(Fy \lor Gy) \supset Hy$		4, 9, M.P.
$\rightarrow$11. Fy		
12. $Fy \lor Gy$		11, Add.
13. Hy		10, 12, M.P.
14. $Fy \supset Hy$		11–13, C.P.
15. $Ay \supset (Fy \supset Hy)$		5-14, C.P.
16. $(x)[Ax \supset (Fx \supset Hx)]$		15, **UG**

EXERCISES

Construct formal proofs of validity for the following arguments, using the rule of Conditional Proof wherever its application will result in a shorter proof:

1. No anarchists are bankers. Jones is an anarchist. Therefore Jones is not a banker.

2. All contestants were deceived. Some contestants were engineers. Therefore some engineers were deceived.

3. No fool is a gentleman. Some hunters are gentlemen. Therefore some hunters are not fools.

4. All insurrectionists were jailed. Some insurrectionists were not killed. Therefore some who were jailed were not killed.

5. All leaders are masterful. Brown is not masterful. Therefore Brown is not a leader.

6. Only officers are navigators. Officers all have pistols. Therefore any navigator has a pistol.

7. Reformers are never quiet. None but reformers have been saints. Therefore there have been no quiet saints.

8. There are useful tautologies. Whatever has use has value. Therefore not all tautologies are valueless.

9. All adolescents are bumptious. No cosmopolitan is bumptious. Some debutantes are cosmopolitans. Therefore some debutantes are not adolescents.

10. The English are friendly. Only the generous are friendly. To be generous one must be honest. There are dishonest industrialists. Therefore not all industrialists are English.

11. All airplanes are fast and convenient. Some airplanes are delapidated. Therefore some delapidated things are fast.

12. Snakes and lizards are reptiles. Reptiles and birds are oviparous. Therefore snakes are oviparous.

13. Every citizen is either a patriot or a traitor. Every patriot is honorable. Some citizens are not honorable. Therefore some citizens are traitors.

14. All members who were present were both surprised and resentful. All members who were interested were present. Therefore all members who were interested were surprised.

15. All crows are black. All black crows are pests. Therefore all crows are black pests.

16. All people are consumers. Some people are wealthy. All wealthy consumers are extravagant. Therefore some people are extravagant.

17. Waitresses and helpers will be discharged if they are clumsy or inefficient. Therefore any waitress will be discharged if she is clumsy.

✓ Leblanc rev. Copi JSL XIX 283

×× Cf Hilbert-Ackermann pp 120-121 ; Kneales 705-6 ;
Leblanc 218-20 ; Anderson & Johnstone p 336 et circa ;
Church 253-4 *Proving Invalidity* Nonker 115-118   85
Mendelson 156

18. All terriers are lively. Lively terriers are all courageous. Any lively terrier which is courageous is a hunter. Therefore all terriers are hunters.

19. Painters and sculptors are artists. All artists and radicals are Bohemians. Bohemians are unconventional and original. Some painters are neither original nor talented. Therefore some sculptors are talented but not unconventional.

20. No man who is a defendant will be convicted if he is innocent. Any man who is tried is a defendant. Any defendant who is not convicted will be acquitted. Every man who is acquitted is innocent. Therefore any man who is tried will be acquitted if and only if he is innocent.

This supplied in 2ⁿᵈ edⁿ (with ref.)

III. PROVING INVALIDITY

Could be made an effective formal test of validity by supplying the Bernays-Schönfinkel upper bound. (367ℓ) on the size of the finite universes which must be considered × ××

In the preceding chapter we proved the invalidity of invalid arguments containing truth-functional compound statements by assigning truth values to their simple constituent statements in such a way as to make their premises true and their conclusions false. We can use a very similar method to prove the invalidity of invalid arguments involving quantifiers. The method of proving invalidity about to be described is closely connected with our basic assumption that the universe is non-empty, that is, that there exists at least one individual in the universe.

The assumption that the universe is non-empty could be satisfied in infinitely many different ways: if there is exactly one individual, or if there are exactly two individuals, or if there are exactly three individuals, or etc. For any such case there is a strict logical equivalence between non-compound general propositions and truth-functional compounds of singular propositions. If there is exactly one individual in the universe, say a, then

$$[(x)\Phi x] \equiv \Phi a \qquad \text{and} \qquad [(\exists x)\Phi x] \equiv \Phi a.$$

If there are exactly two individual in the universe, say a and b, then

$$[(x)\Phi x] \equiv [\Phi a \cdot \Phi b] \qquad \text{and} \qquad [(\exists x)\Phi x] \equiv [\Phi a \lor \Phi b].$$

And for any number k, if there are exactly k individuals in the universe, say a, b, c, . . . , k, then

$$[(x)\Phi x] \equiv [\Phi a \cdot \Phi b \cdot \Phi c \cdot \ \ . \ . \ . \ \cdot \Phi k]$$

and

$$[(\exists x)\Phi x] \equiv [\Phi a \ v \ \Phi b \ v \ \Phi c \ v \ . \ . \ . \ v \ \Phi k].$$

For any possible non-empty universe containing some finite number of individuals, every general proposition is logically equivalent to some truth-functional compound of singular propositions. Hence for any such universe every argument involving quantifiers is logically equivalent to some argument containing only singular propositions and truth-functional compounds of them.

It is clear that an argument involving quantifiers is valid if and only if for every non-empty universe it is logically equivalent to a truth-functional argument which is valid. Hence we can prove the invalidity of an argument by showing that there is a possible non-empty universe for which the given argument is logically equivalent to an *invalid* truth-functional argument. We can accomplish this purpose by translating the given argument involving quantifiers into a logically equivalent argument involving only singular propositions and truth-functional compounds of them, and then using the method of assigning truth values to prove the latter invalid. For example, given the argument

> All whales are heavy.
> All elephants are heavy.
> Therefore all whales are elephants.

we first symbolize it as

$$(x)[Wx \supset Hx]$$
$$(x)[Ex \supset Hx]$$
$$\therefore \ (x)[Wx \supset Ex].$$

In the case of a universe containing exactly one individual, say a, the given argument is logically equivalent to

$$Wa \supset Ha$$
$$Ea \supset Ha$$
$$\therefore \ Wa \supset Ea$$

and the latter is proved invalid by assigning the truth value *true* to 'Wa' and 'Ha' and *false* to 'Ea'. Hence the given argument is *invalid*.

It *can* happen that an invalid argument involving quantifiers is logically equivalent, for a universe containing exactly one individual, to a valid truth-functional argument, although it will be logically equivalent, for any universe containing more than one individual, to an invalid truth-functional argument. For example, consider the argument

> Some dogs are pointers.
> Some dogs are spaniels.
> Therefore some pointers are spaniels.

which we symbolize as

$$(\exists x)[Dx{\cdot}Px]$$
$$(\exists x)[Dx{\cdot}Sx]$$
$$\therefore \ (\exists x)[Px{\cdot}Sx].$$

For a universe containing exactly one individual a it is logically equivalent to

$$Da{\cdot}Pa$$
$$Da{\cdot}Sa$$
$$\therefore \ Pa{\cdot}Sa$$

which is valid. But for a universe containing two individuals a and b it is equivalent to

$$(Da{\cdot}Pa) \text{ v } (Db{\cdot}Pb)$$
$$(Da{\cdot}Sa) \text{ v } (Db{\cdot}Sb)$$
$$\therefore \ (Pa{\cdot}Sa) \text{ v } (Pb{\cdot}Sb)$$

which is proved invalid by assigning *true* to 'Da', 'Db', 'Pa', 'Sb', and *false* to 'Pb' and 'Sa'. Hence the original argument is invalid, since there is a non-empty universe for which it is logically equivalent to an invalid truth-functional argument.

Any invalid argument of this general type can be proved invalid by describing a possible non-empty universe for which its equivalent truth-functional argument is proved invalid by the method of assigning truth values.

Additions in 2nd ed.

EXERCISES

I. Prove that each of the following arguments is invalid:

1. All ballerinas are feminine. Annette is not a ballerina. Therefore Annette is not feminine.
2. All animals are visible. All unicorns are animals. Therefore some unicorns are visible.
3. Some liberals are Republicans. Some Republicans are isolationists. Therefore some isolationists are liberals.
4. All men and only men are rational. Some men are selfish. All men are animals. Some animals are not rational. Therefore there is at least one animal which is not selfish.
5. Lions and tigers are carnivorous mammals. Some lions are dangerous. All tigers have stripes. Some tigers are ferocious. No lions have stripes. Some mammals are neither ferocious nor dangerous. Therefore some carnivores are neither lions nor tigers.

II. Prove the validity or the invalidity of each of the following arguments:

1. No farmer is sophisticated. Adams is sophisticated. Therefore Adams is not a farmer.
2. No foreman is stupid. Brown is not a foreman. Therefore Brown is stupid.
3. All judges are lawyers. Some lawyers are shysters. Therefore some judges are shysters.
4. Some jailers are liberals. All liberals are shrewd. Therefore some jailers are shrewd.
5. All men who have ambition and intelligence are successful. Some ambitious men are not successful. Some intelligent men are not successful. Therefore some men have neither ambition nor intelligence.
6. All mattresses are either soft or uncomfortable. No soft mattress is uncomfortable. Some mattresses are uncomfortable. Therefore some mattresses are not soft.

7. Offices and houses are uncomfortable and disagreeable if they are either stuffy or chilly. Therefore any office will be uncomfortable if it is stuffy.

3. All men and women will be healthy and vigorous if they exercise and do not dissipate. Therefore any man will be healthy if he exercises.

9. No applicant will be either hired or considered who is either untrained or inexperienced. Some applicants are inexperienced beginners. All applicants who are women will be disappointed except those who are hired. Every applicant is a woman. Some women will be hired. Therefore some applicants will not be disappointed.

10. No candidate will be either elected or appointed who is either a liberal or a radical. Some candidates are wealthy liberals. All candidates who are politicians will be disappointed except those who are elected. Every candidate is a politician. Some politicians will be elected. Therefore some candidates will be disappointed.

IV. MULTIPLY GENERAL PROPOSITIONS

Thus far we have limited our attention to singular propositions and to general propositions which contain only a single quantifier. A general proposition which contains exactly one quantifier is said to be *singly* general. We turn next to *multiply* general propositions, which contain two or more quantifiers. In our usage of the term, any compound statement whose components are general propositions is to be counted as a multiply general proposition. For example, the conditional 'If all dogs are carnivorous then some animals are carnivorous', symbolized as '$(x)[Dx \supset Cx] \supset (\exists x)[Ax \cdot Cx]$', is a multiply general proposition. Other multiply general propositions are more complex and require a more complicated notation. To develop the new notation we must turn again to the notion of a propositional function.

All propositional functions considered up to now have had as substitution instances either singular propositions or truth-functional compounds of singular propositions having the same subject terms. But if we now consider a compound statement whose components are singular propositions having *different* subject terms, such as '*Fa·Gb*', we can regard it as a substitution instance either of the propositional function '*Fx·Gb*' or of the propositional function '*Fa·Gx*'. Some propositional functions, we see, may contain singular propositions as parts. And if we consider a compound statement of which one constituent is a general proposition and the other constituent is a singular proposition, such as 'If all dogs are carnivorous then Rover is carnivorous', symbolized as '$(x)[Dx \supset Cx] \supset Cr$', we can regard it as a substitution instance of the propositional function '$(x)[Dx \supset Cx] \supset Cx$'. Thus we see that some propositional functions may contain general propositions as parts.

At this point two new technical terms may properly be introduced. An occurrence of the variable '*x*' which does not occur within, or lie within the scope of, a universal or existential quantifier* '(x)' or '$(\exists x)$' will be called a *free occurrence* of that variable. On the other hand, an occurrence of the variable '*x*' which is either part of a quantifier or lies within the scope of a quantifier '(x)' or '$(\exists x)$' will be called a *bound occurrence* of that variable. † Thus in the expression '$(x)[Dx \supset Cx] \supset Cx$' the first occurrence of the variable '*x*' is *part of a quantifier* and is therefore considered to be *bound*. The second and third occurrences are bound occurrences also. But the fourth occurrence is a free occurrence. Thus we see that propositional functions may contain both free and bound occurrences of variables. On the other hand, all occurrences of variables in propositions must be bound, since every proposition must be either true or false. A propositional function must contain at least one free occurrence of a variable, but no proposition can contain any free occurrences of any variable.

The proposition '*Fa·Gb*' can also be regarded as a substitution instance of '*Fx·Gy*', where the latter is a propositional function containing *two different variables*. Up to now we have explicitly admitted only one individual variable, the letter '*x*'. However, in our previous *use* of the letter '*y*' to denote *any arbitrarily selected*

---

* As explained on page 71.

† An alternative, less common nomenclature refers to free variables as 'real' variables, and to bound variables as 'apparent' variables.

individual, we were in effect using it as a variable without admitting the fact. And in introducing the letter '*w*' by **EI** to denote *some particular* individual having a specified property, without really knowing *which* individual it denoted, we were in effect using '*w*' as a variable also. We now proceed to acknowledge candidly what was implicit in our former usage. Some propositional functions may contain two or more different individual variables. It will be convenient to have a larger supply of individual variables available, so we readjust our notational conventions to include the letters '*u*', '*v*', '*w*', '*x*', '*y*', and '*z*' as individual variables. Propositional functions now include such expressions as '*Fu*', '*Fu* v *Gw*', '(*Fx·Gy*) ⊃ *Hz*', '*Fx* v (*Gy·Hx*)', and the like.

It should be observed that in replacing variables by constants to obtain propositions from propositional functions, the same constant must replace every free occurrence of the same variable. Thus substitution instances of the propositional function '*Fx* v (*Gy·Hx*)' are

> *Fa* v (*Gb·Ha*), *Fa* v (*Gc·Ha*), *Fa* v (*Gd·Ha*), . . .
> *Fb* v (*Ga·Hb*), *Fb* v (*Gc·Hb*), *Fb* v (*Gd·Hb*), . . .
> *Fc* v (*Ga·Hc*), *Fc* v (*Gb·Hc*), *Fc* v (*Gd·Hc*), . . .
> . . . .

but *not* such propositions as '*Fa* v (*Gb·Hc*)'. On the other hand, the *same* constant can replace free occurrences of *different* variables, provided, of course, that if it replaces any free occurrence of a variable it must replace all free occurrences of that variable. Thus additional substitution instances of the propositional function '*Fx* v (*Gy·Hx*)' are '*Fa* v (*Ga·Ha*)', '*Fb* v (*Gb·Hb*)', '*Fc* v (*Gc·Hc*)', . . .

Having admitted the letters '*u*', '*v*', '*w*', '*y*', and '*z*' as individual variables in addition to '*x*', we now adjust our notation for universal and existential quantification to conform to our expanded stock of variables. The proposition 'All *F*'s are *G*'s' may be alternatively symbolized as '(*u*)[*Fu* ⊃ *Gu*]', '(*v*)[*Fv* ⊃ *Gv*]', '(*w*)[*Fw* ⊃ *Gw*]', '(*x*)[*Fx* ⊃ *Gx*]', '(*y*)[*Fy* ⊃ *Gy*]', or '(*z*)[*Fz* ⊃ *Gz*]'.

Similarly the proposition 'There are some H's' may be alternatively symbolized as '$(\exists u)Hu$', '$(\exists v)Hv$', . . . , '$(\exists y)Hy$', or '$(\exists z)Hz$'. The difference between '$(x)Fx$' and '$(y)Fy$' (as between '$(\exists x)Gx$' and '$(\exists y)Gy$') is purely notational, and either may be written in place of the other wherever it occurs. Of course where we have a propositional function containing free occurrences of two or more different variables, such as '$Fx \cdot Gy$', the two propositional functions which result from quantifying it differently as

$$(x)[Fx \cdot Gy] \qquad \text{and} \qquad (y)[Fx \cdot Gy]$$

are very different indeed, and their difference is more than merely notational. The substitution instances of the first are

$$(x)[Fx \cdot Ga], \; (x)[Fx \cdot Gb], \; (x)[Fx \cdot Gc], \; . . .$$

while the substitution instances of the second are

$$(y)[Fa \cdot Gy], \; (y)[Fb \cdot Gy], \; (y)[Fc \cdot Gy], \; . . .$$

If it so happens that every individual has the property F but only some individuals have the property G, then some substitution instances of the first will be true propositions, while all substitution instances of the second will be false, a considerable difference indeed! This example should serve to indicate the need for speaking not of "*the* universal (or existential) quantification of a propositional function" but rather of "the universal (or existential) quantification of a propositional function *with respect to the variable 'x'* " or "the universal (or existential) quantification of a propositional function *with respect to the variable 'y'* " and so on.

It should be clear that since '$(x)[Fx \supset Gx]$' and '$(y)[Fy \supset Gy]$' are alternative translations of the proposition 'Everything which is an F is also a G', the universal quantification of '$Fx \supset Gx$' with respect to 'x' has the same meaning and is logically equivalent to the universal quantification with respect to 'y' of the propositional function which results from replacing all free occurrences of 'x' in '$Fx \supset Gx$' by 'y'—for the result of that replacement is '$Fy \supset Gy$'. In the early stages of our work it will be desirable to have at most one quantification with respect to a given variable in a single proposition. This is not strictly *necessary*, but it is helpful in preventing confusion. Thus the first multiply general proposition considered, 'If all dogs are carnivorous then some animals are carnivorous', is more conveniently symbolized as '$(x)[Dx \supset Cx] \supset (\exists y)[Ay \cdot Cy]$' than as '$(x)[Dx \supset Cx] \supset (\exists x)[Ax \cdot Cx]$', although neither is *incorrect*.

It has been remarked that no proposition can contain a free occurrence of any variable. Hence in symbolizing any proposition we must take care that every occurrence of every variable used lies within the scope of a quantifier with respect to that variable. Some examples will help to make the matter clear. The proposition

> If something is wrong with the house then everyone
> in the house complains.

is properly symbolized as a conditional whose antecedent and consequent contain different quantifiers:

> $(\exists x)[x$ is wrong with the house$] \supset (y)[(y$ is a person
> in the house$) \supset (y$ complains$)]$.

Here the scope of the initial quantifier does not extend past the main implication sign. But if we turn now to another proposition which bears a superficial resemblance to the first:

> If something is wrong then it should be rectified.

it would be *incorrect* to symbolize it as

> $(\exists x)[x$ is wrong$] \supset (x$ should be rectified$)$.

For since the scope of the initial quantifier ends at the implication sign, the occurrence of 'x' in the consequent *cannot* refer back to the initial quantifier because it does not lie within its scope. We have here a free occurrence of a variable, which means that the proposed symbolization is not a proposition and therefore not an adequate translation of the given statement. The error is not to be corrected by *simply* extending the scope of the initial quantifier through rebracketing, moreover, for the symbolic expression

$$(\exists x)[(x \text{ is wrong}) \supset (x \text{ should be rectified})]$$

although a proposition, does not have the same meaning as the original proposition in English. Instead, it says merely that there is at least one thing which should be rectified if it is wrong, but the sense of the English sentence is clearly that if *anything* is wrong then it should be rectified. Hence a correct symbolization is neither of the preceding, but rather

$$(x)[(x \text{ is wrong}) \supset (x \text{ should be rectified})].$$

The situation is more complicated, but no different in principle, when one quantifier occurs *within the scope of another quantifier*. Here the same warning against dangling or unquantified variables must be sounded. The proposition

> If something is missing then if nobody calls the police someone will be unhappy.

is properly symbolized as

> $(\exists x)[x \text{ is missing}] \supset \{(y)[(y \text{ is a person}) \supset \sim(y \text{ calls the police})] \supset (\exists z)[(z \text{ is a person}) \cdot (z \text{ will be unhappy})]\}.$

But the following proposition, which is superficially analogous to the preceding:

> If something is missing then if nobody calls the police it will not be recovered.

is *not* to be symbolized as

> $(\exists x)[x \text{ is missing}] \supset \{(y)[(y \text{ is a person}) \supset \sim(y \text{ calls the police})] \supset \sim(x \text{ will be recovered})\}$

for the last occurrence of the variable 'x' is outside the scope of the initial quantifier, being left dangling. It too cannot be corrected simply by rebracketing, as

$(\exists x)\{(x$ is missing$) \supset \{(y)[(y$ is a person$) \supset \sim(y$ calls the police$)] \supset \sim(x$ will be recovered$)\}\}$

for this expression fails equally to preserve the sense of the English sentence, in the same way as in the previous example. That sense is expressed by the formula

$(x)\{(x$ is missing$) \supset \{(y)[(y$ is a person$) \supset \sim(y$ calls the police$)] \supset \sim(x$ will be recovered$)\}\}$

which is therefore a correct symbolization of the given proposition.

EXERCISES

Symbolize each of the following propositions, in each case using the abbreviations which are suggested:

1. If anything is missing someone will call the police. (Mx-x is missing, Px-x is a person, Cx-x will call the police.)
2. If anything is missing the maid probably took it. (Mx-x is missing, Tx-x was probably taken by the maid.)
3. If any diamonds are large then some diamonds are expensive. (Dx-x is a diamond, Lx-x is large, Ex-x is expensive.)
4. If any diamonds are large then, if all large diamonds are expensive, they are expensive. (Dx-x is a diamond, Lx-x is large, Ex-x is expensive.)
5. If all students who are present are either botany majors or zoology majors then either some botany majors are present or some zoology majors are present. (Sx-x is a student, Px-x is present, Bx-x is a botany major, Zx-x is a zoology major.)
6. If any student is present then either no botany majors are present or he is a botany major. (Sx-x is a student, Px-x is present, Bx-x is a botany major.)
7. If all visitors are friendly and only relatives are visitors then if there are any visitors some relatives are friendly. (Vx-x is a visitor, Fx-x is friendly, Rx-x is a relative.)
8. If there are any visitors and only relatives are visitors then they must be relatives. (Vx-x is a visitor, Rx-x is a relative.)
9. If all wives are ambitious and no husbands are successful then some wives will be miserable. (Wx-x is a wife, Ax-x is ambitious, Hx-x is a husband, Sx-x is successful, Mx-x will be miserable.)

10. If any husband is unsuccessful then if all wives are ambitious he will be miserable. (*Hx-x* is a husband, *Sx-x* is successful, *Wx-x* is a wife, *Ax-x* is ambitious, *Mx-x* will be miserable.)

V. REVISED QUANTIFICATION RULES

1. Inferences Involving Propositional Functions. In constructing a formal proof or demonstration that a given argument is valid, the premisses with which we begin and the conclusion with which we end are all propositions. But wherever the rules of Existential Instantiation or Universal Generalization are used some of the intermediate steps must contain free variables, and will therefore be propositional functions rather than propositions. Each step of a demonstration must be either a premiss, or an assumption of limited scope, or follow validly from preceding steps by an elementary valid argument form, or follow from a sequence of preceding steps by the principle of Conditional Proof. Three questions naturally arise at this point: In what sense can a propositional function be said to follow *validly* from other propositional functions? In what sense can a propositional function be said to follow *validly* from propositions? And in what sense can a proposition be said to follow *validly* from propositional functions?

These questions are not difficult to answer. Propositional functions contain free variables, and are therefore neither true nor false. But a propositional function becomes a proposition when all its free variables are replaced by constants, and the resulting substitution instance is either true or false. One propositional function can be said to follow *validly* as conclusion from one or more other propositional functions as premisses when every replacement of free occurrences of variables by constants (the same constants replacing the same variables in both premisses and conclusion, of course) results in a valid argument. For example, the propositional function '*Gx*' follows validly from the propositional functions '*Fx* ⊃ *Gx*' and '*Fx*', because every replacement of '*x*' by a constant results in an argument of the form *modus ponens*. We may say of such an inference that it is valid by the principle of *modus ponens* despite the fact that propositional functions rather than propositions are involved. It should be clear that any inference is valid which proceeds by way of any of the elementary valid argument forms of our original list, regardless of whether the premisses and conclusion are propositions or propositional functions. In passing we may note that this is so even where the conclusion contains more free variables than the premisses, as when by the principle of Addition we validly infer the propositional function of two variables '*Fx* v *Gy*' from the propositional function of one variable '*Fx*'.

The original list of elementary valid argument forms also permits the inference of propositional functions from propositions, as when by the principle of Addition we infer the propositional function '*Fa* v *Gx*' from the proposition '*Fa*'. That such inferences as these are valid, in the sense explained, is obvious. Moreover, propositions can validly be inferred from propositional functions by elementary valid arguments, as when by the principle of Simplification we infer the proposition '*Fa*' from the propositional function '*Fa·Gx*'.

We can now adopt a more general definition of formal proof or demonstration, which parallels our earlier definition exactly except that steps of a proof can be either propositions or propositional functions. If each step which follows the initial premisses follows validly from preceding steps, in the generalized sense of 'valid' just explained, then the last step validly follows from the initial premisses. And if our initial premisses and conclusion are propositions rather than propositional functions, then the conclusion validly follows from the initial premisses in the original sense of valid which applies to arguments whose premisses and conclusions are all statements or propositions. This fact can be seen by the following considerations. As we go from our original premisses to propositional functions, if we go validly, then if the premisses are true, all substitution instances of the inferred propositional functions must be true also. And as we go from previously inferred propositional functions to other propositional functions, if we go validly, then all substitution instances of the latter must be true also. Finally, when we go from validly inferred propositional functions to the final conclusion which is a proposition, then if we go validly, since all substitution instances of the former are true, the final conclusion must be true also.

The preceding remarks require some modification to take account of Existential Generalization and Instantiation, but the modifications are best introduced as restrictions on the quantification rules themselves. The quantification rules must be reformulated in any case, for as previously stated they were designed to apply only to propositions, not to propositional functions. The two rules for generalizing, **UG** and **EG**, must be reformulated so as to permit the quantification (or binding) of free variables, while the instantiation rules **UI** and **EI** must be reformulated so as to permit the freeing of bound variables, that is, to permit the inference of propositional functions rather than (pretended) substitution instances of them.

In our earlier discussion of propositional functions (of the single variable 'x') we introduced the Greek letters *phi* and *psi*, and let 'Φx' and 'Ψx' denote any propositional function of 'x', such as 'Fx', 'Gx', '$Fx \cdot Hx$', '$(Fx \cdot Gx) \supset Hx$', . . . no matter how complicated such functions might be. It will be useful to continue to use these Greek letters, but now letting 'Φx' denote any propositional function which contains at least one free occurrence of the variable 'x', even including those propositional functions which contain free occurrences of other variables. Thus 'Φx' may denote any of the following:

$$Fx, \; Fx \text{ v } Gx, \; Ga \supset Hx, \; Fw \text{ v } Fx, \; (\exists z)[Gz \text{ v } Hx], \; . . .$$

Similarly, 'Φy' may denote any of the propositional functions

$$Fy, \; Fy \text{ v } Gy, \; Ga \supset Hy, \; Fw \text{ v } Fy, \; (\exists z)[Gz \text{ v } Hy], \; . . .$$

To be able to refer to *any* propositional function in *either* of the preceding groups it will be convenient to introduce the Greek letters *mu* and *nu* ('μ' and 'ν') to denote any individual symbol, whether constant or variable. Thus '$\Phi\mu$' may denote any of the preceding propositional functions of either 'x' or 'y', according as 'μ' is taken as denoting 'x' or 'y'. Similarly, according as 'μ' is taken as denoting 'x' or 'y', '$(\mu)\Phi\mu$' will denote the universal quantification with respect to 'x' or 'y' of any of the preceding propositional functions of 'x' or 'y', and '$(\exists\mu)\Phi\mu$' will denote the existential quantification.

The Greek letters *phi* and *psi* may also be used in conjunction with an individual constant to denote either propositions or propositional functions containing that constant. Thus 'Φa' may denote any of the expressions

$$Fa, \; Fa \; v \; Ga, \; Ga \supset Ha, \; Fw \; v \; Fa, \; (\exists z)[Gz \; v \; Ha], \; \ldots$$

and 'Φb' may denote any of the expressions

$$Fb, \; Fb \; v \; Gb, \; Ga \supset Hb, \; Fw \; v \; Fb, \; (\exists z)[Gz \; v \; Hb], \; \ldots$$

By the convention already introduced, '$\Phi\mu$' may denote any expression of the two preceding groups according as 'μ' is taken as denoting 'a' or 'b'. This notation will be extremely useful in reformulating our quantification rules.

2. Revised Universal Instantiation. The revision of our quantification rules will be accompanied by examples of valid arguments which they must permit, and also by examples of invalid arguments whose avoidance must be accomplished by means of restrictions placed on those rules. The following inferences are clearly valid:

$$\frac{(x)Fx}{\therefore Fa}, \; \frac{(y)[Fy \; v \; Gb]}{\therefore Fa \; v \; Gb}, \; \frac{(z)[Fz \; v \; Gb]}{\therefore Fb \; v \; Gb}, \; \frac{(x)[Fx \; v \; Gy]}{\therefore Fc \; v \; Gy}, \; \frac{(x)\{Fx \cdot (\exists x)[Gx \cdot Hy]\}}{\therefore Fb \cdot (\exists x)[Gx \cdot Hy]},$$

$$\ldots$$

They may be described generally as being of the form $(\mu)\Phi\mu$ $\therefore \Phi v$ where μ is an individual variable, v is an individual constant, and Φv results from $\Phi\mu$ by replacing all free occurrences of μ in $\Phi\mu$ by v. Of course there can be no free occurrence of μ in $(\mu)\Phi\mu$, but there must be at least one free occurrence of μ in $\Phi\mu$. On the other hand, not every occurrence of μ in $\Phi\mu$ need be free: for example, where 'μ' denotes 'x' and '$\Phi\mu$' denotes '$Fx \supset (\exists x)[Gx \; v \; Hy]$', only the first occurrence of μ in $\Phi\mu$ is free, since the second is part of the existential quantifier $(\exists\mu)$ and the third is within the scope of that quantifier.

Also valid are such inferences as

$$\frac{(x)Fx}{\therefore Fy}, \frac{(x)Fx}{\therefore Fx}, \frac{(y)[Fy \text{ v } Gb]}{\therefore Fx \text{ v } Gb}, \frac{(z)[Fz \text{ v } Gx]}{\therefore Fx \text{ v } Gx}, \frac{(x)\{Fx\cdot(\exists x)[Gx\cdot Hy]\}}{\therefore Fz\cdot(\exists x)[Gx\cdot Hy]}, \cdots$$

which are also of the form $(\mu)\Phi\mu \therefore \Phi\upsilon$ as above, except that *both* μ and υ are individual variables. Here the premiss $(\mu)\Phi\mu$ may be a proposition but the conclusion $\Phi\upsilon$ must be a propositional function.

Just as we count valid the inference '$(z)[Fz \text{ v } Gb] \therefore Fb \text{ v } Gb$' where the instantiating constant 'b' occurs in the premiss as well as in the conclusion, so we wish to count as valid such inferences as

$$\frac{(x)[Fx \text{ v } Gy]}{\therefore Fy \text{ v } Gy}, \frac{(y)[Fx \supset Gy]}{\therefore Fx \supset Gx}, \frac{(z)[Fx \supset (Gy\cdot Hz)]}{\therefore Fx \supset (Gy\cdot Hy)}, \cdots$$

in which the instantiating *variable* occurs free in the premiss as well as in the conclusion. In general, when $\Phi\upsilon$ is inferred from $(\mu)\Phi\mu$ validly, υ must occur free in $\Phi\upsilon$ at every place where μ occurs free in $\Phi\mu$, but there *may* be more free occurrences of υ in $\Phi\upsilon$ than there are free occurrences of μ in $\Phi\mu$. There will be more whenever υ occurs free in $\Phi\mu$.

All the preceding inferences must be legitimized by our principle of Universal Instantiation. It will be convenient to establish a single set of conventions governing the expressions '$\Phi\mu$' and '$\Phi\upsilon$' so that each may be used in the same sense in the statements of all four quantification rules. The expression '$\Phi\mu$' will denote any propositional function in which there is at least one free occurrence of the variable denoted by 'μ'. The expression '$\Phi\upsilon$' will denote the result of replacing all free occurrences of μ in $\Phi\mu$ by υ, with the added provision that when υ is a variable it must occur free in $\Phi\upsilon$ at all places at which μ occurs free in $\Phi\mu$. The reason for this restriction will be explained immediately after the statement of our reformulated principle of Universal

Instantiation. This principle is now stated as an elementary valid argument form:

$$\textbf{UI:} \quad \frac{(\mu)\Phi\mu}{\therefore \ \Phi\upsilon}$$

provided that if υ is a variable it must occur free in $\Phi\upsilon$ at all places where μ occurs free in $\Phi\mu$.

This restriction serves to prevent such inferences as

$$\frac{(x)[(\exists y)(Fx \equiv \sim Fy)]}{\therefore \ (\exists y)(Fy \equiv \sim Fy)}$$

for that inference* would be invalid in some non-empty universes, for example, in a universe consisting of just the two individuals a and b, where a has but b lacks the property F. There '$Fa \equiv \sim Fb$' and '$Fb \equiv \sim Fa$' are both true, so that the premiss is true, but the conclusion is false, being contradictory.

3. Revised Existential Generalization. Turning now to Existential Generalization, we observe that the following are all valid inferences:

$$\frac{Fa}{\therefore \ (\exists x)Fx}, \quad \frac{Fa}{\therefore \ (\exists y)Fy}, \quad \frac{Fa \lor Gb}{\therefore \ (\exists x)[Fx \lor Gb]}, \quad \frac{Fa \cdot Gb}{\therefore \ (\exists z)[Fa \cdot Gz]},$$

$$\frac{Fa \supset Ga}{\therefore \ (\exists y)[Fy \supset Ga]}, \ \cdots$$

They may be described generally as being of the form $\Phi\upsilon \ \therefore$ $(\exists\mu)\Phi\mu$, where υ is an individual constant, μ is an individual variable, and $\Phi\upsilon$ results from replacing all free occurrences of μ in $\Phi\mu$ by υ. Here both premisses and conclusions are propositions. Also valid are such inferences involving propositional functions as:

$$\frac{Fx}{\therefore \ (\exists y)Fy}, \quad \frac{Fa \lor Gy}{\therefore \ (\exists x)[Fa \lor Gx]}, \quad \frac{Fx \supset Gy}{\therefore \ (\exists z)[Fx \supset Gz]}, \quad \frac{Fx \cdot Gx}{\therefore \ (\exists y)[Fy \cdot Gx]}, \ \cdots$$

* Which may be paraphrased as: For any individual x there is an individual y such that x has the property F if and only if y does not have the property F; therefore there is an individual y such that y has the property F if and only if y does not have the property F.

which are of the same pattern as the preceding except that here v is a variable instead of a constant. Where Φv and $\Phi\mu$ are governed by the same conventions as in our statement of the revised rule of Universal Instantiation, the revised rule of Existential Generalization may be stated as the following elementary valid argument form:

$$\textbf{EG}: \frac{\Phi v}{\therefore\ (\exists\mu)\Phi\mu}$$

provided that if v is a variable it must occur free in Φv at all places where μ occurs free in $\Phi\mu$.

If we failed to observe this restriction, that would make it possible to deduce contradictory conclusions from unobjectionable premises by such an erroneous deduction as

1. $(x)[(\exists y)(Fx \equiv \sim Fy)]/ \therefore\ (\exists z)(Fz \equiv \sim Fz)$
2. $(\exists y)(Fz \equiv \sim Fy)$ 1, **UI**
3. $Fz \equiv \sim Fw$ 2, **EI**
4. $(\exists z)(Fz \equiv \sim Fz)$ 3, **EG** (erroneous)

Having both **UI** and **EG** available, we may illustrate their use by proving the validity of the argument

> All men are mortal.
> _____
>
> Therefore if Socrates is a man then some men are mortal.

by the following conditional proof:

1. $(x)[Hx \supset Mx]$ $/ \therefore\ Hs \supset (\exists x)[Hx \cdot Mx]$
2. Hs
3. $Hs \supset Ms$ 1, **UI**
4. Ms 2, 3, M.P.
5. $Hs \cdot Ms$ 2, 4, Conj.
6. $(\exists x)[Hx \cdot Mx]$ 5, **EG**
7. $Hs \supset (\exists x)[Hx \cdot Mx]$ 2–6, C.P.

A simpler demonstration suffices to establish the validity of any argument of the form $(\mu)\Phi\mu \therefore\ (\exists\mu)\Phi\mu$. Here the proof proceeds:

1. $(\mu)\Phi\mu\ /\therefore\ (\exists\mu)\Phi\mu$
2. Φv 1, **UI**
3. $(\exists\mu)\Phi\mu$ 2, **EG**

It should be noted that where we have a propositional function containing v as its *only* free variable, then where we replace *all* free occurrences of v by μ and quantify existentially with respect to μ, for the inference to be valid it is not necessary for all substitution instances of the premiss to be true, but only for it to have at least one true substitution instance. We shall return to this point in discussing the two remaining quantification rules.

4. Revised Existential Instantiation. Turning now to Existential Instantiation, we want such inferences as '$(\exists x)Fx \therefore Fx$' and '$(\exists x)Fx \therefore Fy$' to count as valid in a proof *only* if no other condition has previously been placed on the instantiating variable. These inferences are valid *only* if the instantiating variable has no free occurrence in any previous step of the proof. Otherwise we should be able to derive a contradiction from true premisses—granted that some but not all things have the property F, we should be able to prove that something both has and does not have that property. This (erroneous) inference would proceed:

1. $(\exists x)Fx$
2. $(\exists y) \sim Fy$ $/ \therefore (\exists z)(Fz \cdot \sim Fz)$
3. Fw 1, **EI**
4. $\sim Fw$ 2, **EI** (erroneous)
5. $Fw \cdot \sim Fw$ 3, 4, Conj.
6. $(\exists z)(Fz \cdot \sim Fz)$ 5, **EG**

We must therefore state **EI** with the restriction that the instantiating variable must have its first free occurrence in the propositional function inferred. Moreover, no claim is made that *all* substitution instances of the inferred propositional function are true; we maintain only that if the premiss is true then the conclusion is a propositional function which has *at least one* true substitution instance. Hence a propositional function inferred by **EI** can validly have **EG** applied to it, but *not* **UG**. The inferences legitimized by **EI** are of the form $(\exists\mu)\Phi\mu \therefore \Phi v$, but the latter can be listed as an elementary valid argument form *only with the indicated restriction*. Our statement of the principle of

Existential Instantiation as an elementary valid argument form is

$$\textbf{EI}: \frac{(\exists\mu)\Phi\mu}{\therefore\ \Phi\upsilon}$$

provided that υ is a variable that occurs free in $\Phi\upsilon$ at all places where μ occurs free in $\Phi\mu$, and that υ occurs free in no earlier step.

The first restriction serves to prevent such obviously invalid inferences as

$$\frac{(\exists x)(\exists y)(Fx \cdot \sim Fy)}{\therefore\ (\exists y)(Fy \cdot \sim Fy)}$$

5. Revised Universal Generalization.   In stating the principle of Universal Generalization we must be careful to restrict its application to variables which have *not* been introduced by **EI**, for the inference from '$(\exists x)Fx$' to '$(x)Fx$' is surely not valid. The principle **UG** cannot legitimately be used to go from $\Phi\upsilon$ to $(\mu)\Phi\mu$ when the variable υ has been introduced by **EI**. Moreover, the indicated inference is illegitimate when the variable υ has a free occurrence in any earlier propositional function which was inferred by **EI**, even though υ itself was not introduced by **EI**. The reason for this restriction can be illustrated by the following (erroneous) proof of the validity of an *invalid* argument:

1. $(x)(\exists y)[Fx \equiv \sim Fy]$ / $\therefore\ (\exists y)(x)[Fx \equiv \sim Fy]$
2. $(\exists y)[Fw \equiv \sim Fy]$ 1, **UI**
3. $Fw \equiv \sim Fz$ 2, **EI**
4. $(x)[Fx \equiv \sim Fz]$ 3, **UG** (erroneous)
5. $(\exists y)(x)[Fx \equiv \sim Fy]$ 4, **EG**

That argument is invalid, since its premiss is true and its conclusion false for a non-empty universe consisting of just the two individuals a and b, where a has but b lacks the property F. Our statement of **UG** must include a restriction to prevent such erroneous inferences as that from 3 to 4 in the preceding 'proof'. Its illegitimacy does not lie in its generalizing with respect to a variable which was introduced by **EI**, for it is generalizing

[margin note:] Rewritten in 2nd ed.

with respect to 'w', and 'w' was introduced by **UI**. But 'w' has a free occurrence in step 3, which was inferred by **EI**, and that suffices to spoil the inference. To repeat, the inference from Φv to $(\mu)\Phi\mu$ is not valid when v has a prior free occurrence in any step which was inferred by **EI**.

Where the variable being generalized has had no free occurrence in any propositional function inferred by **EI**, the following inferences are perfectly valid:

$$\frac{Fx}{\therefore (x)Fx}, \quad \frac{Fx}{\therefore (y)Fy}, \quad \frac{Gx \cdot Hy}{\therefore (z)[Gz \cdot Hy]}, \quad \frac{(\exists x)[Fx \supset Gy]}{\therefore (z)[(\exists x)[Fx \supset Gz]]}, \cdots$$

But we do not wish to permit such inferences as

$$\frac{Fx \cdot Gy}{\therefore (y)[Fy \cdot Gy]}, \quad \frac{Gx \vee Hy}{\therefore (x)[Gx \vee Hx]}, \quad \frac{Fy \supset Hz}{\therefore (z)[Fz \supset Hz]}, \cdots$$

for that would permit false conclusions to be inferred from true premisses—as in the following (erroneous) proof:

1. $(\exists x)(y)[Fx \supset \sim Fy]$ $/\therefore (x)[Fx \supset \sim Fx]$
2. $(y)[Fx \supset \sim Fy]$ 1, **EI**
3. $Fx \supset \sim Fy$ 2, **UI**
4. $(x)[Fx \supset \sim Fx]$ 3, **UG** (erroneous)

To prevent this kind of error we permit the use of Universal Generalization to go from Φv to $(\mu)\Phi\mu$ only if v is a variable that occurs free in Φv at all places where μ occurs free in $\Phi\mu$.

Nor can we permit such inferences as

$$\frac{Fx \cdot Gx}{\therefore (y)[Fy \cdot Gx]}, \quad \frac{Gy \vee Hy}{\therefore (x)[Gy \vee Hx]}, \quad \frac{Fz \supset Hz}{\therefore (x)[Fx \supset Hz]}, \cdots$$

for that would permit erroneous proofs like the following:

1. $(x)[Fx \equiv Fx]$ $/\therefore (\exists y)(x)[Fy \equiv Fx]$
2. $Fy \equiv Fy$ 1, **UI**
3. $(x)[Fy \equiv Fx]$ 2, **UG** (erroneous)
4. $(\exists y)(x)[Fy \equiv Fx]$ 3, **EG**

To prevent this kind of error we permit the use of Universal Generalization to go from Φv to $(\mu)\Phi\mu$ only if v is a variable that occurs free in Φv at only those places where μ occurs free in $\Phi\mu$.

Still a fourth restriction must be placed on the principle of Universal Generalization. This last restriction arises in connection with assumptions of limited scope in Conditional Proofs of validity. When $(\mu)\Phi\mu$ is validly inferred from Φv, v must be a variable which is not free in any assumption within whose scope Φv lies. Otherwise we could have, in any demonstration, regardless of its initial premisses, the following (improper) sequence of steps:

$$
\begin{array}{ll}
\rightarrow Fy & \\
\quad (x)Fx & \textbf{UG} \text{ (erroneous)} \\
\hline
Fy \supset (x)Fx & \text{C.P.} \\
(y)[Fy \supset (x)Fx] & \textbf{UG}
\end{array}
$$

which would have the proposition 'If anything has property F then everything has property F', which is false for most properties F, following as conclusion from any premisses whatsoever. This kind of error can be prevented by prohibiting any use of the principle of Universal Generalization to infer $(\mu)\Phi\mu$ from Φv when the latter lies in the scope of an assumption in which v has a free occurrence.

The principle of Universal Generalization, with the indicated necessary restrictions, can now be stated as

$$
\textbf{UG:} \quad \frac{\Phi v}{\therefore\ (\mu)\Phi\mu}
$$

provided that v is a variable that occurs free in Φv at all places and only those places where μ occurs free in $\Phi\mu$, and that v does not occur free either in any propositional function inferred by **EI** or in any assumption within whose scope Φv lies.

The original list of elementary valid argument forms plus the strengthened principle of Conditional Proof and the revised quantification rules permit us to demonstrate the validity of any valid argument in whose premisses and conclusion only *indi-*

vidual variables are quantified. Their completeness in this respect will not be proved, however, until the end of Chapter Nine.

6. Shorter Proofs of Validity.   At this stage of our work it is desirable to cut down the length of our demonstrations by permitting short cuts to be taken in the application of the original list of elementary valid argument forms. We can combine any use of the principle of Double Negation with any other step, which will permit us to go directly from '$\sim\!A \supset B$' to 'A v B', or vice versa, without having to write down the intermediate step '$\sim\!\sim\!A$ v B'. We can short cut tedious uses of the principle of Commutation by permitting not only '$A \therefore A$ v B' by the principle of Addition, but also such inferences as '$A \therefore B$ v A'. Since the definition of Material Implication and the principle of Distribution can always be used to obtain '$A \supset (B \cdot C)$' from '$(A \supset B) \cdot (A \supset C)$', and vice versa, our demonstrations can be shortened by permitting Distribution to be applied directly to conditionals having conjunctions as their consequents. This is tantamount to adding the form '$[p \supset (q \cdot r)]$ $\equiv [(p \supset q) \cdot (p \supset r)]$' to our list as an alternative version of the principle of Distribution. By repeated application of the principles of Association and Commutation we can rearrange the terms of any conjunction or disjunction in any way we please. Hence we can shorten our demonstrations by omitting parentheses, brackets, etc., from conjunctions of any three or more singular propositions. Thus such propositions as '$A \cdot \{B \cdot [C \cdot (D \cdot E)]\}$', '$(A \cdot B) \cdot [C \cdot (D \cdot E)]$', '$(A \cdot B) \cdot [(C \cdot D) \cdot E]$', '$[(A \cdot B) \cdot C] \cdot (D \cdot E)$', '$[A \cdot (B \cdot C)] \cdot (D \cdot E)$', '$\{[(A \cdot B) \cdot C] \cdot D\} \cdot E$', '$A \cdot [(B \cdot C) \cdot (D \cdot E)]$', . . . will all be written indifferently as '$A \cdot B \cdot C \cdot D \cdot E$', and *any* permutation will be justified simply by the principle of Commutation. Moreover, if it is desired to infer the conjunction of *some* of the indicated conjuncts, in any order, this can be done in one step and justified by the principle of Simplification. Thus from '$A \cdot B \cdot C \cdot D \cdot E$' we can infer '$E \cdot B \cdot D$' in a single step.

In proving the validity of some arguments all four of our quantification rules must be used. Consider the following moderately complex argument:

If all drugs are contaminated then all negligent technicians are scoundrels. If there are any drugs which are contaminated then all of them are contaminated and unsafe. All germicides are drugs. Only the negligent are absent-minded. Therefore if any technician is absent-minded then if some germicides are contaminated then he is a scoundrel.

Using fairly obvious abbreviations, it may be symbolized and proved valid as follows:

1. $(x)[Dx \supset Cx] \supset (y)[(Ny \cdot Ty) \supset Sy]$
2. $(\exists x)[Dx \cdot Cx] \supset (y)[Dy \supset (Cy \cdot Uy)]$
3. $(x)[Gx \supset Dx]$
4. $(x)[Ax \supset Nx] / \therefore (x)\{(Tx \cdot Ax) \supset \{(\exists y)[Gy \cdot Cy] \supset Sx\}\}$
→5. $Tu \cdot Au$
┌→6. $(\exists y)[Gy \cdot Cy]$

7. $Gw \cdot Cw$	6, **EI**
8. $Gw \supset Dw$	3, **UI**
9. Gw	7, Simp.
10. Dw	8, 9, M.P.
11. Cw	7, Simp.
12. $Dw \cdot Cw$	10, 11, Conj.
13. $(\exists x)[Dx \cdot Cx]$	12, **EG**
14. $(y)[Dy \supset (Cy \cdot Uy)]$	2, 13, M.P.
15. $Dz \supset (Cz \cdot Uz)$	14, **UI**
16. $(Dz \supset Cz) \cdot (Dz \supset Uz)$	15, Dist.
17. $Dz \supset Cz$	16, Simp.
18. $(x)[Dx \supset Cx]$	17, **UG**
19. $(y)[(Ny \cdot Ty) \supset Sy]$	1, 18, M.P.
20. $(Nu \cdot Tu) \supset Su$	19, **UI**
21. Au	5, Simp.
22. $Au \supset Nu$	4, **UI**
23. Nu	22, 21, M.P.
24. Tu	5, Simp.
25. $Nu \cdot Tu$	23, 24, Conj.
26. Su	20, 25, M.P.
27. $(\exists y)[Gy \cdot Cy] \supset Su$	6–26, C.P.
28. $(Tu \cdot Au) \supset \{(\exists y)[Gy \cdot Cy] \supset Su\}$	5–27, C.P.
29. $(x)\{(Tx \cdot Ax) \supset \{(\exists y)[Gy \cdot Cy] \supset Sx\}\}$	28, **UG**

EXERCISES

Construct a formal proof of validity for each of the following arguments:

1. All the accused are guilty. All who are convicted will hang. Therefore, if all who are guilty are convicted then all the accused will hang. (*Ax, Gx, Cx, Hx.*)

2. If there are any geniuses then all great composers are geniuses. If anyone is temperamental, all geniuses are temperamental. Therefore, if anyone is a temperamental genius, then all great composers are temperamental. (*Gx-x* is a genius, *Cx-x* is a great composer, *Px-x* is a person, *Tx-x* is temperamental.)

3. Any car with good brakes is safe to drive and safe to ride in. So if a car is new then if all new cars have good brakes it is safe to drive. (*Cx-x* is a car, *Bx-x* has good brakes, *Dx-x* is safe to drive, *Rx-x* is safe to ride in, *Nx-x* is new.)

4. Either all the guests enjoyed themselves or some of the guests concealed their real feelings. No honest person would conceal his real feelings. Therefore if the guests were all honest persons then they all enjoyed themselves. (*Gx-x* is a guest, *Ex-x* enjoyed himself, *Cx-x* conceals his real feelings, *Hx-x* is honest, *Px-x* is a person.)

5. Any businessman who is a poet must be a wealthy man. Wealthy men are all conservatives. If some conservative does not like poetry then no poets are conservatives. Therefore if there is a wealthy man who does not like poetry then no businessmen are poets. (*Bx-x* is a businessman, *Px-x* is a poet, *Wx-x* is a wealthy man, *Cx-x* is a conservative, *Lx-x* likes poetry.)

6. All radioactive substances either have a very short life or have medical value. No uranium isotope which is radioactive has a very short life. Therefore if all uranium isotopes are radioactive then all uranium isotopes have medical value. (*Rx-x* is radioactive, *Sx-x* has a very short life, *Mx-x* has medical value, *Ux-x* is a uranium isotope.)

7. No sane witness would lie if his lying would implicate him in a crime. Therefore if any witness implicated himself in a crime, then if all witnesses were sane, that witness did not lie. (*Sx-x* is sane, *Wx-x* is a witness, *Lx-x* lies, *Ix-x* implicates himself in a crime.)

8. If any jewelry is missing then if all the servants are honest it will be returned. If any servant is honest they all are. So if any jewelry is

missing then if at least one servant is honest it will be returned (*Jx-x* is jewelry, *Mx-x* is missing, *Sx-x* is a servant, *Hx-x* is honest, *Rx-x* will be returned.)

9. If there are any liberals then all philosophers are liberals. If there are any humanitarians, then all liberals are humanitarians. So if there are any humanitarians who are liberals then all philosophers are humanitarians. (*Lx-x* is a liberal, *Px-x* is a philosopher, *Hx-x* is a humanitarian.)

10. If something is lost then if everyone values his possessions it will be missed. If anyone values his possessions, so does everyone. Therefore if something is lost then if someone values his possessions then something will be missed. (*Lx-x* is lost, *Px-x* is a person, *Vx-x* values his possessions, *Mx-x* is missed.)

VI. LOGICAL TRUTHS INVOLVING QUANTIFIERS

In Chapter Two truth tables were used not only to establish the *validity* of certain arguments but also to certify the *logical truth* of certain propositions (tautologies such as '$A \vee \sim A$'). The notion of a logically true proposition is therefore a familiar one. As we have seen, not all valid arguments can be established by the method of truth tables: some of them must be demonstrated by means of our quantification rules. Similarly, not all logically true propositions can be certified by the method of truth tables: some of them must be *demonstrated* by means of our quantification rules.

The method used in demonstrating the logical truth of tautologies was set forth in Chapter Three. A demonstration of the logical truth of the tautology '$A \supset (A \vee B)$' can be set down as

$\rightarrow$1. A
  2. $A \vee B$ 1, Add.
  3. $A \supset (A \vee B)$ 1–2, C.P.

In demonstrating the logical truth of propositions involving quantifiers, we shall have to appeal not only to the original list of elementary valid argument forms and the strengthened principle of Conditional Proof, but to our four quantification rules as well. Thus a demonstration of the logical truth of the proposition '$(x)Fx \supset (\exists x)Fx$' can be set down as

> 1. $(x)Fx$
> 2. Fy 1, **UI**
> 3. $(\exists x)Fx$ 2, **EG**
> 4. $(x)Fx \supset (\exists x)Fx$ 1–3, C.P.

(In discussing 'logical truth' we explicitly limit our consideration to non-empty universes, just as in discussing *validity*.)

Other logically true propositions involving quantifiers require more complicated demonstrations. For example, the logically true proposition '$(x)Fx \supset \sim(\exists x) \sim Fx$' has the following demonstration:

> 1. $(x)Fx$
> 2. $(\exists x) \sim Fx$
> 3. $\sim Fy$ 2, **EI**
> 4. $(\exists x) \sim Fx \supset \sim Fy$ 2–3, C.P.
> 5. $Fy \supset \sim(\exists x) \sim Fx$ 4, Trans., D.N.
> 6. Fy 1, **UI**
> 7. $\sim(\exists x) \sim Fx$ 5, 6, M.P.
> 8. $(x)Fx \supset \sim(\exists x) \sim Fx$ 1–7, C.P.

Similarly, the truth of '$\sim(\exists x) \sim Fx \supset (x)Fx$' is demonstrated by the following:

> 1. $\sim(\exists x) \sim Fx$
> 2. $\sim Fy$
> 3. $(\exists x) \sim Fx$ 2, **EG**
> 4. $(\exists x) \sim Fx \vee Fy$ 3, Add.
> 5. Fy 4, 1, D.S.
> 6. $\sim Fy \supset Fy$ 2–5, C.P.
> 7. $Fy \vee Fy$ 6, Impl., D.N.
> 8. Fy 7, Taut.
> 9. $(x)Fx$ 8, **UG**
> 10. $\sim(\exists x) \sim Fx \supset (x)Fx$ 1–9, C.P.

Given the logical truths established by the two preceding demonstrations, we can conjoin them to obtain the equivalence '$(x)Fx \equiv \sim(\exists x) \sim Fx$', which was already noted as a logical truth in Section I of the present chapter. Since our proof of this equivalence did not depend upon any peculiarities of the propositional function 'Fx', the equivalence holds for *any* propositional function. And since our proof did not refer to any peculiarities of the variable 'x', the equivalence holds not only for any propositional function but for any individual variable. The equivalence *form* $(v)\Phi v \equiv \sim(\exists v) \sim \Phi v$ is thus seen to be *logically true*, and can be added to the other logical equivalences in our list of elementary valid argument forms. It permits us validly to interchange $(v)\Phi v$ and $\sim(\exists v) \sim \Phi v$ wherever they may occur. This connection between the two quantifiers by way of negation will now be adopted as an additional rule of inference, and may be used in constructing subsequent demonstrations. When it is so used, the letters '**QN**' (for *quantifier negation*) should be written to indicate which principle is being appealed to. It should be obvious that the forms

$$\sim(v)\Phi v \equiv (\exists v) \sim \Phi v$$
$$(v) \sim \Phi v \equiv \sim(\exists v)\Phi v$$
$$\sim(v) \sim \Phi v \equiv (\exists v)\Phi v$$

are all logically equivalent to each other and to the form **QN**, and are therefore logically true.

Some fairly obvious logical truths are simply stated and easily proved with our present symbolic apparatus. A logically true equivalence, for any propositional functions 'Fx' and 'Gx', is

$$[(x)Fx \cdot (x)Gx] \equiv (x)(Fx \cdot Gx)$$

which asserts that: everything has the property F and everything has the property G if and only if everything has the properties F and G. The demonstrations of the two implications involved may be written side by side:

1.	$(x)Fx \cdot (x)Gx$	
2.	$(x)Fx$	1, Simp.
3.	$(x)Gx$	1, Simp.
4.	Fy	2, **UI**
5.	Gy	3, **UI**
6.	$Fy \cdot Gy$	4, 5, Conj.
7.	$(x)(Fx \cdot Gx)$	6, **UG**
8.	$[(x)Fx \cdot (x)Gx] \supset (x)(Fx \cdot Gx)$	
	1–7, C.P.	

1.	$(x)(Fx \cdot Gx)$	
2.	$Fy \cdot Gy$	1, **UI**
3.	Fy	2, Simp.
4.	Gy	2, Simp.
5.	$(x)Fx$	3, **UG**
6.	$(x)Gx$	4, **UG**
7.	$(x)Fx \cdot (x)Gx$	5, 6, Conj.
8.	$(x)(Fx \cdot Gx) \supset [(x)Fx \cdot (x)Gx]$	
	1–7 C.P.	

Another logical equivalence involves the disjunction of existential quantifications:

$$[(\exists x)Fx \lor (\exists x)Gx] \equiv (\exists x)(Fx \lor Gx).$$

It states that if either something has the property F or something has the property G, then something has either the property F or the property G, and conversely. It may be demonstrated as follows: First we prove $[(\exists x)Fx \lor (\exists x)Gx] \supset (\exists x)(Fx \lor Gx)$:

1.	$(\exists x)Fx \lor (\exists x)Gx$	
2.	$(\exists x)Fx$	
3.	Fy	2, **EI**
4.	$Fy \lor Gy$	3, Add.
5.	$(\exists x)(Fx \lor Gx)$	4, **EG**
6.	$(\exists x)Fx \supset (\exists x)(Fx \lor Gx)$	2–5, C.P.
7.	$(\exists x)Gx$	
8.	Gz	7, **EI**
9.	$Fz \lor Gz$	8, Add.
10.	$(\exists x)(Fx \lor Gx)$	9, **EG**
11.	$(\exists x)Gx \supset (\exists x)(Fx \lor Gx)$	7–10, C.P.
12.	$[(\exists x)Fx \supset (\exists x)(Fx \lor Gx)] \cdot [(\exists x)Gx \supset (\exists x)(Fx \lor Gx)]$	
		6, 11, Conj.
13.	$(\exists x)(Fx \lor Gx) \lor (\exists x)(Fx \lor Gx)$	12, 1, C.D.
14.	$(\exists x)(Fx \lor Gx)$	13, Taut.
15.	$[(\exists x)Fx \lor (\exists x)Gx] \supset (\exists x)(Fx \lor Gx)$	1–14, C.P.

Then we prove $(\exists x)(Fx \lor Gx) \supset [(\exists x)Fx \lor (\exists x)Gx]$:

1.	$(\exists x)(Fx \vee Gx)$	
2.	$Fy \vee Gy$	1, **EI**
3.	Fy	
4.	$(\exists x)Fx$	3, **EG**
5.	$(\exists x)Fx \vee (\exists x)Gx$	4, Add.
6.	$Fy \supset [(\exists x)Fx \vee (\exists x)Gx]$	3–5, C.P.
7.	Gy	
8.	$(\exists x)Gx$	7, **EG**
9.	$(\exists x)Fx \vee (\exists x)Gx$	8, Add.
10.	$Gy \supset [(\exists x)Fx \vee (\exists x)Gx]$	7–9, C.P.
11.	$\{Fy \supset [(\exists x)Fx \vee (\exists x)Gx]\}\cdot\{Gy \supset [(\exists x)Fx \vee (\exists x)Gx]\}$	
		6, 10, Conj.
12.	$[(\exists x)Fx \vee (\exists x)Gx] \vee [(\exists x)Fx \vee (\exists x)Gx]$	11, 2, C.D.
13.	$(\exists x)Fx \vee (\exists x)Gx$	12, Taut.
14.	$(\exists x)(Fx \vee Gx) \supset [(\exists x)Fx \vee (\exists x)Gx]$	1–13, C.P.

Another logical truth is in the form of a conditional rather than an equivalence. Written as

$$[(x)Fx \vee (x)Gx] \supset (x)(Fx \vee Gx)$$

it asserts that if either everything is an F or everything is a G, then everything is either an F or a G. Its demonstration too involves making several assumptions of limited scope, and can be written as follows:

1.	$(x)Fx \vee (x)Gx$	
2.	$(x)Fx$	
3.	Fy	2, **UI**
4.	$Fy \vee Gy$	3, Add.
5.	$(x)(Fx \vee Gx)$	4, **UG**
6.	$(x)Fx \supset (x)(Fx \vee Gx)$	2–5, C.P.
7.	$(x)Gx$	
8.	Gy	7, **UI**
9.	$Fy \vee Gy$	8, Add.
10.	$(x)(Fx \vee Gx)$	9, **UG**
11.	$(x)Gx \supset (x)(Fx \vee Gx)$	7–10, C.P.
12.	$[(x)Fx \supset (x)(Fx \vee Gx)]\cdot[(x)Gx \supset (x)(Fx \vee Gx)]$	6, 11, Conj.
13.	$(x)(Fx \vee Gx) \vee (x)(Fx \vee Gx)$	12, 1, C.D.
14.	$(x)(Fx \vee Gx)$	13, Taut.
15.	$[(x)Fx \vee (x)Gx] \supset (x)(Fx \vee Gx)$	1–14, C.P.

The converse of this conditional is *not* logically true, however. The converse states that if everything is either F or G then either everything is F or everything is G. That this converse is not always true can be seen by replacing 'G' by '$\sim F$', for '$(x)(Fx \text{ v} \sim Fx)$' is true for any predicate 'F', while there are few for which '$(x)Fx$ v $(x) \sim Fx$' holds. Another logical truth which is conditional in form is

$$(\exists x)(Fx \cdot Gx) \supset [(\exists x)Fx \cdot (\exists x)Gx].$$

Its demonstration is perfectly straightforward, and can be left as an exercise for the reader. That its converse is not true in general can be seen by again replacing 'G' by '$\sim F$'. For most predicates 'F' the proposition '$(\exists x)Fx \cdot (\exists x) \sim Fx$' is true (e.g. 'something is round and something is not round'), but for any 'F' the proposition '$(\exists x)(Fx \cdot \sim Fx)$' is logically false.

It has already been observed that propositional functions can contain propositions as constituent parts. Examples of such propositional functions are

$$Fx \cdot Ga, \quad Gy \text{ v } (z)Hz, \quad (\exists w)Gw \supset Fz, \quad \ldots$$

When such propositional functions as these are quantified, to obtain the propositions

$$(x)[Fx \cdot Ga], \quad (\exists y)[Gy \text{ v } (z)Hz], \quad (z)[(\exists w)Gw \supset Fz], \quad \ldots$$

we have propositions lying within the scopes of quantifiers, although the quantifiers have no real affect on those propositions. When a quantifier with respect to a given variable is prefixed to an expression its only effect is to bind previously free occurrences of that variable. In the expressions written above, the propositions 'Ga', '$(z)Hz$', and '$(\exists w)Gw$', although lying within the scopes of the quantifiers '(x)', '$(\exists y)$', and '(z)', respectively, are not really affected by them. Wherever we have an expression containing a quantifier within whose scope a *proposition* lies, the entire expression is logically equivalent to another expression in which the scope of the quantifier does *not* extend over the proposition in question. An example or two will make this clear.

In the following, let '*p*' be any *proposition*, and '*Fx*' any propositional function containing at least one free occurrence of the variable '*x*'. Our first equivalence here is between the universal quantification of '*Fx·p*' and the conjunction of the universal quantification of '*Fx*' with '*p*', which is more briefly expressed as

$$(x)(Fx\cdot p) \equiv [(x)Fx\cdot p].$$

The demonstration of this equivalence can be written as

→1. $(x)(Fx\cdot p)$		→1. $(x)Fx\cdot p$	
2. $Fy\cdot p$	1, **UI**	2. $(x)Fx$	1, Simp.
3. Fy	2, Simp.	3. Fy	2, **UI**
4. $(x)Fx$	3, **UG**	4. p	1, Simp.
5. p	2, Simp.	5. $Fy\cdot p$	3, 4, Conj.
6. $(x)Fx\cdot p$	4, 5, Conj.	6. $(x)(Fx\cdot p)$	5, **UG**
7. $(x)(Fx\cdot p) \supset [(x)Fx\cdot p]$		7. $[(x)Fx\cdot p] \supset (x)(Fx\cdot p)$	
1–6, C.P.		1–6, C.P.	

Another logical equivalence holds between the universal quantification of '*p* ⊃ *Fx*' and the conditional statement whose antecedent is '*p*' and whose consequent is the universal quantification of '*Fx*'. The first asserts that *given any individual x, p implies that x has F*, and is equivalent to *p implies that given any individual x, x has F*. Our symbolic expression of this equivalence is

$$(x)(p \supset Fx) \equiv [p \supset (x)Fx].$$

Its demonstration is easily constructed:

→1. $(x)(p \supset Fx)$		→1. $p \supset (x)Fx$	
2. $p \supset Fy$	1, **UI**	→2. p	
→3. p		3. $(x)Fx$	1, 2, M.P.
4. Fy	2, 3, M.P.	4. Fy	3, **UI**
5. $(x)Fx$	4, **UG**	5. $p \supset Fy$	2–4, C.P.
6. $p \supset (x)Fx$	3–5, C.P.	6. $(x)(p \supset Fx)$	5, **UG**
7. $(x)(p \supset Fx) \supset [p \supset (x)Fx]$		7. $[p \supset (x)Fx] \supset (x)(p \supset Fx)$	
1–6, C.P.		1–6, C.P.	

The same pattern of equivalence holds for the existential quantification of '*p* ⊃ *Fx*' and the conditional statement '*p* ⊃ (∃*x*)*Fx*'.

The first asserts that *there is at least one individual x such that p implies that x has F*, and is equivalent to *p implies that there is at least one individual x such that x has F*, which is asserted by the second. Its demonstration is very easily constructed, and will be left as an exercise.

However, the pattern of equivalence is different when '*p*' occurs as consequent rather than antecedent. Although the universal quantification of '*Fx ⊃ p*' implies '*(x)Fx ⊃ p*', it is not implied by the latter. There is an equivalence, however, between *given any x, if x has F then p* and *if there is at least one x such that x has F, then p*, which is expressed symbolically as

$$(x)(Fx \supset p) \equiv [(\exists x)Fx \supset p].$$

And although the existential quantification of '*Fx ⊃ p*' is implied by '*(∃x)Fx ⊃ p*', it does not imply the latter. There is an equivalence, however, between *there is at least one x such that if x has F then p* and *if given any x, x has F, then p*, which is expressed symbolically as

$$(\exists x)(Fx \supset p) \equiv [(x)Fx \supset p].$$

The first is demonstrated as follows:

→1. $(x)(Fx \supset p)$			→1. $(\exists x)Fx \supset p$	
→2. $(\exists x)Fx$			→2. Fy	
3. Fy	2, **EI**		3. $(\exists x)Fx$	2, **EG**
4. $Fy \supset p$	1, **UI**		4. $Fy \supset (\exists x)Fx$	2–3, C.P.
5. p	4, 3, M.P.		5. $Fy \supset p$	4, 1, H.S.
6. $(\exists x)Fx \supset p$	2–5, C.P.		6. $(x)(Fx \supset p)$	5, **UG**
7. $(x)(Fx \supset p) \supset$ $[(\exists x)Fx \supset p]$	1–6, C.P.		7. $[(\exists x)Fx \supset p] \supset$ $(x)(Fx \supset p)$	1–6, C.P.

The present logical equivalence supplies an alternative method of symbolizing one of the propositions discussed in Section IV:

> If something is wrong with the house then everyone in the house complains.

The translation given there abbreviates to

$$(\exists x)(Wx) \supset (y)(Py \supset Cy)$$

which, as we have just demonstrated, is logically equivalent to

$$(x)[Wx \supset (y)(Py \supset Cy)].$$

We shall conclude our discussion of logically true propositions involving quantifiers by turning our attention to four logically true propositions which are neither equivalences nor conditionals. They correspond, in a sense, to our four quantification rules:

1. $(y)[(x)Fx \supset Fy]$
2. $(y)[Fy \supset (\exists x)Fx]$
3. $(\exists y)[Fy \supset (x)Fx]$
4. $(\exists y)[(\exists x)Fx \supset Fy]$

The first of these corresponds to **UI**, saying, as it does, that given any individual y, if every individual has the property F, then y does. Its demonstration is almost trivially obvious, proceeding:

$$
\begin{array}{lll}
\rightarrow 1.\ \ (x)Fx & & \\
\ \ \ 2.\ \ Fz & & 1,\ \textbf{UI} \\
\hline
\ \ \ 3.\ \ (x)Fx \supset Fz & & 1\text{–}2,\ \text{C.P.} \\
\ \ \ 4.\ \ (y)[(x)Fx \supset Fy] & & 3,\ \textbf{UG}
\end{array}
$$

The second corresponds to **EG**, asserting that if any given individual y has the property F, then something has F. The third and fourth, corresponding to **UG** and **EI**, respectively, are not so immediately obvious, but nevertheless are logically true and quite easily demonstrated. An intuitive explanation can be given by reference to the ancient Athenian general and statesman Aristides, often called 'the just'. So outstanding was Aristides for his rectitude that the Athenians had a saying that

If anyone is just, Aristides is just.

With respect to *any* property, there is always some individual y such that if anything has that property, y has it. That is what is asserted by the fourth proposition listed above, which corresponds to **EI**. The matter can be put another way. If we turn our attention not to the property of being just, but to its reverse, the property of being corruptible, then the sense of the first

Athenian saying is also expressible as

> If Aristides is corruptible, then everyone is corruptible.

Again generalizing, we may observe that with respect to *any* property there is always some individual y such that if y has that property, everything has it. That is what is asserted by the third proposition listed above, which corresponds to **UG**. Its demonstration proceeds:

$$
\begin{array}{lll}
\rightarrow 1. & \sim(x)Fx & \\
\quad 2. & (\exists x) \sim Fx & 1, \textbf{QN} \\
\quad 3. & \sim Fz & 2, \textbf{EI} \\
\hline
\quad 4. & \sim(x)Fx \supset \sim Fz & \text{1–3, C.P.} \\
\quad 5. & Fz \supset (x)Fx & 4, \text{Trans.} \\
\quad 6. & (\exists y)[Fy \supset (x)Fx] & 5, \textbf{EG}
\end{array}
$$

Although we shall not prove it until the end of Chapter Nine, the methods of proof so far assembled (techniques for 'Natural Deduction', as they are sometimes called) permit the demonstration of all logically true propositions constructed out of truth-functional connectives and the quantification of individual variables. It will also be proved that *only* propositions that are logically true can be demonstrated by these techniques.

EXERCISES

Construct demonstrations for the following:

1. $(\exists x)(Fx \cdot Gx) \supset [(\exists x)Fx \cdot (\exists x)Gx]$
2. $(x)(Fx \supset Gx) \supset [(x)Fx \supset (x)Gx]$
3. $[(\exists x)Fx \supset (\exists x)Gx] \supset (\exists x)(Fx \supset Gx)$
4. $(\exists x)(p \supset Fx) \equiv [p \supset (\exists x)Fx]$
5. $(\exists x)(Fx \cdot p) \equiv [(\exists x)Fx \cdot p]$
6. $(x)(Fx \lor p) \equiv [(x)Fx \lor p]$
7. $(\exists x)(Fx \lor p) \equiv [(\exists x)Fx \lor p]$
8. $(\exists x)(Fx \supset p) \equiv [(x)Fx \supset p]$
9. $(y)[Fy \supset (\exists x)Fx]$
10. $(\exists y)[(\exists x)Fx \supset Fy]$

The Logic of
Relations

I. SYMBOLIZING RELATIONS

Some propositions which contain two or more proper names (of individuals) are correctly interpreted as truth-functional compounds of singular propositions having different subject terms. For example, the proposition

> Lincoln and Grant were presidents.

is properly interpreted as the conjunction of the two singular propositions

> Lincoln was a president   and   Grant was a president.

But for some other propositions having the same verbal pattern that analysis is wholly unsatisfactory. Thus the proposition

> Lincoln and Grant were acquainted.

is definitely *not* a conjunction or any other truth function of the two expressions

> Lincoln was acquainted   and   Grant was acquainted.

On the contrary, dividing the proposition in this way destroys its significance, for its meaning is not that both Lincoln and Grant were (or had) acquaintances, but that they were *acquainted with each other*. The given proposition does not assert that Lincoln and Grant both had a certain *property*, but that they stood in a certain *relationship*. Lincoln is not said simply to be acquainted (whatever that might mean), but *acquainted with Grant*. Other propositions which express relations between two individuals are

> John loves Mary.
> Plato was a student of Socrates.
> Isaac was a son of Abraham.
> New York is east of Chicago.
> Chicago is smaller than New York.

Relations such as these, which can hold between two individuals, are called 'binary' or 'dyadic'. Other relations may relate three or more individuals. For example, the propositions

> Detroit is between New York and Chicago.
> Helen introduced John to Mary.
> America won the Phillipines from Spain.

express *ternary* or *triadic* relations, while *quaternary* or *tetradic* relations are expressed by the propositions

> America bought Alaska from Russia for seven million dollars.
> Jack traded his cow to the peddler for a handful of beans.
> Al, Bill, Charlie, and Doug played bridge together.

Relations enter into arguments in various ways. One example of a relational argument is

> Al is older than Bill.
> Bill is older than Charlie.
> _____
> Therefore, Al is older than Charlie.

* But cp Whitehead & Russell PM between ×37.62 and ×37.63 (p. 291 in paperback
And remarks on p. 157 below [but it's OK, since it occurs in a "context" where
"   — in general are under discussion": p. 157]

A slightly more complex example, which involves quantification, is this:

> Helen likes David.
> Whoever likes David likes Tom.
> Helen likes only good-looking men.
> _____
> Therefore, Tom is a good-looking man.

A still more complex relational inference, which involves multiple quantification, is:

> All horses are animals.
> _____
> Therefore, the head of a horse is the head of an animal.

The latter is a valid inference$^{\times}$ which, as De Morgan observed, all the logic of Aristotle will not permit one to draw. Its validation by our apparatus of quantifiers and propositional functions will be set forth in the next section. (pp. 138-9)

Before discussing the validation of relational arguments, which will require no methods of proof beyond those developed in the preceding chapter, the problem of *symbolizing* relational propositions must be dealt with. Just as a single predicate symbol can occur in different propositions, so a single relation symbol can occur in different propositions. Just as we have the predicate 'human' common to the propositions:

> Aristotle is human.
> Plato is human.
> Socrates is human.

so we have the relational word 'teacher' common to the propositions:

> Socrates was a teacher of Plato.
> Plato was a teacher of Aristotle.

And just as we regard the three subject-predicate propositions as different substitution instances of the propositional function '*x* is human', so we can regard the two relational propositions as different substitution instances of the propositional function '*x* was a teacher of *y*'. Replacing the variable '*x*' by the constant 'Socrates' and the variable '*y*' by the constant 'Plato' gives us the first proposition; replacing the '*x*' by 'Plato' and the '*y*' by 'Aristotle' gives the second. The *order* of replacement is of great importance here: if '*x*' is replaced by 'Aristotle' and '*y*' by 'Plato', the result is the *false* proposition

Aristotle was a teacher of Plato.

Just as a propositional function of one variable like '*x* is human' was abbreviated as '*Hx*', so a propositional function of two variables like '*x* was the teacher of *y*' is abbreviated as '*Txy*'. Similarly, the propositional function '*x* is between *y* and *z*' will be abbreviated as '*Bxyz*', and the propositional function '*x* traded *y* to *z* for *w*' will be abbreviated as '*Txyzw*'. Our first specimen of a relational argument, since it involves no quantifications, is very easily symbolized. Using the individual constants '*a*', '*b*', and '*c*' to denote Al, Bill, and Charlie, and the expression '*Oxy*' to abbreviate '*x* is older than *y*', we have

Oab
Obc
∴ *Oac*

Our second argument is not much more difficult, since none of its propositions contains more than a single quantification. Using the individual constants '*h*', '*d*', and '*t*' to denote Helen, David, and Tom, respectively, '*Gx*' to abbreviate '*x* is a good-looking man', and the symbol '*Lxy*' to abbreviate '*x* likes *y*', the argument can be symbolized as

1. *Lhd*
2. $(x)(Lxd \supset Lxt)$
3. $(x)(Lhx \supset Gx)$
   ∴ *Gt*

The demonstration of its validity is so easily constructed that it may well be set down now, before going on to consider some of the more difficult problems of symbolization. Referring back to the numbered premisses above, the demonstration proceeds:

4.	$Lhd \supset Lht$	2, **UI**
5.	Lht	4, 1, M.P.
6.	$Lht \supset Gt$	3, **UI**
7.	Gt	6, 5, M.P.

Symbolizing relational propositions becomes more complicated when several quantifications occur in a single proposition. Our discussion of the problem will be simplified by confining attention at first to two individual constants, '*a*', and '*b*', and the propositional function '*x* attracts *y*', abbreviated as '*Axy*'. The two statements '*a* attracts *b*' and '*b* is attracted by *a*' obviously have the same meaning, the first expressing that meaning by use of the *active voice*, the second by use of the *passive voice*. Both statements translate directly into the single formula '*Aab*'. Similarly, the two statements '*b* attracts *a*' and '*a* is attracted by *b*' are both symbolized by the formula '*Aba*'. These two different substitution instances of '*Axy*' are logically independent of each other, either can be true without entailing the truth of the other.

We are still on elementary and familiar ground when we come to symbolize

'*a* attracts everything'
'everything is attracted by *a*' } as '$(x)Aax$',

'*a* attracts something'
'something is attracted by *a*' } as '$(\exists x)Aax$',

'everything attracts *a*'
'*a* is attracted by everything' } as '$(x)Axa$',

'something attracts *a*'
'*a* is attracted by something' } as '$(\exists x)Axa$'.

But the problem of symbolizing becomes more complex when we dispense entirely with individual constants and consider relational propositions which are completely general. The simplest propositions of this kind are

1. Everything attracts everything.
2. Everything is attracted by everything.
3. Something attracts something.
4. Something is attracted by something.
5. Nothing attracts anything.
6. Nothing is attracted by anything.

which are symbolized by the following formulas:

1. $(x)(y)Axy$
2. $(y)(x)Axy$
3. $(\exists x)(\exists y)Axy$
4. $(\exists y)(\exists x)Axy$
5. $(x)(y) \sim Axy$
6. $(y)(x) \sim Axy$

In their English formulations, propositions 1 and 2 are clearly equivalent to each other, as are 3 and 4, and 5 and 6. The first two equivalences are easily established for the corresponding logical formulas:

1. $(x)(y)Axy$		1. $(\exists x)(\exists y)Axy$	
2. $(y)Awy$	1, **UI**	2. $(\exists y)Awy$	1, **EI**
3. Awv	2, **UI**	3. Awv	2, **EI**
4. $(x)Axv$	3, **UG**	4. $(\exists x)Axv$	3, **EG**
5. $(y)(x)Axy$	4, **UG**	5. $(\exists y)(\exists x)Axy$	4, **EG**
6. $(x)(y)Axy \supset (y)(x)Axy$		6. $(\exists x)(\exists y)Axy \supset (\exists y)(\exists x)Axy$	
1–5, C.P.		1–5, C.P.	

These demonstrate the logical truth of conditionals rather than of equivalences, but that their converses are true also can be established by simply reversing the orders of steps 1 through 5. (The equivalence between formulas 5 and 6 is clearly established by the same pattern of argument that proves 1 equivalent to 2.)

When we turn to the next pair of statements

7. Everything attracts something.
8. Something is attracted by everything.

there is no longer any logical equivalence or sameness of meaning. Sentence 7 is not entirely unambiguous, and some exceptional contexts might shift its meaning, but its most natural interpretation is *not* that there is some one thing which is attracted by everything, but rather that everything attracts *something or other*. We can approach its symbolization by way of successive paraphrasings, writing first

$$(x)(x \text{ attracts something})$$

and then symbolizing the expression '*x* attracts something' the same way in which we symbolized '*a* attracts something'. This gives us the formula

7. $(x)(\exists y)Axy$.

Sentence 8 is also susceptible of alternative interpretations, one of which would make it synonymous with sentence 7, meaning that something or other is attracted by any (given) thing. But a perfectly straightforward way of understanding sentence 8 is to take it as asserting that some *one thing* is attracted by all things. Its symbolization, too, can be accomplished in a stepwise fashion, writing first

$$(\exists y)(y \text{ is attracted by everything})$$

and then symbolizing the expression '*y* is attracted by everything' the same way in which we symbolized '*a* is attracted by everything'. This gives us the formula

8. $(\exists y)(x)Axy$.

There is a certain *misleading* similarity between formulas 7 and 8. They both consist of the propositional function '*Axy*' to which are applied a universal quantifier with respect to '*x*' and an existential quantifier with respect to '*y*'. But the *order* in which the quantifiers are written is different in each case, and that makes a world of difference in their meanings. Formula 7, in which the universal quantifier comes first, asserts that given anything in the universe, there is something or other which it attracts. But formula 8, in which the existential quantifier comes first, asserts that there is some one thing in the universe such that everything in the universe attracts *it*. Where two quantifiers are applied to one propositional function, if they are both universal or both existential, their order does not matter, as is shown by the equivalence of formulas 1 and 2, 3 and 4, and 5 and 6. But where one is universal and the other existential the order of generalization or quantification is very important indeed.

Although formulas 7 and 8 are not equivalent, they are not independent. The former is validly deducible from the latter. The demonstration is easily constructed as follows:

1. $(\exists y)(x)Axy$
2. $(x)Axv$ 1, **EI**
3. Auv 2, **UI**
4. $(\exists y)Auy$ 3, **EG**
5. $(x)(\exists y)Axy$ 4, **UG**

But the inference is valid only one way. Any attempt to derive formula 8 from 7 must inevitably run afoul of one of the restrictions on **UG**.

A similar pair of inequivalent propositions may be written as

9. Everything is attracted by something.
10. Something attracts everything.

These are clearly inequivalent when the 'something' in 9, coming at the end, is understood as 'something or other', and the 'something' in 10, coming at the beginning, is understood as 'some one thing'. They are symbolized as

9. $(y)(\exists x)Axy$.
10. $(\exists x)(y)Axy$.

Relational propositions are sometimes formulated as though they were simple subject-predicate assertions. For example, '*a* was struck' is most plausibly interpreted to assert that *something struck a*. Such implicit occurrences of relations are often marked by the passive voice of a transitive verb. Our symbolization of

propositions containing implicit relations should be guided by
consideration of the use to which they are to be put. Our motive
in symbolizing arguments is to get them into that form which is
most convenient for testing their validity by the application of
our rules. Our goal, therefore, with respect to a given argument,
is not that of providing a theoretically complete analysis, but
rather of providing one sufficiently complete for the purpose at
hand—the testing of validity. Consequently some implicit relations may be left implicit, while others require a more thorough
analysis, as may be made clear by an example. Consider the
argument

> Whoever visited the building was observed. Anyone
> who had observed Andrews would have remem-
> bered him. Nobody remembered Andrews. There-
> fore, Andrews didn't visit the building.

The first proposition of this argument contains two relations, one
explicit, the other implicit. Explicitly, we have the relation of
someone visiting the building. It is explicit because mention is made
both of the visitor and what was visited by him. Implicitly, we
have the relation of *someone observing someone*, which is implicit
because no mention is made of the someone who does the observing—the omission being marked by the use of the passive
voice. However, because the only other occurrence of 'x visited
the building' is also as a *unit*, in the conclusion, it need
not be treated as a relation at all, but may be symbolized
as a simple predicate. On the other hand, 'x observed y', despite
its merely implicit occurrence in the first premiss, must be explicitly symbolized as a relation if the validity of the argument
is to be proved. For its second occurrence is not a simple repetition of the original unit; it appears instead as an explicit relation,
with the first variable quantified and the second replaced by the
proper name 'Andrews'. Using 'a' to denote Andrews, 'Vx' to
abbreviate 'x visited the building', 'Oxy' to abbreviate 'x observed
y', and 'Rxy' to abbreviate 'x remembers y', a symbolic translation and validation of the given argument may be written as

× C₉ also know, believe. Here interchanging (what look like) the terms doesn't even make sense.
cf also Quine was Q 30, 31

Symbolizing Relations 129

1. $(x)[Vx \supset (\exists y)Oyx]$
2. $(x)[Oxa \supset Rxa]$
3. $(x) \sim Rxa$ $/ \therefore \sim Va$
4. $Oza \supset Rza$ 2, **UI**
5. $\sim Rza$ 3, **UI**
6. $\sim Oza$ 4, 5, M.T.
7. $(y) \sim Oya$ 6, **UG**
8. $\sim(\exists y)Oya$ 7, **QN**
9. $Va \supset (\exists y)Oya$ 1, **UI**
10. $\sim Va$ 9, 8, M.T.

Our demonstration of the validity of this argument would not have been helped at all by symbolizing 'Andrews visited the building' as a substitution instance of the relational 'x visited y' rather than of the simpler 'Vx'. But our demonstration absolutely required us to symbolize 'was observed' explicitly as a relation.

While on the subject of implicit or concealed relations, mention must be made of the philosophically interesting but logically troublesome topic of *pseudo-relations*. Examples of these are *desiring, hoping, planning, wishing-for*, and the like. These can be regarded as *pseudo-relations* because of the fact that certain inferences which are valid in connection with ordinary relations break down or are invalid when made with respect to *apparent* relations of the sort mentioned. If I *attend* a picnic, there must exist a picnic for me to attend. But if I merely *plan* a picnic, and never execute my plans, there need not exist any picnic at all. If I marry a perfect wife, there must exist a perfect wife for me to marry. But if I merely *desire* a perfect wife, it by no means follows that there exists a perfect wife to whom I stand in the relation of desiring. The existence of Santa Claus is not established by believing in him, for *believing in* is a pseudo rather than a genuine relation. We must beware of imputing existence to non-existents by mistaking pseudo-relations for genuine ones.

Most of our previous examples were illustrations of *unlimited* generality, in which it was asserted that *everything* stood in such-and-such a relation, or something did, or nothing did. A great many relational propositions are not so sweeping. Most assertions are more modest, claiming not that *everything* stands in such-and-such a relation, but that everything does *if* it satisfies certain conditions or restrictions. Thus we may say either that

> Everything is attracted by all magnets.

or that

> Everything made of iron is attracted by all magnets.

The second, of course, is the more modest assertion, being less *general* than the first. While the first is adequately symbolized, where '*Mx*' abbreviates '*x* is a magnet', as

$$(x)(y)[My \supset Ayx],$$

the second is symbolized, where '*Ix*' abbreviates '*x* is made of iron', as

$$(x)[Ix \supset (y)(My \supset Ayx)].$$

That the symbolization is correct can be seen by paraphrasing the second proposition in English as

> Given anything at all, *if* it is made of iron then it is attracted by all magnets.

Perhaps the best way to symbolize relational propositions is by the kind of stepwise process that has already been exemplified. Let us illustrate it further, this time for propositions of limited generality. First let us consider the proposition

> Any good amateur can beat some professional.

As a first step we may write

$$(x)\{(x \text{ is a good amateur}) \supset (x \text{ can beat some professional})\}.$$

Next, the consequent of the conditional between the braces

> *x* can beat some professional

is symbolized as a generalization or quantified expression:

$$(\exists y)[(y \text{ is a professional}) \cdot (x \text{ can beat } y)].$$

Now, using the obvious abbreviations, '*Gx*', '*Px*', and '*Bxy*' for '*x* is a good amateur', '*x* is a professional', and '*x* can beat *y*', the given proposition is symbolized by the formula

$$(x)[Gx \supset (\exists y)(Py \cdot Bxy)].$$

Using the same method of paraphrasing by successive steps, we may symbolize

Some professionals can beat all amateurs.

first as

$$(\exists x)[(x \text{ is a professional}) \cdot (x \text{ can beat all amateurs})]$$

then as

$$(\exists x)\{(x \text{ is a professional}) \cdot (y)[(y \text{ is an amateur}) \supset (x \text{ can beat } y)]\}$$

and finally (using abbreviations) as

$$(\exists x)[Px \cdot (y)(Ay \supset Bxy)].$$

The same method is applicable in more complex cases, where more than one relation is involved. We symbolize the proposition

Anyone who promises everything to everyone is certain to disappoint somebody.

first by paraphrasing it as

$$(x)\{[(x \text{ is a person}) \cdot (x \text{ promises everything to everyone})]$$
$$\supset [x \text{ disappoints somebody}]\}.$$

The second conjunct of the antecedent

x promises everything to everyone

may be further paraphrased, first as

$$(y)[(y \text{ is a person}) \supset (x \text{ promises everything to } y)]$$

and then as

$$(y)[(y \text{ is a person}) \supset (z)(x \text{ promises } z \text{ to } y)].$$

The consequent in our first paraphrase

x disappoints somebody

has its structure made more explicit by being rewritten as

$$(\exists u)[(u \text{ is a person})\cdot(x \text{ disappoints } u)].$$

The original proposition can now be rewritten as

$$(x)\{\{(x \text{ is a person})\cdot(y)[(y \text{ is a person}) \supset (z)(x \text{ promises } z \text{ to } y)]\} \\ \supset (\exists u)[(u \text{ is a person})\cdot(x \text{ disappoints } u)]\}.$$

Using the obvious abbreviations, 'Px', '$Pxyz$', 'Dxy' for 'x is a person', 'x promises y to z', and 'x disappoints y', the proposition can be expressed more compactly in the formula

$$(x)\{\{Px\cdot(y)[Py \supset (z)Pxzy]\} \supset (\exists u)(Pu\cdot Dxu)\}.$$

With practice, of course, not all such intermediate steps need be written out explicitly.

Quantification words such as 'everyone', 'anyone', 'everybody', 'anybody', and 'whoever', refer to *all persons* rather than to *all things;* and such quantification words as 'someone' and 'somebody' refer to *some persons* rather than to *some things.* It is frequently desirable to represent this reference in our symbolization. But doing so is not always necessary for the purpose of evaluating arguments containing these words, however, and the choice of symbolization procedure is determined on the same grounds on which one decides whether a relational clause or phrase is to be symbolized explicitly as a relation or as a mere predicate.

The words 'always', 'never', and 'sometimes' frequently have a strictly non-temporal significance, as in the propositions

> Good men always have friends.
> Bad men never have friends.
> Men who have no wives sometimes have friends.

which may be symbolized, using obvious abbreviations, as

$$(x)[(Gx\cdot Mx) \supset (\exists y)Fxy]$$
$$(x)[(Bx\cdot Mx) \supset \sim(\exists y)Fxy]$$
$$(\exists x)\{[Mx\cdot\sim(\exists y)(Wy\cdot Hxy)]\cdot(\exists z)Fxz\}.$$

However, some uses of these words are definitely temporal, and when they are, they can be symbolized by the logical machinery already available, as can other temporal words like 'while', 'when', 'whenever', and the like. An example or two should serve to make this clear. Thus the proposition

Dick always writes Joan when they are separated.

asserts that all times when Dick and Joan are separated are times when Dick writes Joan. This can be symbolized using 'Tx' for 'x is a time', '$Wxyz$' for 'x writes y at (time) z', and '$Sxyz$' for 'x and y are separated at (time) z', as

$$(x)\{Tx \supset [Sdjx \supset Wdjx]\}$$

Perhaps the most vivid illustration of the adaptability of the present notation is in symbolizing the following remark, usually attributed to Lincoln:

You can fool some of the people all of the time, and all of the people some of the time, but you cannot fool all of the people all of the time.

The first conjunct: 'You can fool some of the people all of the time' is ambiguous. It may be taken to mean either that *there is at least one person who can always be fooled* or that *for any time there is at least one person (or other) who can be fooled at that time.* Adopting the first interpretation, and using 'Px' for 'x is a person', 'Tx' for 'x is a time', and 'Fxy' for 'you can fool x at (or during) y', the above may be symbolized as

$$\{(\exists x)[Px \cdot (y)(Ty \supset Fxy)] \cdot (\exists y)[Ty \cdot (x)(Px \supset Fxy)]\} \cdot$$
$$(\exists y)(\exists x)[Ty \cdot Px \cdot \sim Fxy)].$$

The actual testing of relational arguments presents no new problems—once the translations into logical symbolism are effected. The latter is the more troublesome part, and so a number of exercises are provided for the student to do before going on.

EXERCISES

I. Using the following 'vocabulary', translate the given formulas into idiomatic English sentences:

Ax-x is silver	*Axy-x* helps *y*
Bx-x is blissful	*Bxy-x* belongs to *y*
Cx-x is a cloud	*Bxyz-x* borrows *y* from *z*
Dx-x is a dog	*Cxy-x* can command *y*
Ex-x is smoke	*Dxy-x* is done at (or by) *y*
Fx-x is fire	*Exy-x* shears *y*
Gx-x is glass	*Fxy-x* is fair for *y*
Hx-x is home	*Gxy-x* gathers *y*
Ix-x is ill	*Hxy-x* hears *y*
Jx-x is work	*Ixy-x* lives in *y*
Kx-x is a lining	*Jxy-x* is jack of *y*
Lx-x is a lamb	*Kxy-x* knows *y*
Mx-x is moss	*Lxy-x* likes *y*
Nx-x is good	*Mxy-x* is master of *y*
Ox-x is a fool	*Nxy-x* loses *y*
Px-x is a person	*Oxy-x* is judged by *y*
Qx-x is a place	*Pxyz-x* blows *y* to *z*
Rx-x rolls	*Qxy-x* keeps company with *y*
Sx-x is a stone	*Rxy-x* is like *y*
Tx-x is a trade	*Sxy-x* says *y*
Ux-x is a house	*Txy-x* should throw *y*
Vx-x is a woman	*Txyz-x* tempers *y* to *z*
Wx-x is wind	*Uxy-x* comes to *y*
Xx-x is a time	*Vxy-x* ventures *y*
Yx-x is a day	*Wxy-x* is at (or in) *y*
Zx-x waits	*Xxy-x* is parent of *y*

g-God

Formulas

1. $(x)[Dx \supset (\exists y)(Yy \cdot Byx)]$
2. $(x)[(\exists y)(Py \cdot Fxy) \supset (z)(Pz \supset Fxz)]$
3. $(x)[(Rx \cdot Sx) \supset (y)(My \supset \sim Gxy)]$
4. $(x)[(Px \cdot Axx) \supset (Agx)]$
5. $(x)[(Px \cdot Zx) \supset (y)(Uyx)]$

6. $(x)[Hx \supset (y)(Qy \supset \sim Ryx)]$
7. $(x)[(Px \cdot \sim Nxg) \supset (y)(\sim Nxy)]$
8. $(x)[(Px \cdot \sim Cxx) \supset (y)(\sim Cxy)]$
9. $(x)\{Cx \supset (\exists y)[(Ay \cdot Ky) \cdot Byx]\}$
10. $(x)[Px \supset (y)(Qxy \supset Oxy)]$
11. $(x)\{Qx \supset [(\exists y)(Ey \cdot Wyx) \supset (\exists z)(Fz \cdot Wzx)]\}$
12. $(x)\{[Px \cdot (y)(Ty \supset Jxy)] \supset (z)(Tz \supset \sim Mxz)\}$
13. $(x)\{[Px \cdot (\exists y)[(Gy \cdot Uy) \cdot Ixy]] \supset (z)(Sz \supset \sim Txz)\}$
14. $(x)\{[Px \cdot (y)(Lxy \supset Sxy)] \supset (\exists z)(Hxz \cdot \sim Lxz)\}$
15. $(x)\{[Wx \cdot (y)[Py \supset \sim(\exists z)(Nz \cdot Pxzy)]] \supset Ix\}$
16. $(x)\{[Px \cdot (y)(\sim Vxy)] \supset (z)(\sim Gxz)\}$
17. $(x)\{Vx \supset (y)[Xy \supset (\exists z)[(Jz \cdot Bzx) \cdot \sim Dzy]]\}$
18. $(x)\{[Lx \cdot (\exists y)(Py \cdot Eyx)] \supset (z)(Wz \supset Tgzx)\}$
19. $(x)\{Px \supset (\exists y)[Py \cdot (\exists z)(Bxzy)]\}$
20. $(x)\{Px \supset (\exists y)[Py \cdot (\exists z)(\sim Bxzy)]\}$
21. $(x)\{Px \supset (y)[Py \supset (z)(\sim Bxzy)]\}$
22. $(x)\{Px \supset (y)[Py \supset (\exists z)(\sim Bxzy)]\}$
23. $(x)\{(Nx \cdot Dx) \supset (y)[Py \supset (Myx \equiv Lxy)]\}$
24. $(x)[Px \supset (\exists y)(Py \cdot Xyx)] \cdot (\exists u)[Pu \cdot (v)(Pv \supset \sim Xuv)]$
25. $(x)\{[Qx \cdot (y)\{[(Py \cdot Wyx) \cdot (z)(\sim Kyz)] \supset By\}] \supset$
$(u)\{[(Pu \cdot Wux) \cdot (v)(Kuv)] \supset Ou\}\}$

II. Symbolize the following sentences, in each case using the indicated symbols:

1. Dead men tell no tales. (Dx-x is dead, Mx-x is a man, Tx-x is a tale, Txy-x tells y.)

2. The early bird gets the worm. (Ex-x is early, Bx-x is a bird, Wx-x is a worm, Gxy-x gets y.)

3. A dead lion is more dangerous than a live dog. (Lx-x is a lion, Ax-x is alive, Dx-x is a dog, Dxy-x is more dangerous than y.)

4. Uneasy lies the head that wears a crown. (Ux-x lies uneasy, Hx-x is a head, Cx-x is a crown, Wxy-x wears y.)

5. Every rose has its thorn. (Rx-x is a rose, Tx-x is a thorn, Hxy-x has y.)

6. Anyone who consults a psychiatrist ought to have his head examined. (Px-x is a person, Sx-x is a psychiatrist, Ox-x ought to have his head examined, Cxy-x consults y.)

7. No one ever learns anything unless he teaches it to himself. (Px-x is a person, Lxy-x learns y, $Txyz$-x teaches y to z.)

8. Delilah wore a ring on every finger, and had a finger in every pie. (*d*-Delilah, *Rx-x* is a ring, *Fxy-x* is a finger of *y*, *Oxy-x* is on *y*, *Px-x* is a pie, *Ixy-x* is in *y*.)

9. The race is not always to the swift, nor the battle to the strong. (*Rx-x* is a race, *Sx-x* is swift, *Bx-x* is a battle, *Kx-x* is strong, *Wxy-x* wins *y*.)

10. Anyone who accomplishes anything will be envied by everyone. (*Px-x* is a person, *Axy-x* accomplishes *y*, *Exy-x* envies *y*.)

11. To catch a fish one must have some bait. (*Px-x* is a person, *Fx-x* is a fish, *Bx-x* is bait, *Cxy-x* catches *y*, *Hxy-x* has *y*.)

12. Every student does some problems, but no student does all of them. (*Sx-x* is a student, *Px-x* is a problem, *Dxy-x* does *y*.)

13. Any contestant who answers all the questions put to him will win any prize he chooses. (*Cx-x* is a contestant, *Qx-x* is a question, *Px-x* is a prize, *Axy-x* answers *y*, *Pxy-x* is put to *y*, *Wxy-x* wins *y*, *Cxy-x* chooses *y*.)

14. Every son has a father but not every father has a son. (*Px-x* is a person, *Mx-x* is male, *Pxy-x* is a parent of *y*.)

15. A person is maintaining a nuisance if he has a dog who barks at every stranger. (*Px-x* is a person, *Nx-x* is a nuisance, *Mxy-x* maintains *y*, *Dx-x* is a dog, *Bxy-x* barks at *y*, *Kxy-x* knows *y*, *Hxy-x* has *y*.)

16. A doctor has no scruples who treats a patient who has no ailment. (*Dx-x* is a doctor, *Sx-x* is a scruple, *Hxy-x* has *y*, *Px-x* is a patient, *Ax-x* is an ailment, *Txy-x* treats *y*.)

17. A doctor who treats a person who has every ailment has a job no one would envy him. (*Dx-x* is a doctor, *Px-x* is a person, *Txy-x* treats *y*, *Ax-x* is an ailment, *Hxy-x* has *y*, *Jx-x* is a job, *Exyz-x* envies *y* his *z*.)

18. If a farmer keeps only hens, none of them will lay eggs that are worth setting. (*Fx-x* is a farmer, *Kxy-x* keeps *y*, *Hx-x* is a hen, *Ex-x* is an egg, *Lxy-x* lays *y*, *Wx-x* is worth setting.)

In symbolizing the following, use only the abbreviations: *Px-x* is a person, *Sx-x* is a store, *Bxyz-x* buys *y* from *z*.

19. Everyone buys something from some store (or other).
20. There is a store from which everyone buys something (or other).
21. Some people make all their purchases from a single store.
22. No one buys everything that it sells from any store.
23. No one buys things from every store.

24. No store has everyone for a customer.
25. No store makes all its sales to a single customer.

II. ARGUMENTS INVOLVING RELATIONS

No new principles need be introduced to deal with relational arguments. The original list of valid argument forms, together with the strengthened method of Conditional Proof and our four quantification rules, enable us (if we have sufficient ingenuity) to construct a demonstration of the validity of every valid argument in which only individual variables are quantified and only truth-functional connectives occur.

However, a certain change of technique is advisable in working with arguments involving relations. In all our previous sample demonstrations, **UI** and **EI** were used to instantiate with respect to a variable different from any quantified in the premiss, and **UG** and **EG** were used to quantify with respect to a variable different from any which occurred free in the premiss. Our inferences were of the following forms:

$$\frac{(x)Fx}{\therefore Fy}, \qquad \frac{(\exists x)Fx}{\therefore Fz}, \qquad \frac{Fx}{\therefore (y)Fy}, \qquad \frac{Fy}{\therefore (\exists w)Fw}.$$

But our statement of the quantification rules does not require that μ and ν be different variables; they may well be the same. And on the whole it is simpler (wherever it is legitimate) to instantiate with respect to the same variable that had been quantified, and to quantify with respect to the same variable that had been free in the premiss. Thus the above inferences may also take the following forms:

$$\frac{(x)Fx}{\therefore Fx}, \qquad \frac{(\exists x)Fx}{\therefore Fx}, \qquad \frac{Fx}{\therefore (x)Fx}, \qquad \frac{Fy}{\therefore (\exists y)Fy}.$$

In this way instantiation is accomplished by simply dropping a quantifier, and generalization is accomplished by simply adding a quantifier. Of course our restrictions on the quantification rules must still be observed. For example, where we have two premisses '$(\exists x)Fx$' and '$(\exists x) \sim Fx$', we can instantiate with respect to one by simply dropping the quantifier, but when this is done, if **EI** is subsequently used on the other, a new variable must be used instead of 'x', for the latter will already have a free occurrence in the proof under construction. Of course we remain perfectly free to use **UI** to instantiate with respect to any particular variable or constant we choose. The preceding remarks can be illustrated by constructing a demonstration of validity for the argument

> There is a man whom all men despise.
>
> Therefore at least one man despises himself.

Its symbolic translation and proof, using 'Mx' and 'Dxy' to abbreviate 'x is a man' and 'x despises y' may be written as follows:

1. $(\exists x)[Mx \cdot (y)(My \supset Dyx)] / \therefore \ (\exists x)(Mx \cdot Dxx)$
2. $Mx \cdot (y)(My \supset Dyx)$　　　　1, **EI**
3. $(y)(My \supset Dyx)$　　　　　　2, Simp.
4. $Mx \supset Dxx$　　　　　　　　3, **UI**
5. Mx　　　　　　　　　　　　2, Simp.
6. Dxx　　　　　　　　　　　4, 5, M.P.
7. $Mx \cdot Dxx$　　　　　　　　5, 6, Conj.
8. $(\exists x)(Mx \cdot Dxx)$　　　　　7, **EG**

In the foregoing proof, the only use of a quantification rule which was accompanied by a change of variable was the use of **UI** in going from step 3 to step 4, which was done because we needed the expression 'Dxx' thus obtained.

Another sample demonstration will be given, this time to establish the validity of the third specimen argument stated at the beginning of the present chapter. Its premiss, 'All horses are animals' will be symbolized as '$(x)(Ex \supset Ax)$', where 'Ex' and 'Ax' abbreviate 'x is a horse' and 'x is an animal', respectively. In its conclusion

> The head of a horse is the head of an animal

the word 'the' has the same sense that it does in such propositions as 'The whale is a mammal' or 'The burnt child dreads the fire'.

We may paraphrase it therefore first as

> All heads of horses are heads of animals.

then as

> $(x)[(x$ is the head of a horse$) \supset (x$ is the head of an animal$)]$.

and finally, writing '*Hxy*' for '*x* is the head of *y*', we may express the conclusion by the formula

$$(x)[(\exists y)(Ey \cdot Hxy) \supset (\exists y)(Ay \cdot Hxy)].$$

Once it is symbolized, the argument is easily proved valid by the techniques already available:

1. $(x)(Ex \supset Ax)/\therefore (x)[(\exists y)(Ey \cdot Hxy) \supset (\exists y)(Ay \cdot Hxy)]$
2. $(y) \sim(Ay \cdot Hxy)$
3. $\sim(Ay \cdot Hxy)$ 2, **UI**
4. $\sim Ay \text{ v } \sim Hxy$ 3, De M.
5. $Ay \supset \sim Hxy$ 4, Impl.
6. $Ey \supset Ay$ 1, **UI**
7. $Ey \supset \sim Hxy$ 6, 5, H.S.
8. $\sim Ey \text{ v } \sim Hxy$ 7, Impl.
9. $\sim(Ey \cdot Hxy)$ 8, De M.
10. $(y) \sim(Ey \cdot Hxy)$ 9, **UG**
11. $(y) \sim(Ay \cdot Hxy) \supset (y) \sim(Ey \cdot Hxy)$ 2–10, C.P.
12. $\sim(y) \sim(Ey \cdot Hxy) \supset \sim(y) \sim(Ay \cdot Hxy)$ 11, Trans.
13. $(\exists y)(Ey \cdot Hxy) \supset (\exists y)(Ay \cdot Hxy)$ 12, **QN**
14. $(x)[(\exists y)(Ey \cdot Hxy) \supset (\exists y)(Ay \cdot Hxy)]$ 13, **UG**

Again, the only time a change of variables accompanied the use of a quantification rule (in step 6) was when the change of variable was needed for subsequent inferences.

The first specimen argument presented in this chapter, which dealt with the relation of *being older than*, raises a new problem, which will be discussed in the following section.

EXERCISES

Construct a formal proof of validity for each of the following arguments:

1. Whoever supports Ickes will vote for Jones. Anderson will vote for no one but a friend of Harris. No friend of Kelly has Jones for a friend. Therefore, if Harris is a friend of Kelly, Anderson will not support Ickes. (Sxy-x supports y, Vxy-x votes for y, Fxy-x is a friend of y, a-Anderson, i-Ickes, j-Jones, h-Harris, k-Kelly.)

2. Whoever belongs to the Country Club is wealthier than any member of the Elks Lodge. Not all who belong to the Country Club are wealthier than all who do not belong. Therefore not everyone belongs either to the Country Club or the Elks Lodge. (Cx-x belongs to the Country Club, Ex-x belongs to the Elks Lodge, Px-x is a person, Wxy-x is wealthier than y.)

3. All circles are figures. Therefore all who draw circles draw figures. (Cx-x is a circle, Fx-x is a figure, Dxy-x draws y.)

4. There is a professor who is liked by every student who likes any professor at all. Every student likes some professor or other. Therefore there is a professor who is liked by all students. (Px-x is a professor, Sx-x is a student, Lxy-x likes y.)

5. Only a fool would lie about one of Bill's fraternity brothers to him. A classmate of Bill's lied about Al to him. Therefore if none of Bill's classmates are fools, then Al is not a fraternity brother of Bill. (Fx-x is a fool, $Lxyz$-x lies about y to z, Cxy-x is a classmate of y, Bxy-x is a fraternity brother of y, a-Al, b-Bill.)

6. It is a crime to sell an unregistered gun to anyone. All the weapons that Red owns were purchased by him from either Lefty or Moe. So if one of Red's weapons is an unregistered gun, then if Red never bought anything from Moe, Lefty is a criminal. (Rx-x is registered, Gx-x is a gun, Cx-x is a criminal, Wx-x is a weapon, Oxy-x owns y, $Sxyz$-x sells y to z, r-Red, l-Lefty, m-Moe.)

7. No one respects a person who does not respect himself. No one will hire a person he does not respect. Therefore a person who respects no one will never be hired by anybody. (Px-x is a person, Rxy-x respects y, Hxy-x hires y.)

8. Everything on my desk is a masterpiece. Anyone who writes a masterpiece is a genius. Someone very obscure wrote some of the novels on my desk. Therefore some very obscure person is a genius. (Dx-x is on my desk, Mx-x is a masterpiece, Px-x is a person, Gx-x is a genius, Ox-x is very obscure, Nx-x is a novel, Wxy-x wrote y.)

9. Any book which is approved by all critics is read by every literary person. Anyone who reads anything will talk about it. A critic will

approve any book written by any person who flatters him. Therefore if someone flatters every critic then any book he writes will be talked about by all literary persons. (*Bx-x* is a book, *Cx-x* is a critic, *Lx-x* is literary, *Px-x* is a person, *Axy-x* approves *y*, *Rxy-x* reads *y*, *Txy-x* talks about *y*, *Fxy-x* flatters *y*, *Wxy-x* writes *y*.)

10. A work of art which tells a story can be understood by everyone. Some religious works of art have been created by great artists. Every religious work of art tells an inspirational story. Therefore if some people admire only what they cannot understand, then some artists' creations will not be admired by everyone. (*Ax-x* is an artist, *Gx-x* is great, *Px-x* is a person, *Sx-x* is a story, *Ix-x* is inspirational, *Rx-x* is religious, *Wx-x* is a work of art, *Cxy-x* creates *y*, *Axy-x* admires *y*, *Txy-x* tells *y*, *Uxy-x* can understand *y*.)

III. SOME PROPERTIES OF RELATIONS

There are a number of interesting properties that relations themselves may possess. We shall consider only a few of the more familiar ones, and our discussion will be confined to properties of *dyadic* relations.

Dyadic relations may be characterized as *symmetrical*, *asymmetrical*, or *non-symmetrical*. Various symmetrical relations are designated by the phrases: 'is next to', 'is married to', and 'has the same weight as'. A *symmetrical* relation is one such that if one individual has that relation to a second individual, then the second individual must have that relation to the first. A propositional function '*Rxy*' designates a symmetrical relation if and only if

$$(x)(y)(Rxy \supset Ryx).$$

On the other hand, an *asymmetrical* relation is one such that if one individual has that relation to a second individual, then the second individual *cannot* have that relation to the first. Various asymmetrical relations are designated by the phrases: 'is north of', 'is parent of', and 'weighs more than'. A propositional function '*Rxy*' designates an asymmetrical relation if and only if

$$(x)(y)(Rxy \supset \sim Ryx).$$

Not all relations are either symmetrical or asymmetrical, how-ever. If one individual loves a second, or is a brother of a second, or weighs no more than a second, it does not follow that the second loves the first, or is a brother to the first (possibly being a sister instead), or weighs no more than the first. Nor does it follow that the second does *not* love the first, or is *not* a brother to him, or *does* weigh more than the first. Such relations as these are *non-symmetrical*, and are defined as those which are neither symmetrical nor asymmetrical.

Dyadic relations may also be characterized as *transitive, in-transitive,* or *non-transitive.* Various transitive relations are desig-nated by the phrases: 'is north of', 'is an ancestor of', and 'weighs the same as'. A *transitive* relation is one such that if one individual has it to a second, and the second to a third, then the first must have it to the third. A propositional function '*Rxy*' designates a transitive relation if and only if

$$(x)(y)(z)[(Rxy \cdot Ryz) \supset Rxz].$$

An *intransitive* relation, on the other hand, is one such that if one individual has it to a second, and the second to a third, then the first *cannot* have it to the third. Some intransitive relations are designated by the phrases: 'is mother of', 'is father of', and 'weighs exactly twice as much as'. A propositional function '*Rxy*' designates an intransitive relation if and only if

$$(x)(y)(z)[(Rxy \cdot Ryz) \supset \sim Rxz].$$

Not all relations are either transitive or intransitive. We define a *non-transitive* relation as one which is neither transitive nor intransitive; examples of non-transitive relations are designated by: 'loves', 'is discriminably different from', and 'has a different weight than'.

Finally, relations may be *reflexive, irreflexive,* or *non-reflexive.* Various definitions of these properties have been proposed by different authors, and there seems to be no standard terminology established. It is convenient to distinguish between reflexivity and total reflexivity. A relation is *totally reflexive* if every individual has that relation to itself. For example, the phrase 'is identical with' designates the totally reflexive relation of identity. A propositional function 'Rxy' designates a totally reflexive relation if and only if

$$(x)Rxx.$$

On the other hand, a relation is said to be *reflexive* if any individuals which stand in that relation to each other also have that relation to themselves. Obvious examples of reflexive relations are designated by the phrases: 'has the same color hair as', 'is the same age as', and 'is a contemporary of'. A propositional function 'Rxy' designates a reflexive relation if and only if

$$(x)(y)[(Rxy \supset (Rxx{\cdot}Ryy)].$$

It is obvious that all totally reflexive relations are reflexive.

An irreflexive relation is one which no individual has to itself. A propositional function 'Rxy' designates an irreflexive relation if and only if

$$(x) \sim Rxx.$$

Examples of irreflexive relations are common indeed; the phrases: 'is north of', 'is married to', and 'is parent of' all designate irreflexive relations. Relations which are neither reflexive nor irreflexive are said to be *non-reflexive*. The phrases: 'loves', 'hates', and 'criticizes' designate non-reflexive relations.

Relations may have various combinations of the properties described. The relation of *weighing more than* is asymmetrical, transitive, and irreflexive, while the relation of *having the same weight as* is symmetrical, transitive, and reflexive. However, some properties entail the presence of others. For example, all asymmetrical relations must be irreflexive, as can easily be demonstrated. Let 'Rxy' designate any asymmetrical relation; then by definition:

1. $(x)(y)(Rxy \supset \sim Ryx)$.

From this premiss we can deduce that R is irreflexive, that is, that $(x)\sim Rxx$:

2. $(y)(Rxy \supset \sim Ryx)$ 1, **UI**
3. $Rxx \supset \sim Rxx$ 2, **UI**
4. $\sim Rxx \lor \sim Rxx$ 3, Impl.
5. $\sim Rxx$ 4, Taut.
6. $(x) \sim Rxx$ 5, **UG**

Other logical connections among these properties of relations are easily stated and proved, but our interest lies in another direction.

The relevance of these properties to relational arguments is easily seen. An argument to which one of them is relevant might be stated thus:

> Tom has the same weight as Dick.
> Dick has the same weight as Harry.
> The relation of *having the same weight as* is transitive.
> ———————————————————————
> Therefore Tom has the same weight as Harry.

When it is translated into our symbolism as

$$Wtd$$
$$Wdh$$
$$(x)(y)(z)[(Wxy \cdot Wyz) \supset Wxz]$$
$$\therefore Wth$$

the method of its validation is immediately obvious. We said that the argument 'might' be stated in the way indicated. But such a statement of the argument would be the rare exception rather than the rule. The ordinary way of propounding such an argument would be to state only the first two premisses and the conclusion, on the grounds that *everyone knows* that *having the same weight as* is a transitive relation. Relational arguments are often used, and many of them depend essentially on the transitivity, or symmetry, or one of the other properties of the relations involved. But *that* the relation in question *has* the relevant property is seldom—if ever—stated explicitly as a premiss. The reason is easy to see. In most discussions a large body of propositions can be presumed to be common knowledge. The majority of speakers and writers save themselves trouble

by not repeating well-known and perhaps trivially true propositions which their hearers or readers can perfectly well be ex-
pected to supply for themselves. An argument which is incom-
pletely expressed, part of it being 'understood', is an *enthymeme*.

Because it is incomplete, an enthymeme must have its sup-
pressed premiss or premisses taken into account when the
problem arises of testing its validity. Where a necessary premiss
is missing, the inference is technically invalid. But where the
unexpressed premiss is easily supplied and obviously true, in all
fairness it ought to be included as part of the argument in any
evaluation of it. In such a case one assumes that the maker of the
argument did have more 'in mind' than he stated explicitly.
In most cases there is no difficulty in supplying the tacit premiss
that the speaker intended but did not express. Thus the first
specimen argument stated at the beginning of this chapter:

> Al is older than Bill.
> Bill is older than Charlie.
> ———————————————
> Therefore Al is older than Charlie.

ought to be counted as valid, since it becomes so when the
trivially true proposition that *being older than* is a transitive relation, is added as an auxiliary premiss. When the indicated missing premiss is supplied, a formal proof of the argument's validity
is very easily set down.

Of course premisses other than relational ones are often left
unexpressed. For example, in the argument

> Any horse can outrun any dog. Some greyhounds
>   can outrun any rabbit. Therefore any horse can
>   outrun any rabbit.

not only is the needed premiss about the transitivity of *being able
to outrun* left unexpressed, but also the non-relational premiss
that all greyhounds are dogs. When these are added—and they
are certainly not debatable issues—the validity of the argument
can be demonstrated as follows:

1. $(x)[Hx \supset (y)(Dy \supset Oxy)]$ premisses/ $\therefore$
2. $(\exists y)[Gy \cdot (z)(Rz \supset Oyz)]$ $(x)[Hx \supset (z)(Rz \supset Oxz)]$
3. $(x)(y)(z)[(Oxy \cdot Oyz) \supset Oxz]$ additional premisses
4. $(y)(Gy \supset Dy)$

→5. Hx		
6. $Hx \supset (y)(Dy \supset Oxy)$	1, UI	
7. $(y)(Dy \supset Oxy)$	6, 5, M.P.	
8. $Gy \cdot (z)(Rz \supset Oyz)$	2, EI	
9. Gy	8, Simp.	
10. $Gy \supset Dy$	4, UI	
11. Dy	10, 9, M.P.	
12. $Dy \supset Oxy$	7, UI	
13. Oxy	12, 11, M.P.	
14. $(z)(Rz \supset Oyz)$	8, Simp.	
→15. Rz		
16. $Rz \supset Oyz$	14, UI	
17. Oyz	16, 15, M.P.	
18. $Oxy \cdot Oyz$	13, 17, Conj.	
19. $(y)(z)[(Oxy \cdot Oyz) \supset Oxz]$	3, UI	
20. $(z)[(Oxy \cdot Oyz) \supset Oxz]$	19, UI	
21. $(Oxy \cdot Oyz) \supset Oxz$	20, UI	
22. Oxz	21, 18, M.P.	
23. $Rz \supset Oxz$	15–22, C.P.	
24. $(z)(Rz \supset Oxz)$	23, UG	
25. $Hx \supset (z)(Rz \supset Oxz)$	5–24, C.P.	
26. $(x)[Hx \supset (z)(Rz \supset Oxz)]$	25, UG	

Missing premisses are not always so easily noticed and supplied as in the present example. When it is not so obvious which necessary premisses are missing from an enthymematically expressed argument, then in beginning a proof of its validity it is a good policy to leave a little space just below the given premisses, in which additional premisses can be written when need arises for their use. The only point to be stressed is that no statement which is as doubtful or debatable as the argument's own conclusion is to be admitted as a supplementary premiss, for in a valid argument which is enthymematically stated only the sheerest platitudes should be left unexpressed for the hearer or reader to fill in for himself.

EXERCISES

Prove the validity of the following enthymemes—adding only obviously true premises where necessary:

1. A Cadillac is more expensive than any low-priced car. Therefore no Cadillac is a low-priced car. (*Cx-x* is a Cadillac, *Lx-x* is a low-priced car, *Mxy-x* is more expensive than *y*.)

2. Alice is Betty's mother. Betty is Charlene's mother. Therefore if Charlene loves only her mother then she does not love Alice. (*a*-Alice, *b*-Betty, *c*-Charlene, *Mxy-x* is mother of *y*, *Lxy-x* loves *y*.)

3. Any man on the first team can outrun every man on the second team. Therefore no man on the second team can outrun any man on the first team. (*Fx-x* is a man on the first team, *Sx-x* is a man on the second team, *Oxy-x* can outrun *y*.)

4. Every boy at the party danced with every girl who was there. Therefore every girl at the party danced with every boy who was there. (*Bx-x* is a boy, *Gx-x* is a girl, *Px-x* was at the party, *Dxy-x* danced with *y*.)

5. Anyone is unfortunate who bears the same name as a person who commits a crime. Therefore anyone who commits a burglary is unfortunate. (*Px-x* is a person, *Ux-x* is unfortunate, *Cx-x* is a crime, *Bx-x* is a burglary, *Cxy-x* commits *y*, *Nxy-x* bears the same name as *y*.)

6. All the watches sold by Kubitz are made in Switzerland. Anything made in a foreign country has a tariff paid on it. Anything on which a tariff was paid costs its purchaser extra. Therefore it will cost anyone extra who buys a watch from Kubitz. (*Wx-x* is a watch, *Tx-x* has a tariff paid on it, *Fx-x* is a foreign country, *Cxy-x* costs *y* extra, *Mxy-x* is made in *y*, *Bxyz-x* buys *y* from *z*, *s*-Switzerland, *k*-Kubitz.)

7. Vacant lots provide no income to their owners. Anyone who owns real estate must pay taxes on it. Therefore anyone who owns a vacant lot must pay taxes on something which provides no income to him. (*Vx-x* is a vacant lot, *Rx-x* is real estate, *Ixy-x* provides income to *y*, *Txy-x* pays taxes on *y*, *Oxy-x* owns *y*.)

8. All admirals wear uniforms having gold buttons. Therefore some naval officers wear clothes which have metal buttons. (*Ax-x* is an admiral, *Ux-x* is a uniform, *Gx-x* is gold, *Bx-x* is a button, *Nx-x* is a naval officer, *Cx-x* is clothing, *Mx-x* is metal, *Wxy-x* wears *y*, *Hxy-x* has *y*.)

9. Whenever Charlie moved to Boston, it was after he had met Al. Whenever Charlie got married, it was before he ever saw Dave. Therefore if Charlie moved to Boston and subsequently got married, then he met Al before he ever saw Dave. (Tx-x is a time, Ax-Charlie met Al at (time) x, Bx-Charlie moved to Boston at (time) x, Mx-Charlie got married at (time) x, Dx-Charlie saw Dave at (time) x, Pxy-x precedes y.)

10. A fish that chases every shiner will be hooked by an angler who uses a shiner for bait. A greedy fish will chase every shiner. So if all anglers are sportsmen, then no pike which is not hooked by a sportsman who uses minnows for bait is greedy. (Fx-x is a fish, Sx-x is a shiner, Cxy-x chases y, Hxy-x hooks y, Ax-x is an angler, Bxy-x uses y for bait, Gx-x is greedy, Px-x is a pike, Rx-x is a sportsman, Mx-x is a minnow.)

IV. IDENTITY AND THE DEFINITE DESCRIPTION

The notion of *identity* is a familiar one. Perhaps the most natural occasion for its use is in the process of *identification*, as when in a police line-up a witness identifies a suspect, asserting that

> The man on the right *is* the man who snatched my purse.

Other identifications are common, as in a geography class when it is asserted that

> Mt. Everest *is* the tallest mountain in the world.

or when in a literature class it is asserted that

> Scott *is* the author of *Waverley*.

A relationship is asserted by each of the preceding propositions to hold between the individuals denoted by its two terms. The relation asserted to hold is that of *identity*. In each of the preceding at least one term was a *definite description*, which is a phrase of the form 'the so-and-so'. In identifications, however, both terms may be proper names. Just as the two propositions

> Brutus killed Caesar.

and

> Booth killed Lincoln.

assert the relation of *killing* to hold between the individuals denoted by the proper names appearing in them, so the propositions

> Lewis Carroll was Charles Lutwidge Dodgson.

and

> Mark Twain was Samuel Clemens.

assert the relation of *identity* to hold between the individuals
denoted by the proper names appearing in them.

The usual notation for the relation of identity is the ordinary
equals-sign '$=$'. It is intuitively obvious that the relation of
identity is transitive, symmetrical, and totally reflexive. In our
symbolic notation we can write

$$(x)(y)(z)\{[(x = y)\cdot(y = z)] \supset (x = z)\}$$
$$(x)(y)[(x = y) \supset (y = x)]$$
$$(x)(x = x).$$

All of these are immediate consequences of the definition of
identity contained in Leibniz's principle of the Identity of
Indiscernibles:

> $x = y$ if and only if every property of x is a prop-
> erty of y, and conversely.

This principle permits us to infer, from the premisses $v = \mu$ and
any proposition containing an occurrence of the symbol v, as
conclusion any proposition which results from replacing any
occurrences of v in the second premiss by the symbol μ. Any
inference of this pattern is valid, and in a proof should have the
letters 'Id.' written beside it. A specimen deduction or two will
make this clear. The argument

> O. Henry was William Sidney Porter.
> O. Henry was a writer.
> _____
> Therefore William Sidney Porter was a writer.

may be symbolized and proved valid by the following, in which we use the letters 'h' and 'p' to abbreviate the proper names 'O. Henry' and 'William Sidney Porter', and the symbol 'Wx' for 'x was a writer':

1. $h = p$
2. Wh /∴ Wp
3. Wp 1, 2, Id.

Another illustration is provided by the argument

> George Eliot wrote *The Mill on the Floss*.
> George Eliot is Mary Ann Evans.
> Mary Ann Evans is a lady.
> ―――――――――――――――――――――――
> Therefore a lady wrote *The Mill on the Floss*.

Using the symbols 'g', 'f', 'm', 'Wxy', 'Lx' to abbreviate 'George Eliot', '*The Mill on the Floss*', 'Mary Ann Evans', 'x wrote y', and 'x is a lady', we may formulate the given argument and demonstrate its validity as follows:

1. Wgf
2. $g = m$
3. Lm /∴ $(\exists x)(Lx \cdot Wxf)$
4. Lg 2, 3, Id.
5. $Lg \cdot Wgf$ 4, 1, Conj.
6. $(\exists x)(Lx \cdot Wxf)$ 5, **EG**

An alternative proof for the second argument would be the following:

4. Wmf 1, 2, Id.
5. $Lm \cdot Wmf$ 3, 4, Conj.
6. $(\exists x)(Lx \cdot Wxf)$ 5, **EG**

A third illustration is provided by the argument:

> Only a bald man wears a wig. Kennedy is a man who
> wears a wig. This man is not bald. Therefore this
> man is not Kennedy.

Using the symbols 't', 'k', 'Mx', 'Bx', 'Wx', to abbreviate 'this man', 'Kennedy', 'x is a man', 'x is bald', and 'x wears a wig', we may symbolize the present argument and prove its validity as follows:

1. $(x)[(Mx \cdot Wx) \supset Bx]$
2. $Mk \cdot Wk$
3. $\sim Bt$ $/ \therefore \sim(t = k)$
4. $(Mk \cdot Wk) \supset Bk$ 1, **UI**
5. Bk 4, 2, M.P.
6. $\sim(t = k)$ 3, 5, Id.

This last proof serves to show that we use the principle of Identity not only to infer $\Phi\nu$ from $\Phi\mu$ and $\nu = \mu$, but also to infer $\sim(\nu = \mu)$ from $\Phi\nu$ and $\sim\Phi\mu$.

An important use for the identity symbol is in the formulation of certain common types of exceptive statements. If we wish to symbolize the proposition

> Al is on the team and can outrun anyone else on it.

using 'a' for 'Al', 'Tx' for 'x is on the team', and 'Oxy' for 'x can outrun y', we cannot simply write down

$$Ta \cdot (x)(Tx \supset Oax)$$

for this would entail

$$Oaa$$

which is false because *being able to outrun* is an irreflexive relation. The preceding formula does not translate the given proposition, but rather the necessarily false one:

> Al is on the team and can outrun anyone on it.

In this second proposition the important word 'else' is missing. The first proposition does not assert that Al can outrun *everyone* on the team, but everyone *else* on it, that is, everyone on it who is *other than* or *not identical with* Al. The proper translation of the first proposition is

$$Ta \cdot (x)\{[Tx \cdot \sim(x = a)] \supset Oax\}.$$

If we adopt the convention of abbreviating $\sim(\nu = \mu)$ as $\nu \neq \mu$, the preceding formula may be written

$$Ta \cdot (x)[(Tx \cdot x \neq a) \supset Oax].$$

Making similar use of the identity sign, we may symbolize the propositions

> Only John loves Mary.

and

> Mary can tolerate anyone but John.

as

$$Ljm \cdot (x)(x \neq j \supset \sim Lxm)$$

and

$$\sim Tmj \cdot (x)[(Px \cdot x \neq j) \supset Tmx].$$

A similar technique can be used in symbolizing the notion expressed by the English phrases 'at most' and 'no more than'. Thus the statement

> There is at most one opening.

interpreted not as asserting that there *is* an opening, but that there is *no more* than one, may be symbolized as

$$(x)(y)[(Ox \cdot Oy) \supset x = y].$$

Similarly, the statement

> No more than two visitors are permitted.

interpreted as leaving open the question of there being any at all, may be symbolized as

$$(x)(y)(z)[(Vx \cdot Vy \cdot Vz) \supset (x = z \lor y = z \lor x = y)].$$

The identity sign is also useful in symbolizing the notion of *at least*. It is not needed for 'at least one', because the existential quantifier by itself suffices for this, the statement

> There is at least one applicant.

being symbolized as

$$(\exists x)Ax.$$

But to symbolize

> There are at least two applicants.

we use the identity sign, writing

$$(\exists x)(\exists y)[Ax \cdot Ay \cdot x \neq y].$$

Putting together the notations for 'at least one' and 'at most one' we have a method for symbolizing definite numerical propositions. Thus the statement

There is one book on my desk.

meaning *exactly* one, is symbolized, using 'Bx' for 'x is a book' and 'Dx' for 'x is on my desk', as

$$(\exists x)\{Bx \cdot Dx \cdot (y)[(By \cdot Dy) \supset y = x]\}.$$

And the statement

Every state elects two Senators.

meaning *exactly* two, is symbolized, using 'Sx' for 'x is a state', 'Nx' for 'x is a Senator', and 'Exy' for 'x elects y', as

$$(x)\{Sx \supset (\exists y)(\exists z)[Ny \cdot Nz \cdot Exy \cdot Exz \cdot y \neq z \cdot$$
$$(w)[Nw \cdot Exw) \supset (w = y \text{ v } w = z)]]\}.$$

Finally, the (presumably false) statement

Cerberus has three heads.

is symbolized, using 'Hx' for 'x is a head of Cerberus', as

$$(\exists x)(\exists y)(\exists z)\{Hx \cdot Hy \cdot Hz \cdot x \neq y \cdot y \neq z \cdot x \neq z \cdot$$
$$(w)[Hw \supset (w = x \text{ v } w = y \text{ v } w = z)]\}.$$

The present notation is adequate to the symbolization of arithmetical statements about individuals, but the symbolization of propositions of pure arithmetic requires an expanded logical apparatus such as that suggested in the following section.

Very rarely does an individual have two different proper names ν and μ, so that $\nu = \mu$ is a significant and informative statement. However, individuals are often referred to by means of descriptive phrases rather than by their proper names. Thus when a crime has been committed, and the police have not yet learned who committed it, the newspapers are not silenced for want of a name—the individual in question is referred to as 'the kidnapper of the Lindbergh baby', or 'the driver of the missing car'. The word 'the' has a variety of uses. In one sense it has the force of 'all' or 'any', as in 'The whale is a mammal' or 'The early bird gets the worm'. But in another sense it serves to indicate *existence* and *uniqueness*, as in the phrases

> The author of *Waverley*,
> The man who shot Lincoln,
> The largest city in Illinois,

which denote Scott, Booth, and Chicago, respectively. The standard notation for *this* sense of the word 'the' involves an upside-down iota. The three phrases above are (partially) symbolized as

> $(\imath x)(x$ wrote *Waverley*$)$,
> $(\imath x)(x$ is a man$\cdot x$ shot Lincoln$)$,
> $(\imath x)(x$ is a city in Illinois$\cdot x$ is larger than any other
>   city in Illinois$)$.

In general a formula like '$(\imath x)(x$ wrote *Waverley*$)$' is read as 'the x which wrote *Waverley*', and is treated as a proper name. Thus we can replace the individual variable μ in the propositional function $\Psi\mu$ by $(\imath v)(\Phi v)$ to obtain $\Psi(\imath v)(\Phi v)$ as a substitution instance.

Normally, a definite description functions in argument the same way that a proper name does. The principle of Identity permits us to infer the conclusion 'Scott wrote *Marmion*' from the premisses 'Scott is the author of *Waverley*' and 'the author of *Waverley* wrote *Marmion*'. The proposition 'Something is larger than Detroit' follows validly by **EG** from the premiss 'The largest city in Illinois is larger than Detroit'. Of course **EI** instantiates only with a variable, and **UG** generalizes only from a variable, so there is no difference with respect to these two principles between a proper name and a definite description. But with respect to the principle of Universal Instantiation, certain differences and difficulties arise.

Where the letter '*F*' designates some property, the symbol complex '$(ıx)(Fx)$' denotes the individual which has the property *F if* there is one and only one such individual. But what if no individual, or more than one individual, has this property? In such a case, since there is no unique individual to be denoted by the expression '$(ıx)(Fx)$', that expression does not denote. The problem of interpreting phrases which purport to denote but which do not really do so is usually handled in the following fashion, which is due to Russell.* An explicit definition of a symbol is given by presenting another symbol which is equivalent to it in meaning. Thus the symbol 'bachelor' is defined explicitly by equating it to the phrase 'unmarried man'. An alternative method of explaining the meaning of a symbol is to give a *contextual* rather than an explicit definition for it. A contextual definition of a symbol does not explain the symbol's meaning in isolation, but rather explains the meaning of any statement or context in which that symbol occurs. We do not give an explanation of the word 'the' (or the iota symbol) in isolation, but instead we present a method for interpreting any sentence (or formula) in which it appears. A contextual definition is also referred to as a 'definition in use'. Russell's analysis of the definite description consists of a contextual definition, or definition in use, of the word 'the'—in the sense in which it signifies existence and uniqueness. Consider the proposition

The author of *Waverley* was a genius.

It seems to assert three things: first that

There is an individual who wrote *Waverley*,

* Cf. 'On Denoting', *Mind*, n.s. vol. 14 (1905). An alternative solution to this problem is due to G. Frege, cf. 'On Sense and Nominatum', in *Readings in Philosophical Analysis*, edited by H. Feigl & W. Sellars, New York, 1949. The philosophical implications of this problem are by no means solved as yet; on this cf. 'Russell's Mathematical Logic' by K. Gödel, in *The Philosophy of Bertrand Russell*, Evanston, Illinois, 1946, especially p. 130.

second that

at most one individual wrote *Waverley,*

and finally that

that individual was a genius.

The three parts of its meaning can be symbolized—without using the iota—as follows:

$$(\exists x)(x \text{ wrote } Waverley)$$
$$(y)(y \text{ wrote } Waverley \supset y = x)$$

and

$$x \text{ was a genius.}$$

Putting these three parts together, we obtain

$$(\exists x)\{(x \text{ wrote } Waverley)\cdot(y)(y \text{ wrote } Waverley \supset y = x)\cdot$$
$$(x \text{ was a genius})\}.$$

Here we have a symbolic translation of the given statement which contains neither the troublesome word 'the' nor any synonym for it. In general, any statement of the form

The so-and-so is such-and-such,

or any formula such as

$$\Psi(\imath x)(\Phi x)$$

is regarded as logically equivalent to

$$(\exists x)\{(x \text{ is a so-and-so})\cdot(y)(y \text{ is a so-and-so} \supset y = x)\cdot$$
$$(x \text{ is a such-and-such})\}$$

or as

$$(\exists x)\{\Phi x\cdot(y)(\Phi y \supset y = x)\cdot\Psi x\}.$$

Incidentally, when a property is expressed in the superlative form as 'best', 'fastest', 'heaviest', or the like, any proposition containing it can be expressed using only the comparative forms 'better', 'faster', 'heavier', or the like. Thus the statement

The largest ocean is to the west of America.

can be symbolized, using 'Ox' for 'x is an ocean', 'Wx' for 'x is to the west of America', and 'Lxy' for 'x is larger than y', as

$$(\exists x)\{Ox \cdot (y)[(Oy \cdot y \neq x) \supset Lxy] \cdot Wx\}.$$

A definite description is ordinarily used only when it is believed that it does denote. One normally uses the words 'The so-and-so' only when he believes that there exists one and only one so-and-so. But beliefs are often mistaken, and one sometimes uses such a phrase even when it does not denote. When it does not, any sentence which asserts that *the so-and-so* has such-and-such a property, or stands in this or that relation, is false. Thus, even though it might be true that everything has mass, it is *false* that

The immortal man has mass.

for this sentence asserts the existence of exactly one immortal man, whereas there are none. And unless it occurs in a context which makes clear either that some particular mountain is being referred to, or that *mountains in general* are under discussion, the statement

The mountain has mass.

is false, for it asserts that there is only one mountain, whereas in fact there are many. These remarks should serve to make clear that a phrase of the form 'the so-and-so' or a symbol such as '$(\imath x)(Fx)$' cannot be instantiated by the principle of Universal Instantiation alone. In order to deduce the conclusion '$G(\imath x)(Fx)$' from '$(x)Gx$' we require the additional premiss that there is exactly one individual having the property F. Where that premiss is missing, the inference is invalid. But where it is present, the argument is easily validated as follows:

1. $(x)Gx$
2. $(\exists x)[Fx \cdot (y)(Fy \supset y = x)]$ / $\therefore$ $G(\imath x)(Fx)$
3. $Fx \cdot (y)(Fy \supset y = x)$ 2, **EI**
4. Gx 1, **UI**
5. $Fx \cdot (y)(Fy \supset y = x) \cdot Gx$ 3, 4, Conj.
6. $(\exists x)\{Fx \cdot (y)(Fy \supset y = x) \cdot Gx\}$ 5, **EG**
7. $G(\imath x)(Fx)$ 6—definition

EXERCISES

Demonstrate the validity of the following arguments—using only the identity symbol in addition to the indicated abbreviations:

1. The architect who designed Tappan Hall designs only office buildings. Therefore Tappan Hall is an office building. (*Ax-x* is an architect, *t*-Tappan Hall, *Dxy-x* designed *y*, *Ox-x* is an office building.)

2. The Professor of Greek at Siwash is very learned. Therefore all Professors of Greek at Siwash are very learned. (*Px-x* is a Professor of Greek, *Sx-x* is at Siwash, *Lx-x* is very learned.)

3. The largest state is in the south. All southern states are Democratic. Therefore the largest state is Democratic. (*Sx-x* is a state, *Tx-x* is in the south, *Dx-x* is Democratic, *Lxy-x* is larger than *y*.)

4. The fastest running person is a Scandinavian. Therefore anyone who is not a Scandinavian can be outrun by someone (or other). (*Sx-x* is a Scandinavian, *Px-x* is a person, *Fxy-x* can run faster than *y*.)

5. All entrants will win. There will be at most one winner. There is at least one entrant. Therefore there is exactly one entrant. (*Ex-x* is an entrant, *Wx-x* will win.)

6. Any fish can swim faster than any smaller one. Therefore if there is a largest fish then there is a fastest fish. (*Fx-x* is a fish, *Lxy-x* is larger than *y*, *Sxy-x* can swim faster than *y*.)

7. Adams and Brown were the only men at the banquet who drank. All the men at the banquet who brought liquor drank. Adams did not bring any liquor. If any man at the banquet drank then some man at the banquet who drank must have brought liquor. All who drank became ill. Therefore the man at the banquet who brought liquor became ill. (*a*-Adams, *b*-Brown, *Mx-x* was a man at the banquet, *Dx-x* drank, *Lx-x* brought liquor, *Ix-x* became ill.)

8. Anyone who has climbed Mt. Blanc is braver than anyone who hasn't. Only the youngest member of our team has climbed Mt. Blanc. Everyone on our team is a veteran. Therefore the bravest member of our team is a veteran. (*Cx-x* has climbed Mt. Blanc, *Tx-x* is on our team, *Vx-x* is a veteran, *Bxy-x* is braver than *y*, *Oxy-x* is older than *y*.)

9. There is exactly one penny in my right hand. There is exactly one penny in my left hand. Nothing is in both my hands. Therefore

there are exactly two pennies in my hands. (*Px-x* is a penny, *Rx-x* is in my right hand, *Lx-x* is in my left hand.)

10. All accompanists were bagpipers. All bagpipers were in the cabin. At most two individuals were in the cabin. There were at least two accompanists. Therefore there were exactly two bagpipers. (*Ax-x* was an accompanist, *Bx-x* was a bagpiper, *Cx-x* was in the cabin.)

V. PROPERTY VARIABLES AND PROPERTIES OF PROPERTIES

In all of the preceding discussion, quantification has been confined to individual variables. With the exception of the greek letters *phi* and *psi* used in stating our quantification rules, all property symbols and relation symbols introduced thus far have been *constants*. The letters '*W*', '*S*', and '*B*' in our usage of '*Wx*', '*Sxy*', and '*Bxyz*' as abbreviations for '*x* is wise', '*x* is a son of *y*', and '*x* is between *y* and *z*', have denoted definite or constant properties of, or relations between, individuals. However, property variables and relation variables can be introduced also, and they too may be quantified.

If we set aside the capital letters '*F*', '*G*', '*H*', as property or relation variables, then the same quantification techniques which are already familiar will permit the symbolization of a greater variety of statements. We shall be able to symbolize statements which refer not only to all or some individuals having specified properties or standing in specified relations, but which refer to all or some properties or relations which individuals may have or stand in. The expression

$$Fx$$

consisting of a property variable and an individual variable juxtaposed in that order may be regarded as a propositional function of *two* variables. By instantiation with respect to both variables we obtain such singular propositions as 'Socrates is mortal' and 'Plato is wise', expressed symbolically as '*Ms*' and '*Wp*'. By instantiation with respect to the property variable and generalization with respect to the individual variable we obtain such familiar singly general propositions as

$(x)Mx$ (everything is mortal)
$(\exists x)Wx$ (something is wise)

We have seen all these before. A new kind of proposition, however, although still singly general, is obtained by instantiating with respect to the individual variable and generalizing with respect to the property variable. Here we have

$(F)Fs$ (Socrates has all properties)
$(\exists F)Fp$ (Plato has some property)

Finally, by generalizing with respect to *both* variables, the following doubly general propositions are obtained:

(1) $(x)(F)Fx$ (5) $(F)(x)Fx$
(2) $(x)(\exists F)Fx$ (6) $(F)(\exists x)Fx$
(3) $(\exists x)(F)Fx$ (7) $(\exists F)(x)Fx$
(4) $(\exists x)(\exists F)Fx$ (8) $(\exists F)(\exists x)Fx$

Of these, (1) and (5) are clearly equivalent, (1) stating that

Every individual has every property.

and (5) stating that

Every property belongs to every individual.

Propositions (4) and (8) are also equivalent to each other, with (4) stating that

Some individual has some property.

and (8) stating that

Some property belongs to some individual.

The remaining propositions, however, are all distinct. They may be expressed in English as

(2) Every individual has some property (or other).
(3) There is an individual which has every property.
(6) Every property belongs to some individual (or other).
(7) There is a property which belongs to every individual.

There are no equivalences here, but proposition (3) logically entails proposition (6), and proposition (7) logically entails proposition (2). These implications can be formally established by means of our familiar quantification rules, allowing the symbols 'μ' and 'ν' of the rules to denote property variables as well as individual variables—with the same restrictions in their applicability, of course.

When property variables are introduced and their quantification permitted, a formal, that is, completely symbolic definition, can be given for the identity symbol. The definition is

$$(x = y) = df \ (F)(Fx \equiv Fy).$$

From this definition we have

$$(x)(y)[(x = y) \equiv (F)(Fx \equiv Fy)]$$

following as a logical consequence. And from the latter all the properties of the identity relation can be deduced.

For the most part our preceding discussion has concerned only properties of individuals. But individuals are not the only entities which have properties. In Section III we discussed various properties which can be predicated of *relations*. And properties themselves can have properties: thus the property of being *honest* has the property of being *desirable*, a *virtue* (which is a property) may itself have the property of being *rare*, and the property of being *inconsiderate* is *common*.

Once it has been noted that some properties can be predicated of other properties, the temptation arises to predicate certain properties of themselves. For example, the property of being abstract seems itself to be abstract, whereas the property of being concrete seems not to be itself concrete. Any property which can be truly predicated of itself will be said to be a *predicable* property. Thus being predicable is a property which belongs to all those and only those properties which can be truly predicated of themselves. On the other hand, any property which cannot be truly predicated of itself will be said to be an *impredicable* property. Thus being impredicable is a property which belongs to all those and only those properties which cannot be truly predicated of themselves.

If we now ask whether the property of being impredicable can be truly predicated of itself or not, we are led to the following unhappy conclusion. If the property of being impredicable *can* be truly predicated of itself, then it *has* the property of being impredicable, from which it follows by definition that it *cannot* be truly predicated of itself. On the other hand, if the property of being impredicable *cannot* be truly predicated of itself, then like all other properties which cannot be truly predicated of themselves, it *has* the property of being impredicable, which means that it *can* be truly predicated of itself. We have thus been led to a contradiction.

The contradiction can be derived more clearly by symbolizing the property of being impredicable as 'I', and defining it formally as

$$IF = df \sim FF,$$

which definition has the following general proposition as an immediate logical consequence:

$$(F)(IF \equiv \sim FF).$$

From the latter, by the principle of Universal Instantiation, we can instantiate with respect to 'I' itself to obtain

$$II \equiv \sim II$$

which is an explicit contradiction.*

Several methods have been proposed for avoiding such contradictions. Perhaps the best known is Russell's (simple) Theory of Logical Types,† which can be given the following rough

---

* Cf. Russell's *Principles of Mathematics*, Cambridge, England, 1903, pp. 79–80, 97–98, and 102. Cf. also Carnap's *Logical Syntax of Language*, New York, 1937, p. 211.

† Russell first formulated his theory of logical types in Appendix B of his *Principles of Mathematics*. A more complex version of the theory, designed to cope with certain other problems as well, will be presented in Appendix B of the present volume. Cf. also Russell's 'Mathematical Logic as Based on the Theory of Types'. *American Journal of Mathematics*, vol. 30 (1908), pp. 222–262, and Chapter 2 of the Introduction to the first edition of *Principia Mathematica*, by Whitehead and Russell, Cambridge, England, 1910–1913. The best known alternative resolution of the contradiction is the kind of axiomatic set theory first published by E. Zermelo in 'Untersuchungen über die Grundlagen der Mengenlehre I', *Mathematische Annalen*, vol. 65 (1908), pp. 261–281.

formulation. According to Russell, entities are divided into a hierarchy of different logical types, the lowest of which consists of all individuals, the next of all properties of individuals, the next of all properties of properties of individuals, the next of all properties of properties of properties of individuals, and so on. Relations and their properties give us additional hierarchies, but they will be ignored in the present discussion. The essential point to the theory of types is not merely the division of all entities into different logical types, but the doctrine that any property which may significantly be predicated of an entity of one logical type cannot significantly be predicated of any entity of any other logical type. For some properties the theory of types seems perfectly obvious. Thus an individual thing may be orange in color, but it clearly does not make sense to say of any property that *it* is orange in color. And a property may have many instances, but it does not make sense either to affirm or deny of an individual thing that *it* has many instances.

The primary motivation for accepting the theory of logical types, however, is not its naturalness or obviousness, but the fact that it permits the avoidance of such contradictions as that of the alleged property 'impredicable'. According to this theory the type of a property must be higher than the type of any entity of which it can significantly be predicated. Consequently it does not make sense either to affirm or to deny of any property that it belongs to itself; such expressions as '*FF*' and '$\sim FF$' must be dismissed as meaningless. Consequently no such property as 'impredicable' can be defined, and the contradiction vanishes. The version of the theory of types sketched above— sometimes called the 'Simple Theory of Types'—suffices to rule out all contradictions of this kind. It also has a certain consonance with common sense. However, there are alternative solutions or ways to avoid the contradictions, so that the theory of logical types cannot be regarded as *the* solution. It is very widely accepted, however, and we shall follow it in introducing a new type of symbol to represent properties of properties of individuals.

Some words have more than a single meaning, of course, and may in one sense designate a property of individuals, and in another sense designate a property of properties of individuals. Thus the word 'rare' in one sense designates a property of properties of individuals: a property of individuals is rare if it is exemplified by only a few individuals, and in this sense it cannot significantly be affirmed or denied of individuals themselves. But on the other hand, there is a *different* sense of the word 'rare' in which it designates a property of an individual piece of meat that has been cooked for only a short while, and in this sense it cannot significantly be affirmed or denied of any property. To avoid the danger of ambiguity we shall symbolize properties of properties of individuals by boldface italic capital letters '*A*', '*B*', '*C*', . . . , so that they will not be confused with properties of individuals. With this additional symbolic apparatus we can translate into our notation such propositions as 'Unpunctuality is a fault', and 'Truthfulness is a good quality'. Here we use '*Ux*', '*Tx*', '*FF*', and '*GF*' to abbreviate '*x* is unpunctual', '*x* is truthful', '*F* is a fault', and '*F* is good', and symbolize the two stated propositions as '*FU*' and '*GT*'. More complex propositions can also be symbolized. The propositions

All useful properties are desirable.

and

Some desirable properties are not useful.

can be symbolized, using the symbols '*UF*' for '*F* is useful' and '*DF*' for '*F* is desirable', as

$$(F)(UF \supset DF)$$

and

$$(\exists F)(DF \cdot \sim UF).$$

Finally, the proposition

Tom has all of his mother's good qualities.

can be symbolized, using the additional symbols '*t*' for 'Tom' and '*Mxy*' for '*x* is mother of *y*', either as

$$(F)\{[F(\imath x)(Mxt) \cdot GF] \supset Ft\}$$

or as

$$(\exists x)\{Mxt \cdot (y)(Myt \supset y = x) \cdot (F)[(Fx \cdot GF) \supset Ft]\}.$$

EXERCISES

I. Symbolize the following propositions:

1. Nothing has all properties.
2. Some properties belong to nothing.
3. No two things have all their properties in common.
4. Any two things have some common property.
5. Napoleon had all the properties of a great general. (*n*-Napoleon, *Gx*-*x* is a great general.)
6. David has all of his father's faults and none of his virtues. (*d*-David, *Fxy*-*x* is father of *y*, **F***F*-*F* is a fault, **V***F*-*F* is a virtue.)
7. Jones and Smith share all their good qualities but have no bad qualities in common. (*j*-Jones, *s*-Smith, **G***F*-*F* is a good quality, **B***F*-*F* is a bad quality.)
8. Nothing which possesses every rare property has any ordinary property. (**R***F*-*F* is rare, **O***F*-*F* is ordinary.)
9. A man who possesses all virtues is a virtuous man, but there are virtuous men who do not possess all virtues. (*Mx*-*x* is a man, *Vx*-*x* is a virtuous individual, **V***F*-*F* is a virtue.)
10. Everyone has some unusual property or other; it would be an unusual person who had no unusual properties. (*Px*-*x* is a person, *Ux*-*x* is an unusual individual, **U***F*-*F* is an unusual property.)

II. Demonstrate the following:

1. $[(x)(F)Fx] \equiv [(F)(x)Fx]$
2. $[(\exists x)(\exists F)Fx] \equiv [(\exists F)(\exists x)Fx]$
3. $[(\exists x)(F)Fx] \supset [(F)(\exists x)Fx]$
4. $[(\exists F)(x)Fx] \supset [(x)(\exists F)Fx]$
5. $[(\exists R)(x)(\exists y)Rxy] \supset [(x)(\exists y)(\exists R)Rxy]$
6. Every (dyadic) relation which is transitive and irreflexive is asymmetric.

7. All intransitive dyadic relations are irreflexive.
8. Any dyadic relation which every individual has to some individual or other is totally reflexive if it is both symmetric and transitive.
9. From the premiss '$(x)(y)[(x = y) \equiv (F)(Fx \equiv Fy)]$' (which is true by definition), deduce that the identity relation is symmetric, totally reflexive, and transitive.
10. If circles are ellipses then circles have all properties of ellipses.

CHAPTER SIX

Deductive Systems

I. DEFINITION AND DEDUCTION

In the preceding chapters a number of principles of logic have been set forth. These principles embody some knowledge about logic, but they do not constitute a *science* of logic, for *science* is *organized* knowledge. No mere list or catalog of propositions is ever said to constitute a system of knowledge or a science. We have scientific knowledge only when our propositions are organized in a systematic way, so that we can perceive their interrelations. If a system of logic or a science of logical principles is to be achieved, those principles must be arranged or organized in a systematic fashion. This task will be attempted, on a limited scale, in the following chapters. But first it will be of interest to consider the general questions of what interrelations are important, and how propositions may be organized into a system or science.

All knowledge that we possess can be formulated in propositions, and these propositions are composed of terms. In any science, some propositions can be deduced from or proved on the basis of other propositions. For example, Galileo's laws of falling bodies and Kepler's laws of planetary motion are all derivable from Newton's more general laws of gravitation and motion, and the discovery of these deductive interrelationships was an essential part of the process which has culminated in a *science* of physics. Thus one important sort of relationship for the propositions of a science to possess is that of deducibility. A collection of propositions which embody knowledge about a subject becomes a *science* of that subject when they are arranged or ordered by displaying some of them as conclusions deduced from others.

In any science, some of the terms involved in its propositions can be explained or defined on the basis of other terms. For example, in physics again, *density* is defined as *mass per unit volume*, *acceleration* is defined as the *time rate of change in velocity*, and *velocity* is in turn defined as the *time rate of change of position*. This definition of some terms by means of others also serves to reveal interrelations among the propositions. It shows their concern with a common subject matter, and integrates the concepts of the science just as deductions integrate its laws or statements. A collection of propositions which embody knowledge are helped to become a *science* when some of the words or symbols they contain are defined in terms of their other symbols.

The recognition of definition and deduction as important to science may suggest a specious ideal for scientific systems. It may be imagined that in an ideal science *all* propositions should be *proved*, by deducing them from others, and *all* terms should be *defined*. But this would be 'ideal' only in the sense of being impossible to realize. Terms can be defined only by means of other terms, whose meanings are presupposed and must be antecedently understood if the definitions are to explain the meanings of the terms being defined. And deductions can establish their conclusions only on the basis of premises, which must already have been verified if the conclusions are really to be established by the proofs. Hence, if all terms or symbols of a system are to be defined *within the system*, there must be either infinite sequences of definitions, or circular definitions, as in a pocket dictionary which defines the word 'big' as meaning *large*, and the word 'large' as meaning *big*. Circular definitions are obviously worthless, and infinite sequences of definitions are worthless also, for no term will be really explained until the end is reached, and an infinite sequence has no end. Similarly, to prove *all* propositions there must be either infinite regressions of proofs or circular proofs. And these are equally objectionable.

It must be admitted that *within* a system of propositions which constitutes a science, not all propositions can be proved, and not all terms can be defined. It is not that there is some particular proposition which cannot be proved, or some particular term which cannot be defined, but rather that they cannot *all* be proved or defined without a vicious regression or circularity arising. The ideal of science, then, cannot be a system in which *every* proposition is proved and *every* term defined, but is rather one in which a minimum number of propositions suffice for the deduction of all the rest, and a minimum number of terms suffice for the definition of all the others. The ideal of knowledge is described as a *deductive system*.

II. EUCLIDEAN GEOMETRY

Euclidean Geometry is the oldest example of systematized knowledge or science. Of historical interest and importance in its own right, it has the advantage (for our purpose) of being an example with which the reader has already come into contact during his high school training.

It is generally recognized that geometry, as a science, was originated and developed by the Greeks. Among the most important of the contributors to its development were the mathematicians Pythagoras and Euclid. And yet, geometrical truths were known to the Egyptians thousands of years earlier, as attested by their pyramids, already ancient in the time of Pythagoras (6th century B.C.). Records reveal that the Babylonians, even earlier, were familiar with various principles of geometry. If a considerable body of geometrical knowledge was already possessed before their time, in what sense did the Greeks originate the science of geometry? The answer has already been indicated. Before Pythagoras, man's geometrical knowledge consisted of a collection or catalog of almost wholly isolated facts. Geometrical truths constituted a mere list of useful empirical rules-of-thumb for surveying land or constructing bridges or buildings, and there was no system to their knowledge of geometrical truths. By introducing order into the subject, the Greeks transformed it from a mere body of isolated bits of knowledge into a science.

System was introduced into geometry by the deduction of some of its propositions from others. The propositions of geometry were ordered by listing earlier those which could be used as premises in the demonstrations of those which were put later. This systematization of geometry was begun by Pythagoras and continued by his successors. It culminated in the *Elements* of Euclid (c.300 B.C.), in which all geometrical propositions were arranged in order, beginning with Axioms, Definitions, and Postulates, and continuing with Theorems deduced from the initial propositions. Geometry was cast by the Greeks into the form of a deductive system. Theirs was the first deductive system ever devised, and so great was the achievement that it has served as a model for all scientific thought down to the present time. Even today the most advanced sciences are those which most nearly approximate the form of a deductive system. These are the sciences which have achieved a relatively small number of very general principles from which all other laws and special cases may be derived. Parts of physics have actually been formulated as deductive systems, and similar attempts have been made, with somewhat less impressive results, in parts of biology and psychology also. Perhaps the boldest attempt in this direction was that of Spinoza, whose most important work, the *Ethics*, was written in 'geometrical' form. Starting with axioms and definitions, Spinoza attempted to deduce the rest of his metaphysical and ethical doctrines as theorems provable on the basis of those initial assumptions.

Euclid begins his geometry with definitions of some of the terms used in its development. Thus Definition 1 reads: 'A point is that which has no parts', and Definition 2 reads: 'A line is length without breadth.'* Euclid does not attempt to define *all* his terms, of course. The first two definitions define the terms 'point' and 'line' respectively. The words *used* in these definitions, such as 'parts', 'length', and 'breadth' are not themselves defined but are among the *undefined terms* of the system for Euclid. As more new terms are introduced their definitions make use of previously defined terms as well as the original undefined ones. Thus Definition 4: 'A straight line is . . . [a line] . . . which lies evenly between its extreme points', makes use not only of such undefined terms as 'evenly' and 'between', but also the previously defined terms 'point' and 'line'.

The use of *defined* terms is, from the point of view of logic, a matter of convenience only. Theoretically, every proposition which contains defined terms can be translated into one which contains only *undefined* ones by replacing each occurrence of a defined term by the sequence of undefined terms which was used to define it. For example, Postulate 1: 'Let it be granted that a straight line may be drawn from any one point to any other point', which contains the defined terms 'straight', 'line', and 'point', can be expressed without using defined terms as: 'Let it be granted that a length without breadth which lies evenly between its extreme parts which (themselves) have no parts may be drawn from any one thing which has no parts to any other thing which has no parts'. But the latter is extremely awkward. Although they are theoretically eliminable, in actual practice a considerable economy of space, time, and effort is effected by using relatively brief defined terms to replace lengthy sequences or combinations of undefined ones.

In setting up his deductive system of geometry, Euclid divided his unproved propositions into two groups, one called 'Axioms', the other called 'Postulates'. He gave, however, no reason for making this division, and there seems to be no very clear basis for

---

* These and the following are quoted from the Todhunter edition of *The Elements of Euclid*, No. 891 of Everyman's Library, London and New York.

distinguishing between them. Possibly he felt that some were more *general* than others, or psychologically more *obvious*. The contemporary practice is to draw no such distinction, but to regard all the unproved, initial propositions of a deductive system as having the same standing, and to refer to them all, indifferently, as 'axioms' or as 'postulates', without attaching any difference in meaning to those two terms.

Every deductive system, on pain of falling into circularity or a vicious regression, must contain some axioms (or postulates) which are assumed but not proved within the system. They need not be *precarious* assumptions, or *mere* assumptions. They may be very carefully and convincingly established—but they are *not proved within the system itself*. Any argument intended to establish the truth of the axioms is definitely *outside* the system, or *extra-systematic*.

The older conception of Euclidean geometry held not only that all of its theorems followed logically from its axioms, and were therefore just as *true* as the axioms, but also that the axioms were *self-evident*. It is in this tradition to regard any statement as 'axiomatic' only when its truth is beyond all doubt, being evident in itself and not requiring any proof. It should be clear from what has already been said, however, that we are *not* using the word 'axiom' in *that* sense. No claim is made that the axioms of any system are self-evidently true. Any proposition of a deductive system is an axiom of that system if it is assumed rather than proved in that system. This modern point of view has arisen largely as a consequence of the historical development of geometry and physics.

The self-evident truth of the Euclidean axioms (and postulates) was long believed. It was not believed quite whole-heartedly, however. Most of the axioms, such as Axiom 9: 'The whole is greater than its part', were not questioned; but while there was no doubt about the *truth* of Axiom 12 (the famous 'parallel Postulate'), there was considerable scepticism about its 'self-evidence'. Axiom 12 reads: 'If a straight line meet two straight lines, so as to make the two interior angles on the same

side of it taken together less than two right angles, these straight
lines, being continually produced, shall at length meet on that
side on which are the angles which are less than two right
angles'.* Proclus, a fifth century A.D. commentator, wrote of it:
This ought even to be struck out of the Postulates altogether; for
it is a theorem involving many difficulties . . . '.† That is,
although its *truth* was not questioned, its *self-evidence* was denied,
which was deemed sufficient reason to relegate it from its exalted
position as axiom to the less dignified status of a mere theorem.

The history of mathematics is filled with attempts to prove
the proposition in question as a theorem, either by deducing it
from the remaining axioms of Euclid, or from those axioms supplemented by some more nearly 'self-evident' additional assumption. The latter kind of attempt was pretty uniformly unsuccessful, because every additional or alternative assumption strong
enough to permit the deduction of the parallel postulate turned
out to be no more self-evident than Euclid's own hypothesis.
The first kind of attempt failed also; it was just not possible to
deduce the parallel postulate from the others. The most fruitful
attempt was that of the Italian mathematician Gerolamo
Saccheri (1667–1733), who *replaced* the parallel postulate by
alternative, contrary assumptions, and then sought to derive a
contradiction from them together with Euclid's other axioms.
Had he succeeded in doing so, he would have obtained a
reductio ad absurdum proof of the parallel postulate. He derived
many theorems, which he regarded as *absurd* because they were
so different from common sense or ordinary geometrical intuition. He believed himself to have succeeded thus in demonstrating the parallel postulate, and in 'vindicating Euclid'. But
his derived theorems, while 'absurd' in the sense of violating
ordinary geometrical intuitions, were *not* 'absurd' in the logical
or mathematical sense of being self-contradictory. Instead of

---

* Listed as Postulate 5 by Sir Thomas L. Heath, in *The Thirteen Books of
Euclid's Elements*, Cambridge University Press, 1926. For an interesting discussion of
the history of the parallel postulate, the reader is referred to pages 202 ff. of Volume
I of that work.
† *Ibid.*, p. 202

proving the parallel postulate, Saccheri (unknowingly) did something more important: he was the first to set up and develop a system of non-Euclidean geometry.

The parallel postulate is in fact *independent* of the other Euclidean postulates—although it was not *proved* to be so until the modern period. It is independent of the other postulates in the sense that neither it nor its denial is deducible from them. Alternative systems of 'geometry', non-Euclidean geometries, were subsequently developed, notably by Lobachevsky and Riemann. These were long regarded as ingenious fictions, mere mathematical playthings, in contrast with the Euclidean geometry which was 'true' of the real space about us. But subsequent physical and astronomical research along lines suggested by Einstein's theory of relativity has tended to show that—to the extent that the question is significant—'real' or physical space is more probably non-Euclidean than Euclidean. In any event, the truth or falsehood of its axioms is a purely *external* property of any deductive system. The truth of its propositions is an extra-systematic consideration. It is no doubt important to the extent that a deductive system is ordered *knowledge;* but when we concentrate our attention on the system as such, its *order* is its more important characteristic.

From the purely mathematical or logical point of view, a deductive system can be regarded as a vast and complex argument. Its premisses are the axioms, and its conclusion is the conjunction of all the theorems deduced. As with any other argument, the logical question does not concern the truth or falsehood of the premisses, but the validity of the inference. Granted the truth of the axioms, does the truth of the theorems necessarily follow? That is the question with which the logician and the mathematician are concerned. The answer is, of course, yes—*if* the demonstrations of the theorems are all valid arguments. Hence the most important aspect of any deductive system is the cogency with which its theorems are proved. In the rigorous development of deductive systems in abstraction from the extra-systematic explanation of their undefined terms, the question of truth or falsehood is obviously irrelevant.

III. FORMAL DEDUCTIVE SYSTEMS

There are serious errors in the system of geometry set forth by Euclid in his *Elements*. Indeed, a mistake occurs in his very first proof. The flaw in his proof, paradoxically enough, was the result of his knowing too much about his subject, so that he did not appeal to his explicitly stated axioms alone as premises, but depended also upon what might be called his geometrical intuition.* Where a chain of argument involves familiar notions, there is always the danger of assuming more than the explicitly stated premises warrant. That is particularly serious in the development of a deductive system, for any attempted systematization which appeals to new and unacknowledged assumptions in the derivations of its theorems thereby *fails* to achieve its aim. In a deductive system the theorems must be deduced *rigorously* from the stated postulates. If they are not, however true they may be, the result falls short of the goal of systematization.

Since lapses from rigor are most often occasioned by too great familiarity with the subject matter, mathematicians have found it helpful to minimize or eliminate such familiarity in the interest of achieving greater rigor. In the case of geometry, that end is accomplished by abstracting from the meanings of such geometrical words as 'point', 'line', and 'plane', and developing the theorems as purely formal consequences of the postulates. The familiar geometrical words, with all their associations and suggestions, are replaced by arbitrary symbols. Instead of deductive systems explicitly and avowedly concerned with geometrical entities, mathematicians today develop *formal* deductive systems whose primitive or undefined terms include arbitrary, uninterpreted symbols, usually letters of the Greek or Latin alphabets. Since the undefined terms of a *formal* deductive system include arbitrary symbols, its postulates are not propositions at all, but mere formulas, and so are the theorems.

---

* Euclid's proof and a brief discussion of his mistake can be found on pages 241–243 of Volume I of *The Thirteen Books of Euclid's Elements*, by Heath. An example of how the same type of error can lead to conclusions which are false or even self-contradictory can be found on pages 77–78 of *Mathematical Recreations and Essays*, by W. W. Rouse Ball, The Macmillan Co., 1940.

Deductive relationships can exist, of course, among mere formulas as well as among propositions. Thus the formula 'all *F*'s are *H*'s' is logically deducible from the formulas 'all *F*'s are *G*'s' and 'all *G*'s are *H*'s'. Since the postulates and theorems of a formal deductive system are formulas rather than propositions, the proofs of theorems can proceed unhampered by familiar associations and unconscious assumptions. Moreover, since the formulas are not propositions, the question of truth is strictly irrelevant and does not arise.

More than rigor is gained by the formal development of deductive systems. Since some of the symbols of a formal deductive system are arbitrary uninterpreted symbols, it may be possible to give them different, alternative interpretations. And since the theorems are formal consequences of the axioms, any interpretation of the arbitrary symbols which makes the axioms true will necessarily make the theorems true also. The additional advantage of generality is thus gained. An example may help to make this clear. Given some knowledge about astronomy, it may be desired to set up a deductive system for that subject. To avoid the errors into which familiarity with the subject matter may lead in deducing theorems from the axioms chosen, the system may be developed *formally*. Instead of taking, say, 'stars' and 'planets' among the undefined terms, one may take '*A*'s and '*B*'s. The axioms and theorems will contain these symbols, and when the system is developed, all its formulas may be interpreted by letting the symbol '*A*' designate stars and the symbol '*B*' designate planets. Now, if the axioms are *true* when so interpreted, the theorems must be true also, and the formal system with this interpretation will constitute a science or deductive system of astronomy. But it may be possible to find a *different* interpretation of the symbols '*A*' and '*B*' which also makes the axioms true (and hence the theorems also). The formulas of the system might be made into different but equally true statements by letting the symbol '*A*' designate atomic nuclei and the symbol '*B*' designate electrons. Could this be done (and at one stage in the recent history of atomic physics it seemed highly plausible), the original formal system with this second interpretation would constitute a science or deductive system of atomic physics. Hence developing a deductive system formally, *i.e.*, not interpreting its undefined terms until after its theorems have all been derived, not only helps achieve rigor in its development, but also achieves greater generality in virtue of the possibility of finding alternative interpretations for it. This kind of advantage is often realized in pure mathematics. For example, different interpretations of its arbitrary primitive symbols will transform the same formal deductive system into the theory of real numbers, on the one hand, or into the theory of points on a straight line, on the other. That fact provides the theoretical foundation for the branch of mathematics called *Analytical Geometry*.

As the term is being used here, a *formal deductive system* is simply a deductive system, consisting of axioms and theorems, some of whose undefined or primitive terms are arbitrary symbols whose interpretation is completely extra-systematic. In addition to those special undefined terms, and others defined by means of them, the formulas (axioms and theorems) of the system contain only such logical terms as 'if . . . then', 'and', 'or', 'not', 'all', 'are', and the like, and possibly (unless the system is intended for arithmetic itself) such arithmetical terms as 'sum' and 'product', and numerical symbols.

IV. PROPERTIES OF FORMAL DEDUCTIVE SYSTEMS

Usually, though not always, a formal deductive system is set up with some particular interpretation 'in mind'. That is, the investigator has some knowledge about a certain subject, and wishes to set up a system adequate for its expression. When the formal system has been constructed, the question naturally arises as to whether or not it is adequate to the formulation of all the propositions it is intended to express. If it is, it may be said to be 'expressively complete' *with respect to that subject matter*. We are here discussing what can be *said* in the system, *not* what can be proved. With respect to a given subject matter, a formal deductive system is 'expressively complete' when it is

× Cf Geach on Frege (Three Phil 133-4) & R a G 24

×× Church (p.108) makes being consistent in the sense of Post a special case of absolute consistency viz the case where a wff consisting of a propositional variable alone is not a theorem.

178   *Deductive Systems*

possible to assign meanings to its undefined terms in such a way that every proposition about that subject matter can be *expressed* as a formula of the system. Whether the *true* propositions can be *proved as theorems* or not is another question, which will be discussed below.

A system is said to be *inconsistent* if two formulas, one of which is the denial or contradictory of the other, can both be proved as theorems within it. A system is *consistent* if it contains no formula such that both the formula and its negation are provable as theorems within it. As was shown in Chapter Three, a contradiction logically entails any proposition whatever. Hence a derivative definition or criterion for consistency can be formulated as follows: Any system is consistent if it contains (that is, can express) a formula which is not provable as a theorem within it. This is known as the 'Post criterion for consistency', having been enunciated by the American mathematician and logician, E. L. Post. Consistency is of fundamental importance. An inconsistent deductive system is worthless, for all of its formulas are provable as theorems, including those which are explicit denials of others. When the undefined terms are assigned meanings, these contradictory formulas become contradictory propositions, which cannot possibly all be true. And since they cannot possibly be true, they cannot serve as a systematization of knowledge—for knowledge is expressed in true propositions only.

If one succeeds in deriving both a formula and its negation as theorems of a system, that proves the system inconsistent. But if one tries and does not succeed in deriving both a formula and its negation as theorems, that does *not* show the system to be consistent, for it may only reflect a lack of ingenuity at making proofs on the part of the investigator. How then can the consistency of a deductive system be established? One method of proving the consistency of a formal deductive system is to find an interpretation of it in which all its axioms and theorems are true propositions. Since its theorems are logical consequences of its axioms, any interpretation which makes its axioms true

Check Post Am. J. of Maths vol 43 (1921) p. 177

will make its theorems true also. Hence it is sufficient for the purpose of proving a system consistent to find an interpretation which makes all of its axioms true.

The axioms of a deductive system are said to be *independent* (or to exhibit *independence*) if no one of them can be derived as a theorem from the others. A deductive system which is not consistent is logically objectionable and utterly worthless, but there is no *logical* objection to a deductive system whose axioms are not independent. However, it is often felt that making more assumptions than necessary for the development of a system is extravagant and inelegant, and should be avoided. When a formula need not be assumed as an axiom, but can be proved as a theorem, it *ought* to be proved and not assumed, for the sake of 'economy'. A set of axioms which are not independent is said to be 'redundant'. A redundant set of axioms is aesthetically inelegant, but it is not logically 'bad'.

If one of the axioms of a system *can* be derived from the remaining ones, the set of axioms is thereby shown to be redundant. But if one tries and is not able to derive any of the axioms from the remaining ones, they are *not* thereby shown to be independent, for the failure to find a demonstration may be due only to the investigator's lack of ingenuity. To prove any particular axiom independent of the others, it suffices to find an interpretation which makes the axiom in question *false* and the remaining ones all *true*. Such an interpretation will prove that the axiom in question is not derivable as a theorem from the others, for if it were, it would be made true by any assignment of meanings which made the others true. If such an interpretation can be found for each axiom, this will prove the set of axioms to be independent.

The notion of *deductive completeness* is a very important one. The term 'completeness' is used in various senses. In the least precise sense of the term we can say that a deductive system is complete if all the *desired* formulas can be proved within it. We may have an extra-systematic criterion for the truth of propositions about the subject matter for which we set the deductive system up. If we have, then we may call that system complete when all of its formulas which become true propositions on the intended interpretation are provable formulas or theorems of the system. (In any sense of the term, an *inconsistent* system will be *complete*, but in view of the worthlessness of inconsistent systems, we shall confine our attention to *consistent* systems in the following discussion.)

There is another conception of *completeness* which can be explained as follows. Any formal deductive system will have a certain collection of special undefined or primitive terms. Since any terms definable within the system are theoretically eliminable, being replaceable in any formula in which they occur by the sequence of undefined terms by means of which they were defined, we shall ignore defined terms for the present. All formulas which contain only these special undefined terms (and logical terms) are expressible within the system. We may speak of the totality of undefined terms as the *base* of the system, and the formulas expressible in the system are all formulas constructed *on that base*. In general, the totality of formulas constructed on the base of a given system can be divided into three groups: first, all formulas which are provable as theorems within the system; second, all formulas whose negations are provable within the system; and third, all formulas such that neither they nor their negations are provable within the system. For *consistent* systems the first and second groups are *distinct*, that is, have no formulas in common. Any system whose third group is empty, containing no formulas at all, is said to be *deductively complete*. An alternative way of phrasing this sense of completeness is to say that every formula of the system is such that either it or its negation is provable as a theorem.

A

Another definition of 'completeness', <u>roughly equivalent</u> [x] to <u>the preceding one</u>, is that a deductive system is complete when every formula constructed on its base is either a theorem or else its addition as an axiom would make the system inconsistent.

?

B

An example of an incomplete deductive system would be Euclidean geometry minus the parallel postulate. For the parallel

[x] An odd remark, since the propositional calculus (e.g.) is NOT complete in sense A but is complete in sense B

postulate is itself a formula constructible on the base of the Euclidean system, yet it is not derivable as a theorem from the remaining ones, and the system remains consistent when the parallel postulate is added. It is clear that although completeness is an important property, an incomplete deductive system may be very interesting and valuable. For by investigating the incomplete system of Euclidean geometry without the parallel postulate, we can discover those properties possessed by space independently of the question of whether it is Euclidean or non-Euclidean. Perhaps a more cautious and less misleading formulation of the same point is to say that by investigating the incomplete system we can discover the *common features* of Euclidean and non-Euclidean geometries. Yet for many purposes, a complete system is to be preferred.

V. LOGISTIC SYSTEMS

Most important of all properties for a deductive system to possess is that of rigor. A system has rigor when no formula is asserted to be a theorem unless it is logically entailed by the axioms. It is for the sake of rigor that arbitrary rather than familiar symbols are taken as undefined or primitive terms, and the system developed *formally*. Listing clearly all the undefined terms, and explicitly stating all the axioms used as premisses for the theorems, will help to specify precisely which formulas are to be esteemed as theorems and which are not. With the increased emphasis on rigor that characterizes the modern period, critical mathematicians have seen that this is not enough. To achieve rigor, more is required.

A system is rigorous only when its theorems are proved logically, or derived logically from its axioms. It has now been realized that however clearly its axioms are stated, a formal system will lack rigor unless the notion of *logical proof* or *logical derivation* is specified precisely also. All deductive systems of the sort that have been mentioned, even formal deductive systems which contain logical terms in addition to their own special uninterpreted symbols, depend upon 'ordinary logic' for their

✗ If this means 'a system with axioms or postulates', then this is not necessary. Cf p. 185 mid.

182   *Deductive Systems*

development. They *assume* logic, in the sense that their theorems are supposed to follow *logically* from their axioms. But they do not specify what this 'logic' is. Hence all earlier deductive systems, for geometry, or physics, or psychology, or the like, contain concealed assumptions which are not explicitly stated. These hidden assumptions are the rules or principles of logic to which one appeals in constructing proofs or derivations of theorems. Hence all such deductive systems fall short of complete rigor, for not all of their presuppositions are acknowledged. Therefore their developments are not entirely rigorous, but more or less loose. The question naturally arises: How can this looseness be eliminated, and greater rigor be achieved? The answer is obvious enough. A deductive system will be developed more rigorously when it is specified not only what axioms are assumed as premises in deriving the theorems, but also what principles of inference are to be used in the derivations. The axioms must be supplemented by a list of valid argument forms, or principles of valid inference.

The demand for rigor and for system does not stop even here, however. For the sake of rigor, in addition to its own special axioms, a deductive system must specify explicitly what forms of inference are to be accepted as valid. But it would be unsystematic—and probably impossible—simply to list or catalog *all* required rules of logic or valid modes of inference. A deductive system of logic itself <u>must</u> be set up. Such a deductive system will have deduction itself as its subject matter. A system of this type, often referred to as a *logistic system*, must differ from the ordinary, less formal varieties in several important respects. Since its subject matter is deduction itself, the logical terms 'if . . . then', 'and', 'or', 'not', and so on, cannot occur in it with their ordinary meanings simply assumed. In their stead must be uninterpreted symbols. And the logical principles or rules of inference that *it* assumes must be few in number and explicitly stated.

A second fundamental difference between logistic systems and other formal deductive systems is that in the latter the notion of a 'well formed' or significant formula need not be specified, whereas it is absolutely required in a logistic system. In an ordinary (non-formal) deductive system, it will be obvious which sequences of its words are significant propositions of English (or of whatever natural language in which the system is expressed). In a formal but non-logistical deductive system, the sequences of its symbols are easily divided into those which 'make sense' and those which do not, for they will contain such ordinary logical words as 'if . . . then', 'and', 'or', or 'not', by whose disposition in the sequence it can be recognized as significant or otherwise. An example will make this clear. In a formal deductive system which contains '*A*', '*B*', and '*C*' as uninterpreted primitive symbols, the sequence of symbols 'If any *A* is a *B*, then it is a *C*' is clearly a complete and 'significant' formula which may or may not be provable as a theorem. But the sequence of symbols 'If any *A* is a *B*' is obviously *incomplete*, while the sequence 'And or or *A B* not not if' is clearly nonsense. These are recognized as 'complete' or 'well formed', as 'incomplete' or 'ill formed' by the presence in them of *some* symbols whose meanings are understood. In a logistic system, however, *Church* *all* symbols are uninterpreted, so there are no familiar words *p. 48 ff* within its formulas (or sequences of symbols) to indicate which are 'well formed' and which are not. Where the symbols '*A*', '*B*', '$\sim$', and '$\supset$' are uninterpreted, there must be some method of distinguishing between a well formed formula like '$A \supset \sim B$' and one like '$AB \supset \sim$', which is not well formed. By our knowledge of the normal interpretations of these symbols we can recognize the difference and classify them correctly, but for the *rigorous* development of our system we must be able to do this in abstraction from the (intended) meanings of the symbols involved.

The matter may be expressed in the following terms. As ordinarily conceived, a non-formal deductive system (interpreted, like Euclidean geometry) is an arrangement or organization of propositions about some specified subject matter. Consisting of propositions, it is a *language* in which the subject matter may be discussed. Understanding the language, we can divide all sequences of its words into those which are meaningful statements and those which are meaningless or nonsensical. This division is effected in terms of meanings and is thus done *non-formally*. In a logistic system the situation is different, for prior to the extra-systematic assignment of meanings or interpretation, *all* sequences of symbols are without meaning. Yet we want, prior to and independent of its interpretation, a comparable division of all of its formulas into two groups. When meanings are assigned to the primitive symbols of a logistic system, some of its formulas will become statements or propositions, while others will not. We may informally characterize a formula which on the intended interpretation becomes a significant statement as a 'well formed formula' (customarily abbreviated '*wff*'). Any formulas which on the intended interpretation do *not* become significant statements are *not* well formed formulas. In a logistic system there must be a *purely formal* criterion for distinguishing well formed formulas from all others. To characterize the criterion as 'purely formal' is to say that it is *syntactical* rather than *semantical*, pertaining to the formal characteristics and arrangements of the symbols in abstraction from their meanings. Thus a logistic system must contain only uninterpreted symbols, and must provide a criterion for dividing sequences of these symbols into two groups, the first of which will contain all well formed formulas, the second containing all others. Of the well formed formulas, some will be designated as Axioms (or Postulates) of the logistic system.

It is also desired to divide all well formed formulas which are not axioms into two groups, those which are theorems and those which are not. The former are those which are derivable from the axioms or postulates, *within the system*. Although uninterpreted, the well formed formulas of a logistic system constitute a 'language' in which derivations or proofs can be set down. Some well formed formulas will be assumed as postulates, and other well formed formulas will be derived from them as theorems. It might be proposed to define 'theorem' as any *wff* which is the conclusion of a valid argument whose premisses include only axioms of the system. This proposed definition of 'theorem' will be acceptable only if the notion of a *valid* argument within the logistic system can be defined formally. Since all *wffs* of the system are uninterpreted, the ordinary notion of validity cannot be used to characterize arguments within the system, for the usual notion of validity is *semantical*, an argument being regarded as valid if and only if the *truth* of its premisses entails the *truth* of its conclusion. Consequently, a purely formal or syntactical *criterion of validity* must be provided for arguments expressed *within the system*. 'Valid' arguments within the system may have not merely postulates or already established theorems as premisses and new theorems as conclusions, but may have as premisses *any wffs*, even those which are neither postulates nor theorems, and as conclusions *wffs* which are not theorems. Of course it is desired that any argument within the system which is syntactically 'valid' will become, on the intended or 'normal' interpretation, a semantically valid argument.

Any logistic system, then, will contain the following elements: (1) a list of primitive symbols which, together with any symbols defined in terms of them, are the only symbols which occur within the system; (2) a purely formal or syntactical criterion for dividing sequences of these symbols into formulas which are well formed (*wffs*) and those which are not; (3) a list of *wffs* assumed as postulates or axioms; (4) a purely formal or syntactical criterion for dividing sequences of well formed formulas into 'valid' and 'invalid' arguments; and (5), derivatively from (3) and (4), a purely formal criterion for distinguishing between theorems and non-theorems of the system.

Different logistic systems may be constructed as systematic theories of different parts of logic. The simplest logistic systems are those which formalize the logic of truth-functional compound statements. These systems are called *propositional calculi* or, less frequently, *sentential calculi*. One particular propositional calculus will be presented and discussed in the following chapter.

CHAPTER SEVEN

A Propositional
Calculus

I. OBJECT LANGUAGE AND METALANGUAGE

The logistic system to be constructed in this chapter will correspond to that part of the English language which contains truth-
functional compound statements. Our logistic system will be a
language, although for the sake of rigor in developing its theorems,
it will be regarded as uninterpreted. We shall *talk about* this
language. It will be the *object* of our discussion, and is therefore
called the 'object language'. Since it is uninterpreted, its symbols
and formulas have no meaning, and we cannot *use* it until it is
given an interpretation—which will be postponed until after its
development. We must therefore use a *different* language in order
to talk about our object language. The language *used* in talking
about a language is called a 'metalanguage'. In any investigation of language, there is an object language which is the *object*
of investigation, and there is a metalanguage which is *used* by
the investigators in talking about the object language.

An object language may be discussed from alternative points

186

of view. Its relationship to its users may be investigated, as in a study of dialect changes in English usage and pronunciation in various parts of the country. Or the meaning or interpretation of a language may be investigated, as in compiling a dictionary, and in this latter inquiry a *semantical* metalanguage must be used. Finally the formal structure of a language may be investigated, as in a grammar textbook, or in describing the development of theorems in an uninterpreted logistic system, for which a *syntactical* metalanguage or *Syntax Language* is used. In discussing the object language to be constructed here, we shall sometimes need to use a semantical metalanguage, and sometimes a syntactical one. In discussing its adequacy for expressing all truth-functional compound statements, and its consistency and completeness, we shall have to use a semantical metalanguage, for these topics involve its intended interpretation. But in describing the purely formal criteria for its well formed formulas and the syntactical 'validity' of its arguments, only a Syntax Language need be used, for no references to meanings are made in these connections.

The language to be used as metalanguage in discussing our logistic system will be ordinary English, plus elementary arithmetic, with the addition of some special symbolic devices which will be introduced and explained as they are needed. It is assumed, of course, that the reader understands the metalanguage, for the entire discussion occurs within it. Only this one metalanguage will be used, and it will function in some parts of our inquiry as a semantical metalanguage, in other parts as a Syntax Language.

It should be emphasized that 'object language' and 'metalanguage' are *relative terms*. Any language, no matter how simple or how complex, is an object language when it is being talked *about*. And any language (which must be an interpreted, or meaningful one, of course) is a metalanguage when it is being *used* to discuss an object language. Since *our* object language is uninterpreted, we cannot use it as a metalanguage, but in another context, where the object language is an interpreted or meaningful language, one and the same language can function as both object language and metalanguage. Thus in our first chapter the English language was being discussed (and hence was the object language), and the discussion was carried on in English (which was therefore the metalanguage also). A sufficiently rich or complex language can succeed in formulating the whole of its own syntax, and a good deal of its own semantics. But no language, on pain of contradiction, can express the whole of its own semantics; certainly not the truth conditions for all of its own statements. That limitation can easily be shown.

That no language can express exhaustively its own semantics is shown by the following version of the 'Paradox of the Liar'.* Consider the following English statement:

The sentence printed on page 188, line 13 of this book is not true.

Let us abbreviate the preceding statement by the letter 'S'. Now just as it is obvious that 'Snow is white' is true if and only if *snow is white*, so it is equally obvious that

'S' is true if and only if *the sentence printed on page* 188, *line* 13 *of this book is not true.*

But counting the lines and looking at the page number verifies that 'S' is identical with *the sentence printed on page* 188, *line* 13 *of this book*. Hence

'S' is true if and only if 'S' *is not true.*

which is an explicit contradiction. That such a contradictory result can appear as a consequence of apparently innocent assumptions ought not to be regarded as a joke or a sophistry. It is a serious matter which reveals that the assumptions were not so innocent as they appeared. The source of the trouble is generally agreed to lie in the attempt to formulate the truth conditions for the statements of a language within that language itself. At least, if that is avoided by distinguishing sharply between object language and metalanguage, and not trying to make an object language serve as its own semantical metalanguage, the contradiction does not arise. An alternative method of avoid-

* Due to J. Lukasiewicz.

ing such contradictions is discussed in Appendix B at the end of this book. *pp* 337-8

II. PRIMITIVE SYMBOLS AND WELL FORMED FORMULAS

We now proceed to set up our logistic system. There will be two kinds of primitive symbols within our propositional calculus: 'propositional' symbols and 'operator' symbols. We shall use just four of the latter kind, these being

$$\cdot, \sim, (,).$$

We shall want infinitely many propositional symbols, for which we use the first four capital letters of the alphabet (in boldface type), with and without subscripts:

$$
\begin{array}{cccccc}
A & A_1 & A_2 & A_3 & \cdot\ \cdot\ \cdot\ \cdot \\
B & B_1 & B_2 & B_3 & \cdot\ \cdot\ \cdot\ \cdot \\
C & C_1 & C_2 & C_3 & \cdot\ \cdot\ \cdot\ \cdot \\
D & D_1 & D_2 & D_3 & \cdot\ \cdot\ \cdot\ \cdot
\end{array}
$$

These are the only symbols that our propositional calculus will contain, and in proving theorems and deriving conclusions from premisses *within the system* they are to be regarded as being completely uninterpreted. They may be thought of, prior to the assignment of meanings, as being repeatable and recognizable *marks* rather than 'symbols' at all—though it will be convenient to refer to them as 'symbols'.

Of course we are guided in setting up our logistic system by the interpretation we intend eventually to give it. This intended interpretation controls our choice of primitive symbols, and also governs our syntactical definition of 'well formed formula'. The set of *all* formulas or finite sequences of primitive symbols of our system will include such sequences as the following:

$$
\begin{array}{l}
B_1 \\
(A)\cdot(A) \\
\sim(D) \sim(\sim) \\
\sim((A_1)\cdot(C_3)) \\
B_2B_3A_7 \sim (\ )(\ )\cdot(\ ) \\
)))((
\end{array}
$$

$$\cdot\ \cdot\ \cdot\ \cdot\ \cdot\ \cdot\ \cdot\ \cdot\ \cdot\ \cdot\ \cdot\ \cdot$$

Only some of these are to count as well formed formulas, however. Our definition of 'well formed formula' will be stated, of course, in our Syntax Language. It will be convenient to introduce some special symbols into our Syntax Language, as an aid in discussing the logistic system clearly and economically. While the first four capital letters of the alphabet, with and without subscripts, printed in boldface type, are symbols in our object language, those same letters printed in light face italic type will be symbols in our metalanguage. Their meanings in the latter will follow the convention that a light face italic letter which is an element of our metalanguage will denote or mean that same letter printed in boldface, which is an element of our object language. In addition we introduce the capital letters '*P*', '*Q*', '*R*', and '*S*', with and without subscripts, and shall refer to them as 'propositional variables'. Whereas the propositional symbols *in* our propositional calculus are uninterpreted and have *no meaning*, the propositional variables '*P*', '*Q*', '*R*', '*S*', '*P$_1$*', . . . *in* our Syntax Language *are interpreted* and *do have meaning*. Every propositional variable of our Syntax Language, until further notice, denotes any sequence of symbols or any formula of our object language—subject to the following restriction. In any sentence or sequence of sentences of our Syntax Language, two distinct propositional variables, say '*P*' and '*Q*', may denote either two distinct formulas of our object language, say '**B$_1$**' and '$\sim((A_1)\cdot(C_3))$', or one and the same formula of our object language. But in any one context, while a propositional variable may denote *any* formula of the object language, it must continue to denote that same formula wherever it occurs in that context. Thus the propositional variables '*P*', '*Q*', '*R*', '*S*', . . . of our metalanguage may have substituted for them *any name* in the metalanguage of *any formula* of the object language. We also introduce the symbols '·', '$\sim$', '(', and ')' into the Syntax Language, and explain their meanings as follows. Where any propositional variable, say '*P*', of our Syntax Language denotes in some context a particular formula of our object language, say '*A*', then the symbol '$\sim(P)$' of our Syntax Language will in that context denote the formula '$\sim(A)$' of our object language. And where any propositional variables, say 'P' and 'Q', denote in some context two formulas of our object language, say 'A' and '$\sim(B_2)$' respectively, then the symbol '$(P){\cdot}(Q)$' of our Syntax Language will in that context denote the formula '$(A){\cdot}(\sim(B_2))$' of our object language.

We cannot simply give a list of all well formed formulas of our object language, since there are infinitely many of them. It is necessary to give an inductive or *recursive* definition of 'well formed formula', which can be stated as follows, using the symbolic conventions explained in the preceding paragraph.

Recursive Definition of Well Formed Formula

(a) Any propositional symbol is a *wff*.
(b) If any formula P is a *wff*, then $\sim(P)$ is a *wff*.
(c) If any formulas P and Q are both *wffs*, then $(P){\cdot}(Q)$ is a *wff*.
  (No formula of the object language shall be considered to be a *wff* unless its being so follows from these rules.)

This definition permits infinitely many well formed formulas, but it provides an *effective* criterion for recognizing them. No matter how long a (finite) sequence of symbols of the object language may be, our recursive definition permits us to decide in a finite number of steps whether or not it is a well formed formula. Let us take a relatively simple example to illustrate this:

$$\sim((A){\cdot}(\sim(B)))$$

The question to be decided is whether the foregoing is a *wff* or not. By part (b) of the recursive definition, it is a *wff* provided that $(A){\cdot}(\sim(B))$ is a *wff*. The latter is a *wff* by part (c) of the definition, provided that both A and $\sim(B)$ are *wffs*. The first of these is a *wff* by part (a) of the definition, and by part (b), the second is a *wff* provided that B is a *wff*, which it is by part (a) of the definition. Thus the formula in question *is* a *wff*. From here on we shall use the propositional variables 'P', 'Q', 'R', 'S', and so on, of our Syntax Language to denote only *well formed* formulas of our object language.

EXERCISES

Using the Recursive Definition for Well Formed Formulas, show which of the following are *wffs* of our object language:

1. $(\sim(A_1))\cdot(A_1)$
2. $\sim(\sim((B_1)\cdot(\sim(C_3))))$
3. $\sim(\sim((B_2)\cdot(\sim(D_4))))$
4. $\sim((\sim(D_3))\cdot(\sim(D_4)))$
5. $(\sim((\sim)\cdot(C_2)))\cdot(\sim((B_3)\cdot(B_3)))$
6. $\sim(((A)\cdot(B))\cdot(\sim(B)))$
7. $\sim((A)\cdot(B))\cdot(\sim((A)\cdot(A)))$
8. $(\sim(\sim(A)\cdot(B)\cdot(C))))\cdot(((\sim(A))\cdot(B))\cdot(\sim(C)))$
9. $\sim((\sim((A)\cdot(\sim(B))))\cdot(\sim((\sim((B)\cdot(C)))\cdot(\sim(\sim((C)\cdot(A))))))$
10. $\sim(((\sim((A)\cdot(\sim(B))))\cdot(A))\cdot(\sim(\sim((A)\cdot(\sim(B))))))$

On the intended or 'normal' interpretation of our logistic system the propositional symbols are to be the symbolic translations of English statements which contain no other statements as (truth-functional) component parts. Where *P* is the symbolic translation of any English statement whatever, $\sim(P)$ will be the symbolic translation of its denial or contradictory. And where *P* and *Q* are the symbolic translations of any two English statements whatever, $(P)\cdot(Q)$ will be the symbolic translation of their conjunction. The question now arises: Is our logistic system adequate, when normally interpreted, to express all truth-functionally compound statements? A system which is adequate to express all truth functions will be said to be '*functionally complete*'. *

We may begin our discussion by showing that our logistic system (which we may name 'R.S.', since it is Rosser's System†) is adequate to the formulation of some familiar truth functions. Denials and conjunctions have already been mentioned, but there are also disjunctions, conditionals, and equivalences to be considered. Where two English statements translate into *P* and

---

* This is a special case of the 'expressive completeness' mentioned in Chapter Six.

† The author is greatly indebted to Professor J. Barkley Rosser of Cornell University for permission to include the following material. The calculi presented here and in Chapter Nine are early versions of logistic systems which appear in revised form in Professor Rosser's *Symbolic Logic for Mathematicians*.

Q, their *weak* disjunction (which is true if either or both are true) is expressible in R.S. as $\sim((\sim(P))\cdot(\sim(Q)))$. Since it is a very common function we introduce an abbreviation for it into our Syntax Language, defining '$P \vee Q$' to denote identically the same *wffs* of the object language R.S. as are denoted by '$\sim((\sim(P))\cdot(\sim(Q)))$'.* Where two English statements translate into P and Q, their *strong* disjunction (which is true if either one is true but not both) is expressible in R.S. as $(\sim((P)\cdot(Q)))\cdot(\sim((\sim(P))\cdot(\sim(Q))))$.

The symbolic translation of an English conditional statement (asserting a material implication, of course) whose antecedent has the symbolic translation P and whose consequent has the symbolic translation Q will be $\sim((P)\cdot(\sim(Q)))$. This notion too is quite common, so we introduce the symbol '$\supset$' into our Syntax Language, using '$P \supset Q$' to denote identically the same *wffs* of R.S. as are denoted by '$\sim((P)\cdot(\sim(Q)))$'. Where two English statements have the symbolic translations P and Q, the statement that they are (materially) equivalent, that is, that they have the same truth values, or that each (materially) implies the other has the symbolic translation $(P \supset Q)\cdot(Q \supset R)$, which is identically the same *wff* of R.S. as $(\sim((P)\cdot(\sim(Q))))\cdot(\sim((Q)\cdot(\sim(P))))$. Since material equivalence too is a frequently used notion, we introduce the symbol '$\equiv$' into our Syntax Language, defining '$P \equiv Q$' as an abbreviation for '$(P \supset Q)\cdot(Q \supset P)$'.

At this point two notational conventions will be adopted for our metalanguage. The first is dispensing with the dot (for conjunction), so that $(P)(Q)$ is identically the same formula of the

---

* Since '$P \vee Q$' is an abbreviation of '$\sim((\sim(P))\cdot(\sim(Q)))$', it is proper to say that $P \vee Q$ is, or is identical with, $\sim((\sim(P))\cdot(\sim(Q)))$, but *not* that $P \vee Q$ is an abbreviation of the latter, for there are no abbreviations in the object language itself. (The symbol '$\vee$' is a significant symbol of the Syntax Language, but *does not even occur* in the object language, although we could introduce it if we wished.) A parallel may help make this clear. Since 'U.S.S.R.' is an abbreviation of 'Union of Soviet Socialist Republics', the U.S.S.R. is identical with the Union of Soviet Socialist Republics, but is not an abbreviation of anything at all, being a large nation covering one-sixth of the globe. Since 'U.S.S.R.' denotes a large nation, the U.S.S.R. *is* a large nation, and has no *meaning* in any literal or semantical sense. Similarly, since '$P \vee Q$' denotes a *wff* of R.S., $P \vee Q$ *is a wff* of R.S., and since R.S. is uninterpreted, its *wffs* are meaningless, so that $P \vee Q$ in particular is meaningless.

object language as $(P)\cdot(Q)$. The other notational convention is to replace parentheses by brackets or braces wherever such replacement is conducive to easier reading.

Even using brackets and braces, too many punctuation marks make reading difficult, so two further conventions which permit a minimum use of punctuation will be adopted. The first convention is to assign the following *order of precedence* to the symbols

$$\equiv \supset v \cdot \sim$$

of our Syntax Language. Of these, each has *greater precedence* or greater scope than any listed to its right. What is intended here can be explained by the following examples. The otherwise ambiguous expression '$\sim PQ$' denotes $(\sim(P))\cdot(Q)$ rather than $\sim((P)\cdot(Q))$, because the connective '·' (which we have agreed to represent by juxtaposition) has greater scope than the operator '$\sim$'; the scope of the connective '·' extends over that of the '$\sim$' symbol. The otherwise ambiguous expression 'P v QR' denotes P v $(Q\cdot R)$ rather than $(P$ v $Q)\cdot R$, because the connective 'v' has, by our convention, precedence over the connective '·', and its scope extends over that of the latter. The otherwise ambiguous expression '$P \supset Q$ v RS' denotes $P \supset [Q$ v $(R\cdot S)]$, because '$\supset$' has precedence over both 'v' and '·', and 'v' has precedence over '·'. And the otherwise ambiguous expression '$P \supset Q \equiv \sim Q \supset \sim P$' denotes $[P \supset Q] \equiv [(\sim Q) \supset (\sim P)]$, because '$\equiv$' has precedence over '$\supset$' and '$\sim$', and '$\supset$' has precedence over '$\sim$'. Our second convention is that of *association to the left*, which means that where the convention of *order of precedence* does not suffice to remove the ambiguity of an expression, its parts should be grouped by parentheses *to the left*. That is, when an expression contains two (or more) occurrences of the same connective, and their relative scopes within the expression are not otherwise indicated, the occurrence to the right shall be understood to have the wider (or widest) scope. This too is best explained by means of an example or two. Since all of its connectives have *equal* order of precedence, the ambiguity of the expression '$P \supset Q \supset P \supset P$' cannot be resolved by our first convention. According to our second convention, however, we interpret it as denoting $[(P \supset Q) \supset P] \supset P$. Part, but not all of the ambiguity of the expression '$P \equiv Q \equiv PQ \lor {\sim}P \, {\sim}Q$' is resolved by the convention regarding order of precedence. Once this convention has been appealed to, we know that it denotes *either* $[P \equiv Q] \equiv [(P{\cdot}Q) \lor ({\sim}P{\cdot}{\sim}Q)]$ *or* $P \equiv \{Q \equiv [(P{\cdot}Q) \lor ({\sim}P{\cdot}{\sim}Q)]\}$. We decide that the former is meant by consulting the second convention, which instructs us to associate to the left.

EXERCISES

Write the following expressions of the Syntax Language in unabbreviated form, complete with parentheses:

1. $P \supset P \lor Q$
2. $PQ \supset P$
3. $(P \supset PQ) \supset (P \supset Q)$
4. ${\sim}{\sim}P \supset P$
5. $Q \lor {\sim}Q$
6. $P \supset Q \equiv {\sim}Q \supset {\sim}P$
7. $(P \supset Q){\cdot}(Q \supset R) \supset (P \supset R)$

The preceding remarks indicate the way in which some truth functions are expressible in R.S. But to prove that R.S. is *functionally complete*, that is, adequate to express *all* possible truth functions of any number of simple statements, more is required. We must have a method in our semantical metalanguage of expressing all possible truth functions of simple statements, and then must prove that all of these, or all their substitution instances, can be expressed in our object language R.S. also, in its normal or standard interpretation. Such a method of expressing all possible truth functions is provided by *truth tables*, which were introduced in Chapter Two. The method and notation of truth tables is therefore imported into our semantical metalanguage, and will be used freely in discussing the various semantical properties possessed by R.S. on its standard interpretation.

Truth functions may have one, two, or any number of arguments (in the mathematical sense in which an 'argument' is an independent variable). Thus $f(P)$ is a truth function of P if and only if its truth or falsehood is completely determined by the truth or falsehood of P. Similarly, $f(P,Q)$ is a truth function of P and Q if and only if its truth value is determined solely by the truth values of P and Q.

There are exactly four different truth functions of a single argument, and these may be expressed by the following truth tables:

P	$f_1(P)$		P	$f_2(P)$		P	$f_3(P)$		P	$f_4(P)$
T	T		T	T		T	F		T	F
F	T		F	F		F	T		F	F

The functions $f_1(P)$, $f_2(P)$, $f_3(P)$, and $f_4(P)$ are completely defined by these four truth tables. They are the *only* truth functions of a single argument, and are called 'monadic' or 'singulary' functions.* That they can be expressed in R.S. in its intended or normal interpretation is easily seen. First we note that the intended or normal interpretations of $\sim(P)$ and $(P)\cdot(Q)$ are given by the truth tables

P	$\sim(P)$
T	F
F	T

and

P	Q	$(P)\cdot(Q)$
T	T	T
T	F	F
F	T	F
F	F	F

That R.S. is adequate to express $f_1(P)$, $f_2(P)$, $f_3(P)$, and $f_4(P)$ is proved by actually formulating them in R.S. The function $f_2(P)$ is true when P is true and false when P is false, and is therefore expressible in R.S. as P itself. The function $f_3(P)$ is false when P is true and true when P is false, and is therefore expressible in R.S. as $\sim(P)$. The function $f_4(P)$ is false no matter which truth value P assumes, and is therefore expressible in

---

* Here we are using 'truth function' in the strict and proper sense of a non-linguistic correlation between or among truth values.

R.S. as $(P) \cdot (\sim P)$. The function $f_1(P)$ is true in every case and can therefore be expressed in R.S. as the denial of $f_4(P)$, that is, as $\sim[(P) \cdot (\sim P)]$. We have thereby shown that all singulary truth functions are expressible in R.S.

There are, of course, more truth functions of two arguments than of a single argument. These are defined by the following truth tables:

P	Q	$f_1(P,Q)$	P	Q	$f_2(P,Q)$	P	Q	$f_3(P,Q)$	P	Q	$f_4(P,Q)$
T	T	T	T	T	T	T	T	T	T	T	T
T	F	T	T	F	T	T	F	T	T	F	T
F	T	T	F	T	T	F	T	F	F	T	F
F	F	T	F	F	F	F	F	T	F	F	F

P	Q	$f_5(P,Q)$	P	Q	$f_6(P,Q)$	P	Q	$f_7(P,Q)$	P	Q	$f_8(P,Q)$
T	T	T	T	T	T	T	T	T	T	T	T
T	F	F	T	F	F	T	F	F	T	F	F
F	T	T	F	T	T	F	T	F	F	T	F
F	F	T	F	F	F	F	F	T	F	F	F

P	Q	$f_9(P,Q)$	P	Q	$f_{10}(P,Q)$	P	Q	$f_{11}(P,Q)$	P	Q	$f_{12}(P,Q)$
T	T	F	T	T	F	T	T	F	T	T	F
T	F	T	T	F	T	T	F	T	T	F	T
F	T	T	F	T	T	F	T	F	F	T	F
F	F	T	F	F	F	F	F	T	F	F	F

P	Q	$f_{13}(P,Q)$	P	Q	$f_{14}(P,Q)$	P	Q	$f_{15}(P,Q)$	P	Q	$f_{16}(P,Q)$
T	T	F	T	T	F	T	T	F	T	T	F
T	F	F	T	F	F	T	F	F	T	F	F
F	T	T	F	T	T	F	T	F	F	T	F
F	F	T	F	F	F	F	F	T	F	F	F

These are *all* the truth functions of two arguments, and are called 'dyadic' or 'binary' functions. That they are all expressible in R.S. is easily shown by actually expressing them by means of the $\sim$ and $\cdot$ symbols: for example, $f_8(P,Q)$ is expressible as $P \cdot Q$, while $f_9(P,Q)$ is expressible as $\sim(P \cdot Q)$.

EXERCISES

1. Express each of the dyadic truth functions $f_1(P,Q)$, $f_2(P,Q)$, . . . , $f_{16}(P,Q)$ as *wffs* of R.S.
2. There are 256 triadic (or ternary) truth functions: $f_1(P,Q,R)$, $f_2(P,Q,R)$, . . . , $f_{256}(P,Q,R)$, each of which is completely determined (or defined) by a different eight-row truth table. Take any ten of them and express each as a *wff* of R.S.

Just as there are three different kinds of truth-functional state-ment forms, there are three different kinds of truth functions. *Tautologous* truth functions are functions whose values are true regardless of the truth or falsehood of their arguments. *Con-tradictory* truth functions are functions whose values are false regardless of the truth or falsehood of their arguments. Finally, *contingent* truth functions are true for some values of their argu-ments and false for others. All of these functions, or more pre-cisely, all substitution instances of the truth-functionally com-pound statement forms which express them, can be formulated in a functionally complete logistic system.

To prove the functional completeness of R.S. it is necessary to show that *any* truth function of *any* number of arguments is ex-pressible by means of $\sim$ and $\cdot$. Any truth function of n arguments is expressible by means of a truth table having n initial columns and 2^n rows. Thus any truth function $f(P_1, P_2, P_3, \ldots, P_n)$ is completely specified by writing a 'T' or an 'F' in every one of the 2^n places in the last column of the following truth table:

	P_1	P_2	$P_3 \ldots \ldots P_n$	$f(P_1, P_2, P_3, \ldots P_n)$
Row 1:	T	T	T . . . . . T	
Row 2:	T	T	T . . . . . F	
. . . .		. . . .		
Row 2^n-1:	F	F	F . . . . . T	
Row 2^n:	F	F	F . . . . . F	

The truth function $f(P_1, P_2, P_3, \ldots, P_n)$ must be either tautologous, contradictory, or contingent. In any case it is expressible in R.S., which will now be proved.

CASE 1. $f(P_1, P_2, P_3, \ldots, P_n)$ is contradictory, false in every case, having an **F** under it in every row of its defin-ing truth table. This function can be expressed as $P_1 \cdot \sim P_1 \cdot P_2 \cdot P_3 \cdot \ldots \cdot P_n$, which is a *wff* of R.S.; it is obviously false in every case, and it expresses a function of n arguments. Hence any contradictory truth function of n arguments is expressible in R.S.

[handwritten in left margin: Proof improved considerably in 2nd ed (takes just over 1 page instead of 2½ or less)]

CASE 2. $f(P_1, P_2, P_3, \ldots, P_n)$ is tautologous, being true in every case, that is, having a **T** in every row of its defining truth table. This function can be expressed as $\sim(P_1 \cdot \sim P_1 \cdot P_2 \cdot P_3 \cdot \ldots \cdot P_n)$, which is a *wff* of R.S.; it is obviously true in every case, and it expresses a function of n arguments. Hence any tautologous truth function of n arguments is expressible in R.S.

CASE 3. $f(P_1, P_2, P_3, \ldots, P_n)$ is contingent, being true in some cases and false in others, that is, having **T**'s in some rows and **F**'s in other rows of its defining truth table. Each row of the defining truth table represents a distinct set of truth values for the arguments of the function $f(P_1, P_2, P_3, \ldots, P_n)$: row 1, that in which all the arguments have the value true; row 2, that in which all but the last one take the value true; . . . ; and row 2^n, that in which all of its arguments have the value false. We may divide the present case in which $f(P_1, P_2, P_3, \ldots, P_n)$ is contingent into three sub-cases, according to the number of **T**'s and **F**'s in its truth table.

Sub-case A. In the truth table defining the contingent function $f(P_1, P_2, P_3, \ldots, P_n)$ there is exactly one row containing a **T**, all the rest having **F**'s. If it is the first row, the function is expressed in R.S. by the *wff* $P_1 \cdot P_2 \cdot \ldots \cdot P_{n-1} \cdot P_n$, which has a **T** in the first row of its truth table, and **F**'s in all other rows. If it is the second row, the function is expressed in R.S. by the *wff* $P_1 \cdot P_2 \cdot \ldots \cdot P_{n-1} \cdot \sim P_n$. The 2^n distinct truth functions, each of which has a **T** in its ith row and **F**'s in all others, are represented in R.S. by the 2^n *wffs*

$$P_1 \cdot P_2 \cdot \ldots \cdot P_{n-1} \cdot P_n$$
$$P_1 \cdot P_2 \cdot \ldots \cdot P_{n-1} \cdot \sim P_n$$
$$\ldots \ldots \ldots \ldots \ldots$$
$$\sim P_1 \cdot \sim P_2 \cdot \ldots \cdot \sim P_{n-1} \cdot P_n$$
$$\sim P_1 \cdot \sim P_2 \cdot \ldots \cdot \sim P_{n-1} \cdot \sim P_n$$

Sub-case B. In the truth table defining the contingent function $f(P_1, P_2, \ldots, P_n)$ there is exactly one row containing an **F**, all the rest having **T**'s. If it is the first row, the function is expressed in R.S. by the *wff* $\sim(P_1 \cdot P_2 \cdot \ldots \cdot P_{n-1} \cdot P_n)$, which has an **F** in the first row of its truth table and **T**'s in all other rows. If it is the second row, the function is expressed in R.S. by the *wff* $\sim(P_1 \cdot P_2 \cdot \ldots \cdot P_{n-1} \cdot \sim P_n)$. The 2^n distinct truth functions, each of which has an **F** in its ith row and **T**'s in all others, are represented in R.S. by the 2^n *wffs*

$$S_1: \sim(P_1 \cdot P_2 \cdot \ldots \cdot P_{n-1} \cdot P_n)$$
$$S_2: \sim(P_1 \cdot P_2 \cdot \ldots \cdot P_{n-1} \cdot \sim P_n)$$
$$\cdots \cdots \cdots \cdots \cdots \cdots$$
$$S_{2^n-1}: \sim(\sim P_1 \cdot \sim P_2 \cdot \ldots \cdot \sim P_{n-1} \cdot P_n)$$
$$S_{2^n}: \sim(\sim P_1 \cdot \sim P_2 \cdot \ldots \cdot \sim P_{n-1} \cdot \sim P_n)$$

Sub-case C. In the truth table defining the contingent function $f(P_1, P_2, \ldots, P_n)$ there are two or more rows containing **F**'s. Any such truth function is expressible in R.S. as a conjunction of two or more of the *wffs* listed in Sub-case B. Suppose the truth function in question has **F**'s in the first two rows, **T**'s in all others. Then it is expressed in R.S. as the conjunction of the two *wffs*, each of which has an **F** in just one of those rows of its truth table: $S_1 \cdot S_2$, that is, $\sim(P_1 \cdot P_2 \cdot \ldots \cdot P_{n-1} \cdot P_n) \cdot \sim(P_1 \cdot P_2 \cdot \ldots \cdot P_{n-1} \cdot \sim P_n)$. In the general case, the truth function $f(P_1, P_2, \ldots, P_n)$ is defined by a truth table exactly k of whose rows contain **F**'s, say the rows $i_1, i_2, \ldots, i_k (0 < k < 2^n)$. Here the truth function is expressed in the R.S. as the conjunction of the k *wffs* listed in Sub-case B, each of which expresses a truth function defined by a truth table with an **F** in only one row, that one being row i_1, row $i_2, \ldots$, or row i_k. The truth function is expressed in R.S. as $S_{i_1} \cdot S_{i_2} \cdot \ldots \cdot S_{i_k}$.

The foregoing sub-cases show how any contingent truth function of any number of arguments is expressible in R.S. Since any truth function is either tautologous, contradictory, or contingent, the preceding three cases exhaust the possibilities, and we have proved that any truth function of any number of arguments is expressible in R.S. This is not a theorem *of* or *in* R.S., but a theorem *about* it, established in our semantical metalanguage. We may therefore list it as

METATHEOREM I. R.S. is functionally complete.

We could have chosen to present a logistic system other than R.S. In addition to parentheses and the propositional symbols *P, Q, R, S* and so on, we could have selected as primitive operators any of the following pairs of symbols: '$\sim$' and '$\mathbf{v}$'; '$\sim$' and '$\supset$'; '$\cdot$' and '$\mathbf{v}$'; '$\cdot$' and '$\supset$'; or '$\mathbf{v}$' and '$\supset$', instead of '$\sim$' and '$\cdot$'. It is instructive to inquire whether or not any of those alternative choices of primitives would have made the resulting system functionally complete (on the normal interpretation of the symbols '$\sim$', '$\cdot$', '$\mathbf{v}$', '$\supset$', which we shall denote by '$\sim$', '$\cdot$', '$\mathbf{v}$', '$\supset$'). Before addressing ourselves to these problems it will be well to explain briefly the two kinds of mathematical induction we shall use in establishing results about (not *in*) R.S.

We shall use the term 'weak induction' to refer to the more commonly used type of mathematical induction. The schema for weak induction is

$f(1)$
for any arbitrary m, if $f(m)$ then $f(m + 1)$
_____
therefore $f(m)$ for every m.

It is frequently used in proving theorems in elementary algebra. For example, one proves that the sum of the first n odd integers is equal to n^2 by first proving the two premisses of the above schema and then drawing the general conclusion indicated. The first premiss, which we shall call the 'α-case', is here established as the trivial equation $1 = 1^2$. Then the second premiss, which we shall call the 'β-case', is established by assuming $f(m)$ true for some arbitrary integer m and from this assumption deriving the conclusion that $f(m + 1)$ is true. In this particular proof, the β-case assumption is

$$1 + 3 + 5 + \ldots + (2m - 1) = m^2.$$

We derive the desired conclusion by adding $(2m + 1)$ to both sides of the equation and performing an elementary regrouping and factoring of terms:

$$1 + 3 + 5 + \ldots + (2m - 1) + (2m + 1) = m^2 + (2m + 1)$$
$$1 + 3 + 5 + \ldots + (2m - 1) + [2(m + 1) - 1] = (m + 1)^2$$

which shows that for an arbitrary m, if the sum of the first m odd integers is m^2, then the sum of the first $(m + 1)$ odd integers is $(m + 1)^2$. We thus have established the β-case; from it and the α-case, by *weak induction*, we draw the desired conclusion that for every m, the sum of the first m odd integers is equal to m^2. Weak induction may be thought of as summarizing an unending sequence of arguments of the form *modus ponens:*

$$\frac{\begin{array}{l} f(1) \\ \text{if } f(1) \text{ then } f(1 + 1); \end{array}}{\therefore f(2)} \qquad \frac{\begin{array}{l} f(2) \\ \text{if } f(2) \text{ then } f(2 + 1); \end{array}}{\therefore f(3)} \ldots ;$$

$$\frac{\begin{array}{l} f(m) \\ \text{if } f(m) \text{ then } f(m + 1); \end{array}}{\therefore f(m + 1)} \ldots$$

The term 'strong induction' will be used to refer to the somewhat less frequently encountered type of mathematical induction whose schema is

$$\frac{\begin{array}{l} f(1) \\ \text{for any arbitrary } m, \text{ if } f(k) \text{ for every } k < m, \text{ then } f(m) \end{array}}{\text{therefore } f(m) \text{ for every } m}$$

Strong induction may also be thought of as summarizing an unending sequence of arguments of the form *modus ponens:*

$$\frac{\begin{array}{l} f(1) \\ \text{if } f(1) \text{ then } f(2); \end{array}}{\therefore f(2)} \qquad \frac{\begin{array}{l} f(1) \text{ and } f(2) \\ \text{if } f(1) \text{ and } f(2) \text{ then } f(3); \end{array}}{\therefore f(3)} \ldots ;$$

$$\frac{\begin{array}{l} f(1) \text{ and } f(2) \text{ and } \ldots \text{ and } f(m - 1) \\ \text{if } f(1) \text{ and } \ldots \text{ and } f(m - 1) \text{ then } f(m); \end{array}}{\therefore f(m)} \ldots$$

To illustrate the use of strong induction, we shall prove that a symbolic logic based on the propositional symbols P, Q, R, S, and the operators $\cdot$ and v is *not* functionally complete. We do so by proving that no well formed formula* of the system based on $\cdot$, v, and P, Q, R, S, . . . can express a truth function which has the value *true* when all of its arguments have the value *false*. In our proof we use strong induction on the number of symbols in the well formed formula $g(P, Q, R, \ldots)$, ignoring parentheses, and counting each occurrence of P, Q, R, . . . , $\cdot$, and v as one symbol.

α-case: In case $g(P, Q, R, \ldots)$ contains just one symbol, to be well formed it must be either P alone, or Q alone, or R alone, or . . . . Where the arguments P, Q, R, . . . all have the value *false*, $g(P, Q, R, \ldots)$ will also have the value *false*, since it is one of them. Hence any well formed formula of the present system which contains exactly one symbol cannot have the value *true* when its arguments all have the value *false*.

β-case: Here we assume that any well formed formula $g(P, Q, R, \ldots)$ containing less than m symbols cannot have the value *true* when all of its arguments have the value *false*, and we shall prove, under this assumption, that any well formed formula containing exactly m symbols cannot have the value *true* when all its arguments have the value *false*. Consider any formula $g(P, Q, R, \ldots)$ which contains exactly m symbols (where $m > 1$). To be well formed, $g(P, Q, R, \ldots)$ must be either

$$g_1(P, Q, R, \ldots) \cdot g_2(P, Q, R, \ldots)$$

or

$$g_1(P, Q, R, \ldots) \text{ v } g_2(P, Q, R, \ldots)$$

where $g_1(P, Q, R, \ldots)$ and $g_2(P, Q, R, \ldots)$ are well formed formulas containing less than m symbols. By the β-case assumption, when P, Q, R, . . . are all *false*, both

---

* We assume a recursive definition analogous to that stated on page 191.

$g_1(P, Q, R, \ldots)$ and $g_2(P, Q, R, \ldots)$ will have the value *false* also. Now given any two propositions which are *false*, both their disjunction and their conjunction are *false;* hence in this case $g(P, Q, R, \ldots)$ has the value *false* also. This establishes the β-case.

Having established both the α and β cases, by strong induction we infer that no well formed formula of the system based on $\cdot$, v, P, Q, R, . . . can express a truth function which has the value *true* when all of its arguments have the value *false*. Hence the system is *not* functionally complete.

EXERCISES

Prove the functional completeness or incompleteness of the logistic systems based on the propositional symbols P, Q, R, S, . . . , parentheses, and the operators:

1. v and $\sim$ 3. $\supset$ and $\sim$
2. $\supset$ and $\cdot$ 4. $\supset$ and v

5. $\sim$ and $+$, where $+$ is the symbol for exclusive disjunction, which may be defined by the truth table:

P	Q	$P + Q$
T	T	F
T	F	T
F	T	T
F	F	F

6. $\supset$ and $+$ 8. $+$ and $\equiv$
7. v and $+$ 9. $+$ and $\cdot$

10. $\equiv$ and $\sim$

III. AXIOMS AND DEMONSTRATIONS

The rules for our system and the proofs of the theorems within it will be much simplified if we assume infinitely many well formed formulas as axioms or postulates. Of course we cannot actually write out an infinite list of axioms *within our object language*, but we can use our Syntax Language to specify exactly which *wffs* of R.S. are axioms and which are not. There can be no objection to having an infinite number of axioms if there is an *effective* process for determining whether or not any *wff* is an axiom. The infinite list of axioms of R.S. may be written as

Axiom 1. $P \supset (P \cdot P)$
Axiom 2. $(P \cdot Q) \supset P$
Axiom 3. $(P \supset Q) \supset [\sim(Q \cdot R) \supset \sim(R \cdot P)]$

Each of these syntactical formulas (formulas within our Syntax Language) represents or designates an infinite list of *wffs* of R.S. Thus Axiom 1 designates all the following:

$$\sim((A) \cdot (\sim((A) \cdot (A))))$$
$$\sim((B) \cdot (\sim((B) \cdot (B))))$$
$$\sim((C) \cdot (\sim((C) \cdot (C))))$$
$$\sim((D) \cdot (\sim((D) \cdot (D))))$$
$$\sim((A_1) \cdot (\sim((A_1) \cdot (A_1))))$$

. . . .
$$\sim((\sim(A)) \cdot (\sim((\sim(A)) \cdot (\sim(A)))))$$
$$\sim((\sim(B)) \cdot (\sim((\sim(B)) \cdot (\sim(B)))))$$
. . . .
$$\sim(((A) \cdot (D)) \cdot (\sim(((A) \cdot (D)) \cdot ((A) \cdot (D)))))$$
$$\sim(((A_3) \cdot (B_7)) \cdot (\sim(((A_3) \cdot (B_7)) \cdot ((A_3) \cdot (B_7)))))$$
. . . .
. . . .

and infinitely many more *wffs* of R.S. It designates, in fact, every *wff* of R.S. which is of the indicated pattern; and it is effectively decidable of any given finite sequence of symbols of R.S. whether it is of this pattern or not. Three patterns are set forth, and every *wff* of R.S. which exemplifies any one of these patterns is assumed as an axiom.

That these axioms are reasonable assumptions is evidenced by the fact that on the normal interpretation of the symbols $\sim$ and $\cdot$ they are all tautologies.

Our logistic system is intended, upon interpretation, to be adequate to the formulation of arguments. Arguments, as we know, consist of premisses and conclusions, all of which are expressed in statements. Corresponding to such arguments we have in our logistic system sequences of well formed formulas of which the last formula is the 'conclusion'. It is desired to set up a criterion which will enable us to distinguish formally between sequences of *wffs* within R.S. which become valid arguments when interpreted normally and sequences which do not.

In Chapter Three a valid argument was characterized as one for which a formal proof or demonstration could be given. A formal proof of an argument's validity was described as a sequence of statements each of which was either a premiss or followed from preceding statements by an elementary valid argument, and whose last statement was the conclusion of the argument being proved valid. Thus the question of the validity of *any* argument was 'reduced' to the question of the validity of certain elementary argument forms or rules of inference. Something like that will be proposed for R.S., but it is not desirable to make such a wholesale set of assumptions about valid elementary inferences as was made in Chapter Three, where nineteen elementary valid argument forms or rules of inference were postulated. However, *some* mode of inference must be assumed for our logistic system or there will be no inference at all legitimized within it. One rule of inference will suffice for the validation of all arguments and (hence) for the proof of all theorems within R.S. We assume *modus ponens*, and state it (in our Syntax Language, of course) as

RULE 1. If P and $P \supset Q$ then Q.

Examples of arguments *in* R.S. which are legitimized as *valid* by the assumption of this rule of inference are

$$\sim((A)\cdot(\sim(B))) \qquad\qquad \sim(((A_1)\cdot(A_2))\cdot(\sim(\sim(C))))$$
$$A \qquad\qquad\text{and}\qquad\qquad (A_1)\cdot(A_2)$$
$$B \qquad\qquad\qquad\qquad \sim(C)$$

The assumption of *modus ponens* as Rule 1 (abbreviated as R 1) of our logistic system, *by itself*, permits only a special variety of

Shouldn't there be something about allowing as a step the "move" from a formula ~~in the sequence~~ to itself expressed by different symbols? Cf. S'_3 on p.211, S'_4 on 213, and the moves annotated 'df.' on pp 214 and ff. See also fn. on p. 193 above.

Axioms and Demonstrations   207

arguments having two premises to be regarded as valid. But R.S. is adequate to the expression of *all* formally valid arguments of the sort which are certifiable by means of truth tables, including extended ones containing any number of premises. So it is desirable to introduce a method for validating extended arguments in R.S. by showing how their conclusions follow from their premises by *repeated* applications of R 1. Here our treatment is roughly analogous to that for extended arguments presented in Chapter Three, although with some important differences. We define a *demonstration* of the validity of an argument having as premises the formulas $P_1, P_2, \ldots, P_n$ and as conclusion the formula Q, to be a sequence of well formed formulas $S_1, S_2, \ldots, S_k$ such that: every S_i is either one of the premises $P_1, P_2, \ldots, P_n$, or is one of the axioms of R.S., or follows from two preceding S's by R 1; and such that S_k is Q. As before, an argument is to be regarded as valid if and only if there exists a *demonstration* of its validity. A special notation is introduced (into the Syntax Language) to represent this idea. We shall introduce and use the special symbol '$\vdash$' (which may be read 'yields') so that

$$P_1, P_2, \ldots, P_n \vdash Q$$

asserts that there is a demonstration of the validity of the argument having $P_1, P_2, \ldots, P_n$ as premises and Q as conclusion. For example, all of the infinitely many arguments denoted by

$$P \supset Q$$
$$\sim(QR)$$
$$\sim(RP)$$

are valid because $P \supset Q, \sim(QR) \vdash \sim(RP)$, the demonstration consisting of the following sequence of S's:

$$S_1: (P \supset Q) \supset [\sim(QR) \supset \sim(RP)]$$
$$S_2: P \supset Q$$
$$S_3: \sim(QR) \supset \sim(RP)$$
$$S_4: \sim(QR)$$
$$S_5: \sim(RP)$$

in which S_1 is Axiom 3, S_2 is the first premise of the argument, S_3 follows from S_1 and S_2 by R 1, S_4 is the second premise, and S_5 follows from S_3 and S_4 by R 1, while S_5 is the conclusion. Any such sequence of S's will be called a *demonstration* of $P_1, P_2, \ldots , P_n \vdash Q$, and each S_i will be called a *step* of the demonstration. Where a demonstration is given for the validity of all arguments in R.S. of a particular form, as in the example cited, any particular argument of that form may be regarded as having been validated by that demonstration, and the general form may be regarded as a *derived rule of inference*.

The definition of *demonstration* given in the preceding paragraphs should have made it clear that the axioms of R.S. function as 'understood' premises of every argument formulated within the system. Where those axioms are the *only* premises of an argument, then (if it is valid) the conclusion is a *theorem* of the system. That a given formula Q is a theorem is expressed by writing '$\vdash Q$'. The notation '$\vdash Q$' is defined more strictly as the assertion that there exists a demonstration of Q, which is a sequence of well formed formulas $S_1, S_2, \ldots , S_k$ such that: every S_i is either an axiom of R.S. or follows from two preceding S's by R 1, and S_k is Q.

It should be noted that *demonstration*, either of a theorem or of the validity of an argument, is an *effective* notion. Given any sequence of S's, however long, it can be decided quite mechanically, in a finite number of operations, whether or not it is a *demonstration*. It can be decided effectively of any S whether or not it is an axiom (and whether or not it is one of the premises, if an argument is involved). And if some S, say S_j, is neither an axiom nor a premise, then since only a finite number of S's precede S_j in the sequence, a finite number of inspections will reveal whether or not two of the preceding steps are S_i and $S_i \supset S_j$, for only if these occur earlier in the sequences of S's will S_j follow from two preceding steps by R 1.

With this definition of *theorem*, the three axioms and the one rule of R.S. can be regarded as a sort of symbolic machine for generating well formed formulas. Each axiom itself generates an infinite number of *wffs*, and by repeated applications of R 1 to them infinitely many more *wffs* are produced as theorems. Two questions quite naturally arise at this point. First, is the system consistent? And second, are all the theorems (on the normal interpretation of the primitive symbols) tautologies?

A logistic system which is a propositional calculus (such as R.S.) will be called *analytic* if and only if all of its theorems become tautologies on their normal interpretations. R.S. is analytic, on this definition, provided that $\vdash P$ implies that P is tautologous. We shall now prove that R.S. has this property.

METATHEOREM II. R.S. is analytic (that is, if $\vdash P$ then P is a tautology).

Proof: We use strong induction on the number of uses of R 1 in the demonstration that $\vdash P$.

α-case: Suppose P results from a single use of R 1. Then R 1 must be applied to the axioms. The axioms are all tautologies, as is easily verified by actually constructing truth tables for them. Hence P results from applying R 1 to S and $S \supset P$, where S and $S \supset P$ are both tautologies. Clearly P must be a tautology in this case, for if it were not, there would be an **F** in at least one row of its truth table, say row j. But since S is a tautology, it has all **T**'s in its truth table, including, of course, a **T** in row j. Hence in the jth row, S would have a **T** and P an **F**, so that $S \supset P$ would have an **F**—contrary to the fact that it is tautologous and has only **T**'s in its truth table. Hence the Metatheorem is true for m uses of R 1 where $m = 1$.

β-case: Here we assume the Metatheorem to be true for any number $k < m$ uses of R 1. Consider the status of any P whose demonstration involves m uses of R 1. The formula P is either an axiom (in which case it is clearly a tautology) or must result from earlier steps S and $S \supset P$ by the mth use of R 1. The earlier step S

is either an axiom (in which case it is clearly a tautology) or is obtained by $k < m$ uses of R 1, and hence is a tautology by the assumption of the β-case. Similarly, the earlier step $S \supset P$ must also be a tautology. Now, since S and $S \supset P$ are tautologies, P must be one also, by the argument of the α-case.

From α and β, by strong induction we conclude that if $\vdash P$ (by *any* number of applications of R 1) then P is a tautology, which means that R.S. is analytic.

Having established the analyticity of R.S., its consistency follows immediately, and may be regarded as a mere corollary of Metatheorem II. In proving it, we use the Post criterion for consistency, according to which a deductive system is consistent if it contains a formula which is not provable in it as a theorem.

COROLLARY: R.S. is consistent.

Proof: The formula $P \cdot \sim P$ is a *wff* of R.S. but is not a tautology, therefore by Metatheorem II it is not a theorem of R.S. Hence R.S. contains a formula which is not provable as a theorem, so that R.S. is consistent by the Post criterion.

We define the 'deductive completeness' of a logistic system for the propositional calculus as the converse of the property of analyticity. An *analytic* system is one such that all of its theorems are tautologies; a propositional calculus will be called *deductively complete* in case all tautologies are provable as theorems within it. The deductive completeness of R.S. is more difficult to establish than the first two Metatheorems, and requires that we first develop some theorems of the system. The proof, then, will be postponed to Section V, while we turn our attention to the development of R.S. itself in the next section.

IV. DEVELOPMENT OF THE CALCULUS

In the actual development of derived rules and theorems of our object language we regard all of its symbols as completely uninterpreted, being motivated by a desire for rigor in its development. *When interpreted normally*, the formulas $\sim RP$ and $P\sim R$ are logically equivalent. But as *wffs* of R.S., *in its development*, they cannot be so regarded, and the *wff* $\sim RP \equiv P\sim R$ cannot be accepted as a theorem until it has been formally derived from the axioms of the system.

It will be convenient to begin with the demonstration of a derived rule of inference for R.S., which will validate infinitely many arguments in it. We state it as

DR 1. $P \supset Q, Q \supset R \vdash \sim(\sim RP)$.

Its demonstration requires a sequence of just five well formed formulas, the third of which we shall write twice, once in unabbreviated and once in abbreviated form:

$$S_1: (P \supset Q) \supset [\sim(Q\sim R) \supset \sim(\sim RP)]$$
$$S_2: P \supset Q$$
$$S_3: \sim(Q\sim R) \supset \sim(\sim RP)$$
$$S_3': (Q \supset R) \supset \sim(\sim RP)$$
$$S_4: Q \supset R$$
$$S_5: \sim(\sim RP)$$

That this sequence of S's is a demonstration is easily verified. The first step, S_1, is Axiom 3 of R.S. It is true that there is an apparent difference between S_1 and our syntactical formulation of Axiom 3:

$$S_1: (P \supset Q) \supset [\sim(Q\sim R) \supset \sim(\sim RP)]$$
$$\text{Ax. 3}: (P \supset Q) \supset [\sim(QR) \supset \sim(RP)]$$

since S_1 contains $\sim R$ wherever Axiom 3 contains R. The point is that we are here *talking about* well formed formulas *of* R.S. Both S_1 and Axiom 3 denote infinitely many *wffs* of R.S., and every *wff* of R.S. which is denoted by S_1 *is also denoted by Axiom* 3. We can put the matter another way. Our first derived rule (DR 1) validates infinitely many arguments formulable within R.S., for example:

(1) $\sim((A)\cdot(\sim(B)))$
       $\sim((B)\cdot(\sim(C)))$
   $\therefore \sim((\sim(C))\cdot(A))$

and

(2) $\sim((B)\cdot(\sim(C)))$
       $\sim((C)\cdot(\sim(D)))$
   $\therefore \sim((\sim(D))\cdot(B))$

as well as

(3) $\sim((A)\cdot(\sim(A)))$
       $\sim((A)\cdot(\sim(A)))$
∴ $\sim((\sim(A))\cdot(A))$

and

(4) $\sim(((A)\cdot(B))\cdot(\sim(\sim(C))))$
       $\sim((\sim(C))\cdot(\sim((D_1)\cdot(D_2))))$
∴ $\sim((\sim((D_1)\cdot(D_2)))\cdot((A)\cdot(B)))$

The sequence of S's in the given demonstration denotes infinitely many sequences of *wffs* of R.S., one for each of the different arguments whose validity is being demonstrated. The first step in the demonstration *in* R.S. for the first of the four examples given is the *wff* of R.S. denoted by S_1 when 'P', 'Q', and 'R' are taken to denote 'A', 'B', and 'C', respectively. But this is identically the same *wff* of R.S. denoted by our syntactical formulation of Axiom 3 when 'P', 'Q', and 'R' in it are taken to denote 'A', 'B', and '$\sim C$', respectively. Hence the first *wff* of the demonstration sequence is one of the infinitely many axioms of R.S. supplied by Axiom 3. The situation is the same with respect to the demonstration of the validity of every other argument *in* R.S. which is validated by DR 1.

It is readily seen that the other steps of the sequence conform to the requirements laid down in our definition of demonstration. The two premisses of the argument occur as S_2 and S_4, while S_3 follows from S_1 and S_2 by R 1, and S_5 follows from $S_3(S_3')$ and S_4 by R 1. It is helpful to write in the 'justification' for each step in the demonstration: 'Ax. 3' to the right of S_1, 'premiss' to the right of S_2, and so on. These labels are not part of the demonstration, but are helpful to both the writer and the reader.

At this point the question naturally arises as to whether derived rules of inference can be appealed to in deriving theorems from the axioms of the system. It is most conveniently discussed in connection with an actual example. Let us take as our first theorem of R.S. the formula

Th. 1. $\vdash \sim(\sim PP)$.

This formula follows directly from Axioms 1 and 2 by means of our first derived rule, DR 1. A sequence of formulas which has already been demonstrated to be a valid argument (by our demonstration of DR 1) is

$$S_1\colon P \supset PP \qquad\qquad \text{Ax. 1}$$
$$S_2\colon PP \supset P \qquad\qquad \text{Ax. 2}$$
$$S_3\colon \sim(\sim PP) \qquad\qquad \text{DR 1}$$

That S_2 is really Ax. 2 should be clear from the previous discussion. Every *wff* of R.S. denoted by our syntactical formulation of Ax. 2, '$PQ \supset P$', is an axiom, and every *wff* of R.S. denoted by the syntactical expression '$PP \supset P$' is (also) denoted by '$PQ \supset P$', so S_2 denotes infinitely many axioms of R.S. And that S_3 really follows by DR 1 from S_1 and S_2 is seen by observing that DR 1 validates any argument of the form

$$P \supset Q$$
$$Q \supset R$$
$$\sim(\sim RP)$$

no matter what *wffs* of R.S. the formulas P, Q, and R may be. Thus DR 1 includes the case in which 'P' and 'R' denote identically the same formulas, while 'Q' and 'PP' also denote the same *wffs*.

Although the sequence S_1, S_2, S_3 may be regarded as a *'proof'* of Theorem 1, it does not constitute a *demonstration*, for by definition a *demonstration* involves the use of R 1 exclusively. But if we have a 'proof' in which a derived rule is used, as DR 1 is used in the given sequence, the *demonstration of the derived rule* can be *inserted* into the sequence to change it into a demonstration proper. Thus in place of S_3 in the given sequence, the demonstration of DR 1 can be substituted, so that we have

$$S_1\colon P \supset PP \qquad\qquad\qquad\qquad\qquad\qquad \text{Ax. 1}$$
$$S_2\colon PP \supset P \qquad\qquad\qquad\qquad\qquad\qquad \text{Ax. 2}$$
$$S_3\colon (P \supset PP) \supset [\sim(PP\sim P) \supset \sim(\sim PP)] \qquad \text{Ax. 3}$$
$$S_4\colon \sim(PP\sim P) \supset \sim(\sim PP) \qquad\qquad\qquad \text{R 1}$$
$$S_4'\colon (PP \supset P) \supset \sim(\sim PP)$$
$$S_5\colon \sim(\sim PP) \qquad\qquad\qquad\qquad\qquad\qquad \text{R 1}$$

This sequence *is* a demonstration; since S_1, S_2, and S_3 are axioms, S_4 follows by R 1 from S_1 and S_3, and S_5 follows by R 1 from S_2 and S_4. Moreover, the present demonstration results from the earlier 'proof' by certain changes which are indicated in the

[margin note:] Copi's private use of the words 'proof' and 'demonstration'

* [we haven't been told anything about the notion of following by definition. It doesn't occur in the definition of demonstration on p. 207.

214   A Propositional Calculus

proof itself. The original sequence, which we call a 'proof', is not a demonstration, but a *description* of a demonstration that can be given. A proof may be regarded as a prescription or recipe for the construction of a demonstration.

The situation is analogous to that which occurs when later theorems of a deductive system are derived not directly from the axioms but from earlier, already established theorems. Here again an example will aid the discussion. We shall take as our second theorem the formula

TH. 2. $\vdash \sim\sim P \supset P$

which <u>follows</u> directly from Th. 1 by <u>definition</u>. Its proof may be written as:

$$S_1: \sim(\sim\sim P\sim P) \qquad \text{Th. 1}$$
$$S_2: \sim\sim P \supset P \qquad \qquad \text{df.}$$

This sequence is clearly *not* a *demonstration*, but it *is* a *proof*, for it tells us exactly how to construct a demonstration of Th. 2. In place of S_1 we need only write out the demonstration of Th. 1— or rather the demonstration of that version of it which is relevant to the desired conclusion, Th. 2. The general statement of Th. 1 is

$$\vdash \sim(\sim PP)$$

which denotes every *wff* which is of this form, no matter which *wff* the syntactical variable 'P' denotes. Every *wff* denoted by '$\sim(\sim\sim P\sim P)$' is of that form, and is therefore included among the infinitely many provable formulas of R.S. which are labelled Theorem 1. The demonstration described by the indicated proof of Th. 2 can be written as follows:

$$S_1: \sim P \supset \sim P\sim P \qquad\qquad\qquad\qquad\qquad\qquad \text{Ax. 1}$$
$$S_2: \sim P\sim P \supset \sim P \qquad\qquad\qquad\qquad\qquad\qquad \text{Ax. 2}$$
$$S_3: (\sim P \supset \sim P\sim P) \supset [\sim(\sim P\sim P\sim\sim P) \supset \sim(\sim\sim P\sim P)] \ \text{Ax. 3}$$
$$S_4: \sim(\sim P\sim P\sim\sim P) \supset \sim(\sim\sim P\sim P) \qquad\qquad \text{R 1}$$
$$S_4': (\sim P\sim P \supset \sim P) \supset \sim(\sim\sim P\sim P) \qquad\qquad\quad \text{df.}$$
$$S_5: \sim(\sim\sim P\sim P) \qquad\qquad\qquad\qquad\qquad\qquad \text{R 1}$$
$$S_5': \sim\sim P \supset P \qquad\qquad\qquad\qquad\qquad\qquad\quad \text{df.}$$

In general, proofs are shorter and therefore easier to write out than are demonstrations. Since any proof can be made into a demonstration by replacing any step which is a previously established theorem by the demonstration of that theorem, and any step which results from the use of a derived rule by the demonstration of that rule, proofs can be regarded as shorthand notations for demonstrations. However, proofs are *different*, and should not be *confused* with demonstrations.

Before proceeding with the development of additional theorems and derived rules for R.S., it should be remarked that Th. 2 can be equally well expressed as $\vdash \sim P \text{ v } P$, which is a version of the principle of the Excluded Middle. For by our definition of the symbol 'v', '$\sim P \text{ v } P$' is an abbreviation of '$\sim(\sim\sim P \sim P)$', which has (Th. 2) '$\sim\sim P \supset P$' as an alternative abbreviation. In the latter form it constitutes part of the principle of Double Negation.

Some additional theorems of R.S., together with their proofs (*not* demonstrations) are these:

Th. 3. $\vdash \sim(QR) \supset (R \supset \sim Q)$

Proof: $\vdash \sim\sim Q \supset Q$	Th. 2
$\vdash (\sim\sim Q \supset Q) \supset [\sim(QR) \supset \sim(R\sim\sim Q)]$	Ax. 3
$\vdash \sim(QR) \supset \sim(R\sim\sim Q)$	R 1
$\vdash \sim(QR) \supset (R \supset \sim Q)$	df.

Th. 4. $\vdash R \supset \sim\sim R$

Proof: $\vdash \sim(\sim RR) \supset (R \supset \sim\sim R)$	Th. 3
$\vdash \sim(\sim RR)$	Th. 1
$\vdash R \supset \sim\sim R$	R 1

Th. 5. $\vdash (Q \supset P) \supset (\sim P \supset \sim Q)$

| *Proof*: $\vdash \sim(Q\sim P) \supset (\sim P \supset \sim Q)$ | Th. 3 |
| $\vdash (Q \supset P) \supset (\sim P \supset \sim Q)$ | df. |

It will be observed that Th. 5 is part of the principle of Transposition, and that Theorems 2 and 4 are parts of the principle of Double Negation. But although both $P \supset \sim\sim P$ and $\sim\sim P \supset P$ have been proved to be theorems, *the* principle of Double Negation, $P \equiv \sim\sim P$, which abbreviates $(P \supset \sim\sim P)\cdot(\sim\sim P \supset P)$, is not (yet) proved to be a theorem. It would follow from Theorems 2 and 4 by the principle of Conjunction, P, $Q \vdash P \cdot Q$, but the latter has not (yet) been established as a valid principle of inference or derived rule for R.S. These remarks are intended to throw additional light on the meaning of the '$\vdash$' symbol. Writing '$\vdash P$' asserts that there is a sequence of *wffs* ending with P which is a demonstration. Writing '$\vdash P$ and $\vdash Q$' asserts that there are *two* sequences of *wffs*, both demonstrations, one ending with P, the other ending with Q. But writing '$\vdash P \cdot Q$' asserts that there is a *single* sequence of *wffs* which is a demonstration and ends with $P \cdot Q$. This assertion, although different, follows from the preceding by the principle of Conjunction, which will be established as DR 14.

The next derived rule is proved as follows:

DR 2. $\sim P \supset \sim Q \vdash Q \supset P$.
Proof:

$(\sim P \supset \sim Q) \supset [\sim(\sim QQ) \supset \sim(Q \sim P)]$	Ax. 3
$\sim P \supset \sim Q$	premiss
$\sim(\sim QQ) \supset \sim(Q \sim P)$	R 1
$\sim(\sim QQ)$	Th. 1
$\sim(Q \sim P)$	R 1
$Q \supset P$	df.

Although Theorem 5, $\vdash (Q \supset P) \supset (\sim P \supset \sim Q)$, is part of the principle of Transposition, DR 2, $\sim P \supset \sim Q \vdash Q \supset P$, is not. That principle asserts that $(Q \supset P) \equiv (\sim P \supset \sim Q)$, which is our abbreviation for $[(Q \supset P) \supset (\sim P \supset \sim Q)] \cdot [(\sim P \supset \sim Q) \supset (Q \supset P)]$. The left hand conjunct is Theorem 5, but the right hand conjunct is *not* DR 2. There is an important difference between

$$\sim P \supset \sim Q \vdash Q \supset P \qquad \text{and} \qquad \vdash (\sim P \supset \sim Q) \supset (Q \supset P).$$

The first asserts that there is a sequence of *wffs* each of which is either $\sim P \supset \sim Q$ or an axiom or follows from two preceding *wffs* by R 1, and whose last *wff* is $Q \supset P$. The second asserts that there is a sequence of *wffs* each of which is an axiom or follows from two preceding *wffs* by R 1, and whose last *wff* is $(\sim P \supset \sim Q) \supset (Q \supset P)$. (The second has not yet been established.) Of course there is some connection between them, as there is between any two statements such as $P \vdash Q$ and $\vdash P \supset Q$. Given the latter, the former is easily established, for to the sequence of *wffs* $S_1, S_2, \ldots, S_k$, (where S_k is $P \supset Q$), which constitutes a demonstration for $\vdash P \supset Q$, we need only add P as S_{k+1} and derive Q as S_{k+2}, for it follows from S_k and S_{k+1} by R 1. But although $\vdash P \supset Q$ follows from $P \vdash Q$, the proof that it does is less simple. It will be established as Metatheorem III (the 'Deduction Theorem'); but until it has been proved it cannot be assumed to hold for R.S.

Some additional derived rules, together with their proofs, are these:

DR 3. $P \supset Q \vdash RP \supset QR$

Proof:	
$(P \supset Q) \supset [\sim(QR) \supset \sim(RP)]$	Ax. 3
$P \supset Q$	premiss
$\sim(QR) \supset \sim(RP)$	R 1
$RP \supset QR$	DR 2

DR 4. $P \supset Q, R \supset S \vdash \sim[\sim(QS)(PR)]$

Proof:	
$P \supset Q$	premiss
$SP \supset QS$	DR 3
$R \supset S$	premiss
$PR \supset SP$	DR 3
$\sim[\sim(QS)(PR)]$	DR 1

DR 5. $P \supset Q, Q \supset R, R \supset S \vdash P \supset S$

Proof:	
$R \supset S$	premiss
$(R \supset S) \supset (\sim S \supset \sim R)$	Th. 5
$\sim S \supset \sim R$	R 1
$(\sim S \supset \sim R) \supset [\sim(\sim RP) \supset \sim(P\sim S)]$	Ax. 3
$\sim(\sim RP) \supset \sim(P\sim S)$	R 1
$P \supset Q$	premiss
$Q \supset R$	premiss
$\sim(\sim RP)$	DR 1
$\sim(P\sim S)$	R 1
$P \supset S$	df.

The last derived rule mentioned may be thought of as a 'generalized' Hypothetical Syllogism. In developing R.S. it is convenient to establish DR 5 before proving the ordinary Hypothetical Syllogism $P \supset Q, Q \supset R \vdash P \supset R$. The latter will be established as DR 6. For ease in proving the next derived rule it is desirable to prove three additional theorems first. Their proofs will be left as exercises for the reader:

Th. 6. $\vdash (R \sim \sim P) \supset (PR)$
Th. 7. $\vdash P \supset P$
Th. 8. $\vdash RP \supset PR$

An additional exercise which will be instructive for the reader is to construct a *demonstration* (not merely a proof) for Theorem 7. It is so obvious a tautology as to seem trivial, and yet its demonstration in R.S. is not short.

Together, DR 5 and Theorem 7 provide an easy proof of the validity of the Hypothetical Syllogism

DR 6. $P \supset Q, Q \supset R \vdash P \supset R$

Some additional theorems and derived rules, whose establishment is necessary for the proof of the next Metatheorem, are these:

Th. 9. $\vdash \sim(PR) \supset \sim(RP)$
DR 7. $P \supset Q, R \supset S \vdash PR \supset QS$

It is convenient to record two corollaries of DR 7:

Cor. 1. $P \supset Q \vdash PR \supset QR$
Cor. 2. $R \supset S \vdash PR \supset PS$
DR 8. $P \supset Q, P \supset R \vdash P \supset QR$
Th. 10. $\vdash (PQ)R \supset P(QR)$

A useful corollary of Th. 10 is the other half of the principle of Association for '·':

Cor. $\vdash P(QR) \supset (PQ)R$
DR 9. $P \supset R, Q \supset S \vdash (P \vee Q) \supset (R \vee S)$
DR 10. $P \supset R, Q \supset R \vdash (P \vee Q) \supset R$
Th. 11. $\vdash (P \vee Q) \supset (Q \vee P)$
Th. 12. $\vdash (P \vee Q) \vee R \supset P \vee (Q \vee R)$

A useful corollary of Th. 12 is the other half of the principle of Association for 'v':

Cor. $\vdash P \vee (Q \vee R) \supset (P \vee Q) \vee R$
Th. 13. $\vdash [P \supset (Q \supset R)] \supset [PQ \supset R]$
Th. 14. $\vdash [PQ \supset R] \supset [P \supset (Q \supset R)]$

These last two theorems are the two halves of the principle of Exportation, but before the principle itself can be derived from them, the principle of Conjunction must be established (as DR 14).

DR 11. $P \supset Q, P \supset (Q \supset R) \vdash P \supset R$
Th. 15. $\vdash P \supset (Q \supset PQ)$
Th. 16. $\vdash P \supset (Q \supset P)$

Having established these derived rules and theorems, we are now able to prove the Deduction Theorem for R.S. as

METATHEOREM III. If $P_1, P_2, \ldots, P_{n-1}, P_n \vdash Q$ then $P_1, P_2, \ldots, P_{n-1} \vdash P_n \supset Q$.

Proof: We assume that $P_1, P_2, \ldots, P_{n-1}, P_n \vdash Q$, that is, that there is a demonstration or sequence of *wffs* $S_1, S_2, \ldots, S_s$ such that each S_i is either an axiom, or a $P_i(i = 1, 2, \ldots, n)$, or follows from two previous S's by R 1, and S_s is Q. Now consider the sequence of *wffs* $P_n \supset S_1$, $P_n \supset S_2, \ldots, P_n \supset S_s$. If we can 'fill in' *wffs* before each $P_n \supset S_i$ in such a way that the resulting total sequence is a demonstration from $P_1, P_2, \ldots, P_{n-1}$, that is, so that each step of the resulting total sequence is either an axiom or a $P_i(i = 1, 2, \ldots, n - 1)$, or follows from two previous steps by R 1, then since $P_n \supset S_s$ is $P_n \supset Q$, we shall have a demonstration that $P_1, P_2, \ldots, P_{n-1} \vdash P_n \supset Q$. That we *can* 'fill in' to get the desired demonstration is proved by weak induction on the number of formulas $P_n \supset S_i$ involved.

(α) In case $i = 1$, we have only the formula $P_n \supset S_1$ to consider. By assumption, S_1 is either an axiom or a $P_i(i = 1, 2, \ldots, n)$.

CASE 1. S_1 is an axiom. Here we fill in with the demonstration of Theorem 16, $\vdash S_1 \supset (P_n \supset S_1)$, and S_1 itself. From the last two formulas we derive $P_n \supset S_1$ by R 1, so that the total sequence of *wffs* up to and including $P_n \supset S_1$ is a demonstration that $\vdash P_n \supset S_1$ and hence that $P_1, P_2, \ldots, P_{n-1} \vdash P_n \supset S_1$.

CASE 2. S_1 is $P_i(i = 1, 2, \ldots, n - 1)$. Here we fill in with the demonstration of Theorem 16, $\vdash S_1 \supset (P_n \supset S_1)$, and S_1 itself. From the last two formulas we derive $P_n \supset S_1$ by R 1, so that the total sequence of *wffs* up to and including $P_n \supset S_1$ is a demonstration that $S_1 \vdash P_n \supset S_1$. Since S_1 is a $P_i(i = 1, 2, \ldots, n - 1)$ we have a demonstration that $P_1, P_2, \ldots, P_{n-1} \vdash P_n \supset S_1$.

CASE 3. S_1 is P_n. Here we fill in with the demonstration of Theorem 7, $\vdash P_n \supset P_n$, that is, $\vdash P_n \supset S_1$, so that the total sequence of *wffs* up to and including $P_n \supset S_1$ is a demonstration that $\vdash P_n \supset S_1$, and hence that $P_1, P_2, \ldots, P_{n-1} \vdash P_n \supset S_1$.

(β) Now suppose that we have properly filled in all the steps up to and including $P_n \supset S_{k-1}$, so that we have a sequence of *wffs* which is a demonstration that $P_1, P_2, \ldots, P_{n-1} \vdash P_n \supset S_{k-1}$. Under this assumption we can show how to fill in properly so as to include $P_n \supset S_k$ in the sequence, which will then be a demonstration that $P_1, P_2, \ldots, P_{n-1} \vdash P_n \supset S_k$. By assumption, S_k is an axiom, a $P_i(i = 1, 2, \ldots, n)$, or results from the application of R 1 to two previous S's, say S_i and $S_j(i, j < k)$.

CASE 1. S_k is an axiom. Insert the demonstration of Theorem 16, $\vdash S_k \supset (P_n \supset S_k)$, and S_k itself, and derive $P_n \supset S_k$ by R 1. The entire sequence will then be a demonstration that $P_1, P_2, \ldots, P_{n-1} \vdash P_n \supset S_k$.

CASE 2. S_k is $P_i(i = 1, 2, \ldots, n - 1)$. Insert the demonstration of Theorem 16, $\vdash S_k \supset (P_n \supset S_k)$, and S_k itself, and derive $P_n \supset S_k$ by R 1. The entire sequence will then be a demonstration that $P_1, P_2, \ldots, P_{n-1} \vdash P_n \supset S_k$.

CASE 3. S_k is P_n. Insert the demonstration of Theorem 7, $\vdash P_n \supset P_n$, that is, $\vdash P_n \supset S_k$, and the entire sequence will be a demonstration that $P_1, P_2, \ldots, P_{n-1} \vdash P_n \supset S_k$.

CASE 4. S_k resulted (in the original demonstration that $P_1, P_2, \ldots P_n \vdash Q$), from the application of R 1 to two earlier S's, say S_i and S_j, where $i, j < k$ and S_i is of the form $S_j \supset S_k$. By the assumption of the β-case we have already filled in up to and including both $P_n \supset S_j$ and $P_n \supset (S_j \supset S_k)$. By DR 11, stated as

$$P \supset Q, P \supset (Q \supset R) \vdash P \supset R$$

we have

$$P_n \supset S_j, P_n \supset (S_j \supset S_k) \vdash P_n \supset S_k.$$

Insert the demonstration of this derived rule, whose last step is $P_n \supset S_k$, and the entire sequence will then be a demonstration that $P_1, P_2, \ldots, P_{n-1} \vdash P_n \supset S_k$.

Now by weak induction we conclude that we can fill in for *any* number of steps $P_n \supset S_i$ in such a way that the resulting sequence will be a demonstration that $P_1, P_2, \ldots, P_{n-1} \vdash P_n \supset S_i$. We can therefore do it for the demonstration of $P_1, P_2, \ldots, P_{n-1}, P_n \vdash Q$ no matter how many steps $S_1, S_2, \ldots, S_s$ it contains. And since S_s is Q, we can construct a demonstration that $P_1, P_2, \ldots, P_{n-1} \vdash P_n \supset Q$. This concludes our demonstration of the Deduction Theorem.

An immediate consequence is the

COROLLARY: If $P \vdash Q$ then $\vdash P \supset Q$.

An equally obvious corollary is the more general conclusion that: The Deduction Theorem holds for *any* propositional calculus which has only the rule *modus ponens* and which contains demonstrations for $P \supset P$, $P \supset (Q \supset P)$, and $(P \supset Q) \supset \{[P \supset (Q \supset R)] \supset (P \supset R)\}$.

The way in which Metatheorem III (abbreviated 'D.T'.) may be used in proofs is indicated in the following proof of DR 6. First we demonstrate the relatively trivial DR 6': $P \supset Q$, $Q \supset R$, $P \vdash R$ by the steps

$P \supset Q$	premiss
P	premiss
Q	R 1
$Q \supset R$	premiss
R	R 1

Then we can prove DR 6 by simply applying the D.T. once, the proof reading

$P \supset Q, Q \supset R, P \vdash R$	DR 6'
$P \supset Q, Q \supset R \vdash P \supset R$	D.T.

Since the D.T. gives us an effective method of constructing a new demonstration for DR 6 on the basis of the old one for DR 6', the preceding two step proof is a perfectly adequate prescription of how to construct the desired demonstration. It should not be thought that effort has been 'wasted' in constructing more difficult proofs of our earlier theorems, for they had to be established first in order to prove the Deduction Theorem itself.

Some additional theorems and derived rules of R.S. are

TH. 17. $\vdash P \supset (Q \lor P)$
COR. $\vdash P \supset (P \lor Q)$
TH. 18. $\vdash (P \lor Q)R \supset (PR \lor QR)$

This theorem constitutes a part of the principle of Distribution—the distribution of '·' with respect to 'v'.

DR 12. $P \supset \sim Q \vdash P \supset \sim(QR)$
DR 13. $P \supset \sim R \vdash P \supset \sim(QR)$
DR 14. $P, Q \vdash PQ$

Here, finally, we have the principle of Conjunction. It permits us to establish the principle of Double Negation as our next theorem, which follows directly from Th. 2 and Th. 4 by DR 14.

TH. 19. $\vdash P \equiv \sim\sim P$

Theorem 19, by itself, however, does not permit us to replace $\sim\sim P$ by P wherever it may occur in the interior of a larger *wff*. That is, where we are able to demonstrate a *wff* $\vdash (- - - \sim\sim P \ldots)$ the mere equivalence of $\sim\sim P$ and P does not permit us simply to infer that $\vdash (- - - P \ldots)$. The inference would be valid, but we must *prove* that it is valid within R.S. The legitimacy of any such substitution or replacement is asserted by our next Metatheorem. Before stating and proving it we shall find it convenient to establish two additional derived rules both having to do with equivalences:

DR 15. $P \equiv Q \vdash \sim P \equiv \sim Q$

and

DR 16. $P \equiv Q, R \equiv S \vdash PR \equiv QS.$

Proofs will be left as exercises for the reader.

Now we are ready to prove the Substitution Theorem for R.S.

METATHEOREM IV. (Substitution Theorem). Let Q and P_1, P_2, . . . , P_n be any *wffs*, and let S be any *wff* which contains no symbols other than ·, $\sim$, $P_i (1 \leq i \leq n)$, and Q. Where S^* is a *wff* which results from replacing any of the occurrences of Q in S by R, then $Q \equiv R \vdash S \equiv S^*$.

Proof: Strong induction is used on the number of symbols in S, counting each occurrence of ·, $\sim$, Q, or any P_i as a single symbol.

(α) $n = 1$. In this case S is either Q alone or a P_i alone.

CASE 1. S is Q and S^* is R. It is obvious that $Q \equiv R \vdash Q \equiv R$ so that $Q \equiv R \vdash S \equiv S^*$.

CASE 2. S is Q and S^* is Q also. Since $\vdash Q \equiv Q$ by Th. 7 and DR 14, $\vdash S \equiv S^*$ so that $Q \equiv R \vdash S \equiv S^*$.

CASE 3. S is a P_i. In this case S^* also is the same P_i. Since $\vdash P_i \equiv P_i$ by Th. 7 and DR 14, $\vdash S \equiv S^*$ so that $Q \equiv R \vdash S \equiv S^*$.

(β) Here the Metatheorem is assumed to be true for any S containing any $k < n$ symbols. Consider any S containing exactly n symbols ($n > 1$). It is clear that S must be either of the structure $\sim S_1$ or $S_1 \cdot S_2$.

CASE 1. S is of the structure $\sim S_1$. Since S contains n symbols, S_1 contains $k < n$ symbols (here $k = n - 1$), so by the β-case assumption, $Q \equiv R \vdash S_1 \equiv S_1^*$, where S_1^* is a *wff* which results from replacing any of the occurrences of Q in S_1 by R. But $S_1 \equiv S_1^* \vdash \sim S_1 \equiv \sim S_1^*$ by DR 15, and since $\sim S_1^*$ is obviously the same as S^*, we have $Q \equiv R \vdash S \equiv S^*$.

CASE 2. S is of the structure $S_1 \cdot S_2$. Here S_1 and S_2 each contain less than n symbols, so by the β-case assumption, $Q \equiv R \vdash S_1 \equiv S_1^*$ and $Q \equiv R \vdash S_2 \equiv S_2^*$. But by DR 16, $S_1 \equiv S_1^*, S_2 \equiv S_2^* \vdash S_1 \cdot S_2 \equiv S_1^* \cdot S_2^*$ and since $S_1^* \cdot S_2^*$ is S^*, $Q \equiv R \vdash S \equiv S^*$.

Hence by strong induction we infer that regardless of the number of symbols in S, $Q \equiv R \vdash S \equiv S^*$.

COROLLARY: If Q, R, S, and S^* are as in Metatheorem IV, then $Q \equiv R, S \vdash S^*$.

The proof of the corollary is obvious.

Of the list of elementary valid argument forms used in validating extended arguments back in Chapter Three, the first nine were argument forms proper, while the last ten were equivalences whose intersubstitutability was assumed. Of the first nine, the first, *modus ponens*, is the primitive rule R 1 of R.S. The third, the Hypothetical Syllogism, has already been established as DR 6; and the eighth, the principle of Conjunction, has been proved as DR 14. The remaining six can easily be proved as derived rules of R.S. They may be listed as

DR 17. $P \supset Q, \sim Q \vdash \sim P$ (*modus tollens*)

DR 18. $P \vee Q, \sim P \vdash Q$ (Disjunctive Syllogism)

DR 19. $(P \supset Q) \cdot (R \supset S), P \vee R \vdash Q \vee S$ (Constructive Dilemma)

DR 20. $(P \supset Q) \cdot (R \supset S), \sim Q \vee \sim S \vdash$

                        $\sim P \vee \sim R$ (Destructive Dilemma)

DR 21. $PQ \vdash P$ (Simplification)

DR 21—Cor. $PQ \vdash Q$

DR 22. $P \vdash P \vee Q$ (Addition)

The various equivalences which made up the last ten items on the elementary valid argument form list can easily be established. The principle of Double Negation has already been proved as Theorem 19. The various principles of Commutation and Association are obtained by simply applying DR 14 to already established theorems and corollaries.

Th. 20. $\vdash P \vee Q \equiv Q \vee P$ (Commutation of 'v')

Th. 21. $\vdash PQ \equiv QP$ (Commutation of '·')

Th. 22. $\vdash [P \vee (Q \vee R)] \equiv [(P \vee Q) \vee R]$ (Association of 'v')

Th. 23. $\vdash P(QR) \equiv (PQ)R$ (Association of '·')

The principle of Transposition is obtainable by DR 14 from Theorem 5 and the result of applying the Deduction Theorem to DR 2.

Th. 24. $\vdash (P \supset Q) \equiv (\sim Q \supset \sim P)$ (Transposition)

The proof of the principle of Exportation is even more obvious.

Th. 25. $\vdash [(PQ) \supset R] \equiv [P \supset (Q \supset R)]$ (Exportation)

The proofs of the final group of theorems of the R.S. will be left as exercises for the reader.

TH. 26. $\vdash P \equiv PP$ (Tautology)

TH. 26—COR. $\vdash P \equiv P \lor P$ (Tautology)

TH. 27. $\vdash \sim(PQ) \equiv (\sim P \lor \sim Q)$ (De Morgan's Theorem)

TH. 28. $\vdash \sim(P \lor Q) \equiv (\sim P \sim Q)$ (De Morgan's Theorem)

TH. 29. $\vdash (P \supset Q) \equiv (\sim P \lor Q)$ (Material Implication)

TH. 30. $\vdash P \cdot (Q \lor R) \equiv PQ \lor PR$ (Distribution of '·' over 'v')

TH. 31. $\vdash (P \equiv Q) \equiv [PQ \lor \sim P \sim Q]$ (Material Equivalence)

TH. 32. $\vdash P \lor QR \equiv (P \lor Q)(P \lor R)$ (Distribution of 'v' over '·')

With the establishment of this final group of theorems, R.S. has been shown to contain all of the logical principles appealed to in validating extended arguments in Chapter Three. Containing also, as it does, the Deduction Theorem and the principle of Double Negation, it is adequate also to the methods of Conditional Proof and Indirect Proof discussed in that Chapter. It still remains to be demonstrated that the system is *deductively complete*, which will be established in the next section.

V. DEDUCTIVE COMPLETENESS

In Theorems 22, 23, and 30 we already have the Association of 'v' and '·', and the Distribution of '·' with respect to 'v'. But as stated, these properties have been established only for cases involving exactly three *wffs*. In proving the deductive completeness of R.S. we must make use of more general Association and Distribution principles. These will be established as our next three Metatheorems. The first of them will establish the general Association and Commutation of the conjunction symbol, '·', stating that no matter in what order or grouping any number of *wffs* are conjoined, the resulting *wff* will be equivalent to the result of conjoining them in any other order or grouping. We may state this formally as follows:

METATHEOREM V. Let P_1, P_2, . . . , P_n be any *wffs* and let Q and R be any two *wffs* constructed out of them by means of '·'. If each $P_i(1 \leq i \leq n)$ occurs exactly once in each of the *wffs* Q and R, then $\vdash Q \equiv R$.

Proof: We use strong induction on the number of 'factors' P_i in Q and R.

α) Where $n = 1$, Q and R are identically the same *wff* P_1, so that $\vdash Q \equiv R$ by Th. 7 and DR 14.

β) Here we assume the Metatheorem true for every $k < n$ factors P_1, P_2, . . . , P_k. Now consider Q and R each built up out of n factors P_1, P_2, . . . , P_n. Q has the structure ST and R has the structure XY (here we introduce 'T', 'X', and 'Y' as additional syntactical variables of our metalanguage). It is clear that S, T, X, and Y each has less than n factors, that S may or may not have at least one factor in common with X, that S may or may not have at least one factor in common with Y, that T may or may not have at least one factor in common with X, and that T may or may not have at least one factor in common with Y. To discuss these various cases we introduce some special symbols:

> Let 'S_x' denote a conjunction of all factors of S which are also factors of X—if there are any. (If there is at least one factor common to S and X we shall say that S_x *exists*, whereas if there are no common factors we shall say that S_x *does not exist.*)
> Let 'S_y' denote a conjunction of all factors of S which are also factors of Y—if there are any.
> Let 'T_x' denote a conjunction of all factors of T which are also factors of X—if there are any.
> Let 'T_y' denote a conjunction of all factors of T which are also factors of Y—if there are any.

Not all of these need exist; but all possibilities must be considered in establishing the β-case for our induction. The first is that in which only S_x and T_y exist. Here S_x is S and T_y is T, so that S and X have identically the same factors, and T and Y have identically the same factors. By the β-case assumption, $\vdash S \equiv X$

and $\vdash T \equiv Y$, hence by DR 16 we have $\vdash ST \equiv XY$, which is $\vdash Q \equiv R$. There are six other cases, which will be left as exercises for the reader. When they have all been covered, Metatheorem V follows by strong induction.

The next principle concerns the general Association and Commutation of the disjunction symbol 'v': no matter in what order or grouping any *wffs* are connected by 'v', the resulting disjunction or 'logical sum' will be equivalent to the result of connecting them by 'v' in any other order or grouping. We may state this formally as

METATHEOREM VI. Let P_1, P_2, . . . , P_n be any *wffs* and let Q and R be any two *wffs* constructed out of them by means of 'v'. If each $P_i(1 \leq i \leq n)$ occurs exactly once in each of the *wffs* Q and R, then $\vdash Q \equiv R$.

The proof will be left as an exercise for the reader.

Finally, we wish to establish a generalized statement of the Distribution of conjunction with respect to disjunction, that is, of '·' over 'v'. This is expressed as

METATHEOREM VII. If Q is the logical sum of P_1, P_2, . . . , P_n, and S is the logical sum of P_1R, P_2R, . . ., P_nR, then $\vdash QR \supset S$.
Proof: We use weak induction on the number of summands P_1, P_2, . . . , P_n.

    α) Where $n = 1$, Q is P_1, QR is P_1R, and S is P_1R also. By Th. 7, $\vdash P_1R \supset P_1R$ which is $\vdash QR \supset S$.

    β) Assume the Metatheorem true for k summands P_1, P_2, . . . , P_k. Now let Q be the logical sum or disjunction of P_1, P_2, . . . , P_k, P_{k+1}, and let S be the logical sum of P_1R, P_2R, . . . , P_kR, $P_{k+1}R$. Now we argue that

$\vdash (P_1 \text{ v } P_2 \text{ v } \ldots \text{ v } P_k)R \supset$
                $(P_1R \text{ v } P_2R \text{ v } \ldots \text{ v } P_kR)$ by the β-case assumption
$\vdash P_{k+1}R \supset P_{k+1}R$ Th. 7
$\vdash [(P_1 \text{ v } P_2 \text{ v } \ldots \text{ v } P_k)R \text{ v } P_{k+1}R] \supset$
    $[(P_1R \text{ v } P_2R \text{ v } \ldots \text{ v } P_kR) \text{ v } P_{k+1}R]$ DR 9

$\vdash[(P_1 \vee P_2 \vee \ldots \vee P_k) \vee P_{k+1}]R \supset$

$\qquad [(P_1 \vee P_2 \vee \ldots \vee P_k)R \vee P_{k+1}R]$ Th. 18

$\vdash[(P_1 \vee P_2 \vee \ldots \vee P_k) \vee P_{k+1}]R \supset$

$\qquad [(P_1R \vee P_2R \vee \ldots \vee P_kR) \vee P_{k+1}R]$ DR 9

By our convention of *association to the left*, the preceding line can also be written as

$\vdash(P_1 \vee P_2 \vee \ldots \vee P_k \vee P_{k+1})R \supset$

$\qquad (P_1R \vee P_2R \vee \ldots \vee P_kR \vee P_{k+1}R)$

$\qquad$ which is $\vdash QR \supset S$ where Q contains $k+1$ summands.

Metatheorem VII now follows by weak induction. ~~show~~ 2ʷᵈ ed

To prove that R.S. is deductively complete, we ~~(must prove)~~ that all tautologies are provable as theorems in the system. Since all tautologies are expressible as *wffs* of R.S. (by MT 1) the deductive completeness of R.S. is expressed as: If S is a tautology then $\vdash S$. ~~(The)~~ criterion for deciding whether or not any *wff* is a   2 tautology is supplied by the method of truth tables. Any *wff* S has a truth table with as many initial columns in it as there are distinct propositional symbols in S. Where there are n of them, say $P_1, P_2, \ldots, P_n$, the tautology S will have this truth table:

P_1	P_2	$\ldots$	P_n	S
T	T	$\ldots$	T	T
T	T	$\ldots$	F	T
.	.	. . .	.	.
.	.	. . .	.	.
.	.	. . .	.	.
F	F	$\ldots$	T	T
F	F	$\ldots$	F	T

Any such truth table has 2^n rows, each of which represents a different assignment of **T**'s and **F**'s to the P_i's, one row for every possible assignment. That only **T**'s appear in the column under S indicates that every possible assignment of **T**'s and **F**'s to the P_i's must assign a **T** to S.

To show that $\vdash S$ for every such S, we establish the following:

first, that each row of its truth table, that is, each assignment of truth values to the P_i's, can be represented by a *wff* of R.S., the first row by Q_1, the second by Q_2, . . . , and the last or $2^n th$ by Q_{2^n};

second, that if Q_1, Q_2, . . . , Q_{2^n} are the 2^n *wffs* representing all possible assignments of T's and F's to the P_i's, then $\vdash (Q_1 \text{ v } Q_2 \text{ v } . . . \text{ v } Q_{2^n})$; and

third, that if a particular assignment of T's and F's to the P_i's assigns a T to S, then where Q_j represents that particular assignment, we have $\vdash Q_j \supset S$.

That these will suffice to prove that $\vdash S$ is easily seen. Where the truth table for S has all T's in the column under S, then $\vdash Q_1 \supset S$, $\vdash Q_2 \supset S$, . . . , $\vdash Q_{2^n} \supset S$. From these, by $2^n - 1$ uses of DR 10 we have $\vdash (Q_1 \text{ v } Q_2 \text{ v } . . . \text{ v } Q_{2^n}) \supset S$. And once we have established that $\vdash (Q_1 \text{ v } Q_2 \text{ v } . . . \text{ v } Q_{2^n})$, we obtain $\vdash S$ by R 1.

Now we proceed to attack the problem in detail. First we must show that every possible assignment of T's and F's to the P_i's of a set $(P_1, P_2, . . . , P_n)$ can be represented by a *wff*. A *wff* is said to *represent* a particular assignment of truth values when (on the normal interpretation of its operator symbols) that truth value assignment is the only one which makes the *wff* in question true. Where T's are assigned to every P_i, this assignment is represented by the conjunction $P_1 \cdot P_2 \cdot . . . \cdot P_n$, which we denote by '$Q_1$'. Where T's are assigned to every P_i except P_n, which is assigned an F, the assignment is represented by the conjunction $P_1 \cdot P_2 \cdot . . . \cdot P_{n-1} \sim P_n$, which we denote by '$Q_2$'. Similarly for every other possible assignment corresponding to every row of the truth table, ending with the conjunction $\sim P_1 \cdot \sim P_2 \cdot . . . \cdot \sim P_n$, which we denote by '$Q_{2^n}$'. In this way any row of any truth table can be represented by a *wff* of R.S., which establishes the *first* result mentioned in the preceding paragraph.

Next we turn our attention to the *second*, which we express as

METATHEOREM VIII. If Q_1, Q_2, . . . , Q_{2^n} represent all possible distinct assignments of truth values to the n distinct propositional symbols P_1, P_2, . . . , P_n, then $\vdash (Q_1 \vee Q_2 \vee \ldots \vee Q_{2^n})$.

Proof: We use weak induction on the number of P_i's.

α) Where $n = 1$, $2^n = 2$, and Q_1 is P_1 and Q_2 is $\sim P_1$. Here we have

$\vdash \sim P_1 \vee P_1$ Th. 2
$\vdash (\sim P_1 \vee P_1) \supset (P_1 \vee \sim P_1)$ Th. 11
$\vdash P_1 \vee \sim P_1$ R 1

which is $\vdash (Q_1 \vee Q_2)$.

β) Assume the Metatheorem true for P_1, P_2, . . . , P_k. Now consider the set P_1, P_2, . . . , P_k, P_{k+1}. Where Q_1, Q_2, . . . , Q_{2^k} represent all possible distinct assignments of truth values to P_1, P_2, . . . , P_k, we have

$\vdash (Q_1 \vee Q_2 \vee \ldots \vee Q_{2^k})$ by the β-case assumption.

Then we continue the argument as follows:

$\vdash \sim P_{k+1} \vee P_{k+1}$ Th. 2
$\vdash (\sim P_{k+1} \vee P_{k+1}) \supset (P_{k+1} \vee \sim P_{k+1})$ Th. 11
$\vdash P_{k+1} \vee \sim P_{k+1}$ R 1
$\vdash (P_{k+1} \vee \sim P_{k+1})(Q_1 \vee Q_2 \vee \ldots \vee Q_{2^k})$ DR 14
$\vdash [(P_{k+1} \vee \sim P_{k+1})(Q_1 \vee Q_2 \vee \ldots \vee Q_{2^k})] \supset$
     $[P_{k+1}(Q_1 \vee Q_2 \vee \ldots \vee Q_{2^k}) \vee$
         $\sim P_{k+1}(Q_1 \vee Q_2 \vee \ldots \vee Q_{2^k})]$ Th. 18
$\vdash P_{k+1}(Q_1 \vee Q_2 \vee \ldots \vee Q_{2^k}) \vee$
         $\sim P_{k+1}(Q_1 \vee Q_2 \vee \ldots \vee Q_{2^k})$ R 1
$\vdash P_{k+1}(Q_1 \vee Q_2 \vee \ldots \vee Q_{2^k}) \equiv$
         $(Q_1 \vee Q_2 \vee \ldots \vee Q_{2^k})P_{k+1}$ Th. 21
$\vdash (Q_1 \vee Q_2 \vee \ldots \vee Q_{2^k})P_{k+1} \vee$
         $\sim P_{k+1}(Q_1 \vee Q_2 \vee \ldots \vee Q_{2^k})$ MT IV, Cor.
$\vdash \sim P_{k+1}(Q_1 \vee Q_2 \vee \ldots \vee Q_{2^k}) \equiv$
         $(Q_1 \vee Q_2 \vee \ldots \vee Q_{2^k}) \sim P_{k+1}$ Th. 21
$\vdash (Q_1 \vee Q_2 \vee \ldots \vee Q_{2^k})P_{k+1} \vee$
         $(Q_1 \vee Q_2 \vee \ldots \vee Q_{2^k}) \sim P_{k+1}$ MT IV, Cor.

$\vdash (Q_1 \text{ v } Q_2 \text{ v } \ldots \text{ v } Q_{2^k})P_{k+1} \supset$

$\qquad\qquad (Q_1P_{k+1} \text{ v } Q_2P_{k+1} \text{ v } \ldots \text{ v } Q_{2^k}P_{k+1}) \quad$ MT VII

$\vdash (Q_1 \text{ v } Q_2 \text{ v } \ldots \text{ v } Q_{2^k})\sim P_{k+1} \supset$

$\qquad\qquad (Q_1\sim P_{k+1} \text{ v } Q_2\sim P_{k+1} \text{ v } \ldots \text{ v } Q_{2^k}\sim P_{k+1}) \quad$ MT VII

$\vdash [(Q_1 \text{ v } Q_2 \text{ v } \ldots \text{ v } Q_{2^k})P_{k+1} \text{ v }$

$\quad (Q_1 \text{ v } Q_2 \text{ v } \ldots \text{ v } Q_{2^k})\sim P_{k+1}] \supset$

$\qquad [(Q_1P_{k+1} \text{ v } Q_2P_{k+1} \text{ v } \ldots \text{ v } Q_{2^k}P_{k+1}) \text{ v }$

$\qquad (Q_1\sim P_{k+1} \text{ v } Q_2\sim P_{k+1} \text{ v } \ldots \text{ v } Q_{2^k}\sim P_{k+1})] \quad$ DR 9

$\vdash (Q_1P_{k+1} \text{ v } Q_2P_{k+1} \text{ v } \ldots \text{ v } Q_{2^k}P_{k+1}) \text{ v }$

$\qquad (Q_1\sim P_{k+1} \text{ v } Q_2\sim P_{k+1} \text{ v } \ldots \text{ v } Q_{2^k}\sim P_{k+1}) \quad$ R 1

$\vdash [(Q_1P_{k+1} \text{ v } Q_2P_{k+1} \text{ v } \ldots \text{ v } Q_{2^k}P_{k+1}) \text{ v }$

$\quad (Q_1\sim P_{k+1} \text{ v } Q_2\sim P_{k+1} \text{ v } \ldots \text{ v } Q_{2^k}\sim P_{k+1})] \equiv$

$\qquad (Q_1P_{k+1} \text{ v } Q_2P_{k+1} \text{ v } \ldots \text{ v } Q_{2^k}P_{k+1} \text{ v }$

$\qquad Q_1\sim P_{k+1} \text{ v } Q_2\sim P_{k+1} \text{ v } \ldots \text{ v } Q_{2^k}\sim P_{k+1}) \quad$ MT VI

$\vdash (Q_1P_{k+1} \text{ v } Q_2P_{k+1} \text{ v } \ldots \text{ v } Q_{2^k}P_{k+1} \text{ v }$

$\qquad Q_1\sim P_{k+1} \text{ v } Q_2\sim P_{k+1} \text{ v } \ldots \text{ v } Q_{2^k}\sim P_{k+1}) \quad$ MT IV, Cor.

The preceding expression contains $2^k + 2^k = 2{\cdot}2^k = 2^{k+1}$ summands, each of which represents a different assignment of truth values to P_1, P_2, $\ldots$, P_{k+1}. By MT V, each Q_iP_{k+1} and each $Q_i\sim P_{k+1}$ is equivalent to a different Q_i', where the 2^{k+1} Q_i's represent all possible distinct assignments of truth values to P_1, P_2, $\ldots$, P_{k+1}. Hence by MT IV, Cor., $\vdash (Q_1' \text{ v } Q_2' \text{ v } \ldots \text{ v } Q_{2^{k+1}}')$. Metatheorem VIII now follows by weak induction.

We next prove that if the truth value assignment represented by Q_j assigns a **T** to S, then $\vdash Q_j \supset S$. We shall prove this by establishing a slightly more general result, which includes also the case in which the truth value assignment assigns an **F** to S instead. This is

METATHEOREM IX. Let Q_j represent any possible assignment of truth values to the n propositional symbols P_1, P_2, $\ldots$, P_n; and let S be any *wff* which has no constituents other than $P_i(1 \leq i \leq n)$. If Q_j assigns a **T** to S, then $\vdash Q_j \supset S$; and if Q_j assigns an **F** to S, then $\vdash Q_j \supset \sim S$.

Proof: We use strong induction on the number of symbols in S, counting each occurrence of $\cdot$, of $\sim$, and of any P_i as a single symbol.

α) Where $n = 1$, S **must** be a single symbol, and since it is a *wff* it must be a $P_i(1 \leq i \leq n)$.

    CASE 1. Q_j assigns a **T** to S, that is, to P_i. Hence P_i rather than $\sim P_i$ must be a factor of Q_j. By MT V, $\vdash Q_j \supset P_i R$, where R is a conjunction of all the factors of Q_j except P_i. Now we argue

$$\vdash P_i R \supset P_i \qquad\qquad \text{Ax. 2}$$
$$\vdash Q_j \supset P_i \qquad\qquad \text{DR 6}$$

which is $\vdash Q_j \supset S$.

    CASE 2. Q_j assigns an **F** to S, that is, to P_i. Hence $\sim P_i$ must be a factor of Q_j. By MT V, $\vdash Q_j \supset \sim P_i R$, where R is a conjunction of all the factors of Q_j except $\sim P_i$. Now we argue

$$\vdash \sim P_i R \supset \sim P_i \qquad\qquad \text{Ax. 2}$$
$$\vdash Q_j \supset \sim P_i \qquad\qquad \text{DR 6}$$

which is $\vdash Q_j \supset \sim S$.

β) Assume the Metatheorem true for any S containing any number $k < n$ symbols. Now consider any S containing $n(>1)$ symbols. The *wff* S must have the structure $S_1 \cdot S_2$ or $\sim S_3$.

    CASE 1. S is of the form $S_1 \cdot S_2$.

    Sub-case A: Q_j assigns a **T** to S. Here Q_j must assign a **T** to S_1 and a **T** to S_2. Since S_1, S_2 each have less than n symbols, we argue as follows:

$$\vdash Q_j \supset S_1 \qquad\qquad \text{by the } \beta\text{-case assumption}$$
$$\vdash Q_j \supset S_2 \qquad\qquad \text{by the } \beta\text{-case assumption}$$
$$\vdash Q_j \supset S_1 \cdot S_2 \qquad\qquad \text{DR 8}$$

which is $\vdash Q_j \supset S$.

    Sub-case B: Q_j assigns an **F** to S. Here Q_j must assign an **F** to S_1 or an **F** to S_2. If to S_1, then $\vdash Q_j \supset \sim S_1$ by the β-case assumption, and hence by DR 12 $\vdash Q_j \supset \sim(S_1 \cdot S_2)$, which is $\vdash Q_j \supset \sim S$. If to S_2

then $\vdash Q_j \supset \sim S_2$ by the β-case assumption, and hence by DR 13 $\vdash Q_j \supset \sim (S_1 \cdot S_2)$, which is $\vdash Q_j \supset \sim S$.

CASE 2. S is of the form $\sim S_3$.

Subcase A: Q_j assigns a **T** to S. Here Q_j must assign an **F** to S_3. Hence by the β-case assumption, $\vdash Q_j \supset \sim S_3$ which is $\vdash Q_j \supset S$.

Subcase B: Q_j assigns an **F** to S. Here Q_j must assign a **T** to S_3. Hence by the β-case assumption, $\vdash Q_j \supset S_3$. But $\vdash S_3 \supset \sim \sim S_3$ by Th. 4, so by DR 6 we have $\vdash Q_j \supset \sim \sim S_3$, which is $\vdash Q_j \supset \sim S$.

Metatheorem IX now follows by strong induction.

The deductive completeness of the system now follows easily, and may be proved as

METATHEOREM X. R.S. is deductively complete (that is, if S is a tautology then $\vdash S$).

Proof: If S is a tautology, then every possible assignment of truth values to its constituents P_1, P_2, . . . , P_n must assign a **T** to S. Hence by MT IX:

$$\vdash Q_1 \supset S$$
$$\vdash Q_2 \supset S$$
$$\cdot \ \cdot \ \cdot \ \cdot \ \cdot$$
$$\vdash Q_{2^n} \supset S$$

where Q_1, Q_2, . . . , Q_{2^n} represent all possible assignments of truth values to P_1, P_2, . . . , P_n. Now by $2^n - 1$ uses of DR 10, we have

$$\vdash (Q_1 \text{ v } Q_2 \text{ v } . . . \text{ v } Q_{2^n}) \supset S.$$

and by MT VIII,

$$\vdash (Q_1 \text{ v } Q_2 \text{ v } . . . \text{ v } Q_{2^n}).$$

From these we derive $\vdash S$ by R 1, which completes the proof of Metatheorem X.

The *decision problem* for any deductive system is the problem of stating an effective criterion for deciding whether or not any statement or well formed formula is a theorem of the system. In view of the analyticity and deductive completeness of R.S. (Metatheorems II and X), the method of truth tables constitutes a solution to the decision problem. Truth tables enable us to decide effectively whether or not any *wff* is a tautology. By MT II, *only* tautologies are theorems, and by MT X, *all* tautologies are theorems. Hence truth tables enable us to decide effectively whether or not any *wff* is a theorem. Moreover, the proofs up to and including that for MT X do not merely assure us that for any tautologous *wff* there exists a demonstration—they prescribe effectively a method of actually constructing its demonstration. The demonstration constructed by following the directions contained in the proof of deductive completeness will in general be longer than one discovered through the exercise of ingenuity and inventiveness. That is to be admitted. But it is significant and important that through the use of the recipe contained in the proofs up to and including that of MT X, a demonstration within the logistic system can be written out for any tautology—*without any need for ingenuity or inventiveness.* That this can be done is guaranteed by our effective solution of the decision problem for the system.*

It is clear from the foregoing that any argument whose validity can be established by the use of truth tables can be proved valid in R.S. In Chapter Three the claim was made that any such argument could be proved valid using the list of nineteen elementary valid argument forms augmented by the principles of Conditional Proof and Indirect Proof. We are now in a position to substantiate that claim, which is equivalent to the assertion that the method of deduction set forth in Chapter Three is deductively complete. We can do so by showing that every argument which can be proved valid in R.S. can also be

* The preceding proof of deductive completeness and solution to the decision problem is an adaptation of Professor E. L. Post's original demonstration which appeared in his 'Introduction to a General Theory of Elementary Propositions', *American Journal of Mathematics*, vol. 43 (1921), pp. 163–185.

proved valid by the methods of Chapter Three. The latter is accomplished by showing that to every demonstration of validity for an argument in R.S. there corresponds a formal proof of validity for the same argument by the methods of Chapter Three.

Every step of a demonstration in R.S. which is a premiss of the argument being proved valid is also a legitimate step in a formal proof of validity for that argument by the methods of Chapter Three. Corresponding to every step of a demonstration in R.S. which is an axiom, we have in the corresponding formal proof of validity the Conditional Proof of that axiom. (The reader has presumably already verified that the three axioms of R.S. can be derived by the method of Conditional Proof since they were included as exercises 13, 14, and 15 of Exercise Set I on page 60.) Finally, every step of a demonstration in R.S. which follows from two preceding steps by R 1 will also legitimately follow in a formal proof of validity by the methods of Chapter Three, since R 1 of R.S. is *modus ponens*, the first elementary valid argument form on the list assumed in Chapter Three.

Thus we see that the method of deduction set forth in Chapter Three is also a deductively complete system of logic.

Revised in 2nd ed. 1st ed version shown to be fallacious by Gerald J. Massey Notre Dame journal of formal logic vol 4 (1963) pp 140-1 (cf JSL Vol 30 No 3 366-7)

CHAPTER EIGHT

Alternative Systems
and Notations

I. ALTERNATIVE SYSTEMS OF LOGIC

There are three different senses in which the phrase 'alternative systems of logic' can be understood. These parallel the three senses of the phrase 'alternative systems of geometry', and can most easily be explained by analogy with the latter. We may speak of Euclidean plane geometry and Euclidean solid geometry as 'alternative systems' in the sense that the first can be studied independently of the second, and they are certainly different in that the second is *more inclusive* than the first. Analogously, we may speak of a Propositional Calculus and a Function Calculus as 'alternative systems of logic' in that the first can be studied independently of the second, and that the second is *more inclusive* than the first—where a Function Calculus contains all the tautologies and rules of the Propositional Calculus *plus* Quantification Axioms, Rules, and Theorems. It is not *this* sense of an alternative system that we shall be concerned with in the present chapter.

A second sense is that in which we can speak of Euclidean geometry and Riemannian (or Lobachevskian) geometry as alternative systems. These are alternative in the sense that, although they may possess some theorems in common, each contains some theorems not included in the other. Parallel to this situation in geometry, there are alternative systems of logic exhibiting the same sort of differences. An ordinary 'two-valued' system of logic, whose formulas—on interpretation—are either *true* or *false*, can be contrasted with 'three-valued' or 'many-valued' systems of logic whose formulas are supposed to take—on interpretation—either three or $n > 3$ different 'truth values'. Alternative systems of logic in this sense have been extensively developed, first by Jan Lukasiewicz in Poland and independently by E. L. Post in this country, more recently by J. B. Rosser and A. R. Turquette.* A study of these is beyond the scope of this book. It is not *this* sense of alternative systems that we shall be concerned with in the present chapter.

The third sense in which one can speak of alternative systems of geometry is that in which different axiomatic bases are assumed, but identically the same theorems are derivable from each of them. Thus many different axiom sets for Euclidean geometry have been devised, all of which yield the same theorems. In alternative systems of this sort, different terms are taken as primitive or undefined, and different formulas are assumed as axioms or postulates. What may be a primitive term in one system may be defined by means of other primitives in the other, and what is assumed as an axiom in one may be derived as a theorem from the axioms of the other—where those axioms correspond to theorems of the first. It is *this* sense

* Cf. J. Lukasiewicz, 'O logice trojwartosciowej', *Ruch Filozoficzny* (Lwow), vol. 5 (1920), pp. 169–171.

E. L. Post, 'Introduction to a General Theory of Elementary Propositions', *American Journal of Mathematics*, vol. 43 (1921), pp. 163–185.

J. B. Rosser, 'On The Many-Valued Logics', *American Journal of Physics*, vol. 9 (1941), pp. 207–212.

J. B. Rosser and A. R. Turquette, 'Axiom Schemes for M-Valued Propositional Calculi', *Journal of Symbolic Logic*, vol. 10 (1945), pp. 61–82, and *Many-valued Logics*, Amsterdam, 1952.

of alternative systems that will be discussed in the present chapter.

The logical truths whose systematization is under consideration are truth functional tautologies. Any system wholly adequate to their expression and development must be *functionally complete*, *analytic*, and *deductively complete*, in the senses in which R.S. was proved to possess these properties in Metatheorems I, II, and X of the preceding chapter. Any such system will be called a *Model System of Logic*, and any other axiom system for logic will be a genuine or acceptable alternative to R.S. if and only if it is a Model System. There are many different Model Systems, different in that they start with different primitive or undefined terms, and different in that they assume different formulas as axioms. They are all equivalent, however, first in being able to express—on their normal interpretations—all truth functions, second in including *all* tautologies as theorems, and third in having *only* tautologies as theorems. One such alternative system will be proved to be a *Model System* in the following section.

II. THE HILBERT-ACKERMANN SYSTEM

The Hilbert-Ackermann system for the propositional calculus has as its primitive symbols infinitely many single letters with and without subscripts:

$$A \quad A_1 \quad A_2 \quad A_3 \quad \cdots$$
$$B \quad B_1 \quad B_2 \quad B_3 \quad \cdots$$
$$C \quad C_1 \quad C_2 \quad C_3 \quad \cdots$$
$$D \quad D_1 \quad D_2 \quad D_3 \quad \cdots$$

which on their normal interpretations express non-compound propositions, and has in addition to parentheses, the two operator symbols '$\sim$' and 'v' (designated in our metalanguage by '$\sim$' and 'v'), which have as their normal interpretations the operations of negation and weak (or inclusive) disjunction. We continue to use the symbols 'P', 'Q', 'R', 'S', with and without subscripts, in our metalanguage, to denote well formed formulas of H.A. (the Hilbert-Ackermann system of logic). The notion of a *wff* of H.A. is defined recursively as follows:

Recursive Rule for *wffs* in H.A.

1. Any single letter of H.A. is a *wff*.
2. If P is a *wff* then $\sim(P)$ is a *wff*.
3. If P and Q are *wffs* then $(P) \vee (Q)$ is a *wff*.

(No formula of H.A. will be regarded as being a *wff* unless its being so follows from this definition.)

The symbols '$\supset$', '$\cdot$', '$\equiv$', are defined *syntactically* for our metalanguage by the following:

$$P \supset Q = \text{df} \sim P \vee Q$$
$$P \cdot Q = \text{df} \sim(\sim P \vee \sim Q)$$
$$PQ = \text{df} P \cdot Q$$
$$P \equiv Q = \text{df} (P \supset Q)(Q \supset P)$$

We shall continue to use the same conventions regarding parentheses which were adopted in the preceding chapter.

Four (patterns of) axioms or postulates are assumed in H.A.

P 1. $(P \vee P) \supset P$
P 2. $P \supset (P \vee Q)$
P 3. $(P \vee Q) \supset (Q \vee P)$
P 4. $(P \supset Q) \supset [(R \vee P) \supset (R \vee Q)]$

Each of these syntactical expressions denotes infinitely many *wffs* of our object language H.A., just as in the metalogical development of R.S.

Finally, a single rule of inference is assumed, which we may state as

R′ 1. If P and $P \supset Q$ then Q.

It should be realized that R′ 1 is different from R 1, because R′ 1 legitimizes arguments within H.A. of the form

$$P$$
$$\sim P \vee Q$$
$$Q$$

while R 1 legitimizes arguments within R.S. of the form

$$P$$
$$\sim(P\sim Q)$$
$$Q$$

and these are clearly different. We may make the contrast more vivid by writing them as

R 1. If P and $\sim(P\sim Q)$ then Q.
R' 1. If P and $\sim P$ v Q then Q.

By MT IV, Cor., and Th. 29 of R.S., any *wff in* R.S. that follows by R 1 from two other *wffs* must also follow by R' 1 and conversely. But this cannot be assumed true of H.A. until it is *proved*.

A 'demonstration in H.A.' of the validity of an argument having premises $P_1, P_2, \ldots, P_n$ and conclusion Q is defined to be a sequence of *wffs* $S_1, S_2, \ldots, S_t$ (of H.A.) each of which is either a postulate P 1, P 2, P 3, or P 4 or a $P_i(1 \leq i \leq n)$ or follows from two preceding S's by R' 1, and such that S_t is Q. That there is such a demonstration in H.A. is written

$$P_1, P_2, \ldots, P_n \models_{\text{HA}} Q$$

Similarly, that the formula P is a theorem of H.A. is written

$$\models_{\text{HA}} P$$

which asserts that there is a sequence of *wffs* $S_1, S_2, \ldots, S_t$ (of H.A.) each of which is either a postulate P 1, P 2, P 3, or P 4 or follows from two preceding S's by R' 1, and such that S_t is P.

The functional completeness of H.A. is easily established; in fact it was one of the exercises listed on page 204 of the preceding chapter. A proof of the analyticity of H.A. is easily given by using truth tables to show that any postulate P 1, P 2, P 3, P 4 is a tautology, and then proving that any *wff* which follows from tautologies by repeated applications of R' 1 must be tautologous also. The detailed proofs are left as exercises for the reader.

There remains only the task of proving H.A. to be deductively complete.

There are two alternative methods by which the deductive completeness of H.A. can be established. The first is that used in proving R.S. to be deductively complete. Involved here would be the development of a considerable number of theorems and derived rules *in* the system, and then the proof of a number of Metatheorems *about* the system, culminating in an analogue of the preceding chapter's Metatheorem X for the Hilbert-Ackermann System. This first method is systematic and elegant, but very lengthy. A shorter method is available. The shorter method of proving H.A. to be deductively complete depends upon the fact that the deductive completeness of R.S. has already been proved. What has been established for R.S. by MT X of the preceding chapter is that any tautological formula S is derivable by one or more applications of R 1 to Ax. 1, Ax. 2, and Ax. 3 of R.S. We wish to prove that H.A. is deductively complete, that is, that any tautological formula S is derivable by one or more applications of R′ 1 to P 1, P 2, P 3, and P 4 of H.A. Now *if* it can be shown that Ax. 1, Ax. 2, and Ax. 3 of R.S. can be derived by repeated applications of R′ 1 to the Hilbert-Ackermann postulates P 1, P 2, P 3, and P 4, and further shown that any *wff S* which is derivable from Ax. 1, Ax. 2, and Ax. 3, by the use of R 1 is also derivable from them by the use of R′ 1, then it will have been shown that any tautological formula S is derivable by repeated applications of R′ 1 to P 1, P 2, P 3, and P 4. The latter, of course, asserts the deductive completeness of H.A. This second, shorter method of proving H.A. to be deductively complete will be adopted here. We begin by establishing Ax. 1, Ax. 2, and Ax. 3 of R.S. as theorems of the Hilbert-Ackermann system. It will be convenient to establish some few derived rules and auxiliary theorems in H.A. first. To this task we now proceed, giving proofs rather than demonstrations in most cases.

THEOREM 1. $\vdash_{\overline{HA}} (Q \supset R) \supset [(P \supset Q) \supset (P \supset R)]$

Demonstration: $(Q \supset R) \supset [(\sim P \vee Q) \supset (\sim P \vee R)]$ P 4
             $(Q \supset R) \supset [(P \supset Q) \supset (P \supset R)]$ df.

FIRST DERIVED RULE (DR' 1). $P \supset Q, Q \supset R \vdash_{\text{HA}} P \supset R$

Proof: $(Q \supset R) \supset [(P \supset Q) \supset (P \supset R)]$ Th. 1

     $Q \supset R$ premiss

     $(P \supset Q) \supset (P \supset R)$ R' 1

     $P \supset Q$ premiss

     $P \supset R$ R' 1

THEOREM 2. $\vdash_{\text{HA}} P \supset P$

Proof: $P \supset (P \vee P)$ P 2

     $(P \vee P) \supset P$ P 1

     $P \supset P$ DR' 1

THEOREM 3. $\vdash_{\text{HA}} P \vee {\sim}P$

Proof: $P \supset P$ Th. 2

     ${\sim}P \vee P$ df.

     $({\sim}P \vee P) \supset (P \vee {\sim}P)$ P 3

     $P \vee {\sim}P$ R' 1

THEOREM 4. $\vdash_{\text{HA}} P \supset {\sim}{\sim}P$

Proof: ${\sim}P \vee {\sim}{\sim}P$ Th. 3

     $P \supset {\sim}{\sim}P$ df.

SECOND DERIVED RULE (DR' 2). $P \supset Q \vdash_{\text{HA}} {\sim}Q \supset {\sim}P$

Proof: $P \supset Q$ premiss

     $Q \supset {\sim}{\sim}Q$ Th. 4

     $P \supset {\sim}{\sim}Q$ DR' 1

     ${\sim}P \vee {\sim}{\sim}Q$ df.

     $({\sim}P \vee {\sim}{\sim}Q) \supset ({\sim}{\sim}Q \vee {\sim}P)$ P 3

     ${\sim}{\sim}Q \vee {\sim}P$ R' 1

     ${\sim}Q \supset {\sim}P$ df.

THEOREM 5. $\vdash_{\text{HA}} P \supset PP$

Proof: $({\sim}P \vee {\sim}P) \supset {\sim}P$ P 1

     ${\sim}{\sim}P \supset {\sim}({\sim}P \vee {\sim}P)$ DR' 2

     $P \supset {\sim}{\sim}P$ Th. 4

     $P \supset {\sim}({\sim}P \vee {\sim}P)$ DR' 1

     $P \supset (PP)$ df.

THEOREM 6. $\vdash_{\text{HA}} {\sim}{\sim}P \supset P$

Proof: ${\sim}P \supset {\sim}{\sim}{\sim}P$ Th. 4

     $({\sim}P \supset {\sim}{\sim}{\sim}P) \supset [(P \vee {\sim}P) \supset (P \vee {\sim}{\sim}{\sim}P)]$ P 4

     $(P \vee {\sim}P) \supset [P \vee {\sim}{\sim}{\sim}P]$ R' 1

$(P \vee \sim P)$ Th. 3
$P \vee \sim\sim\sim P$ R' 1
$(P \vee \sim\sim\sim P) \supset (\sim\sim\sim P \vee P)$ P 3
$\sim\sim\sim P \vee P$ R' 1
$\sim\sim P \supset P$ df.

THEOREM 7. $\vdash_{HA} PQ \supset P$

Proof: $\sim P \supset (\sim P \vee \sim Q)$ P 2
$\sim(\sim P \vee \sim Q) \supset \sim\sim P$ DR' 2
$\sim\sim P \supset P$ Th. 6
$\sim(\sim P \vee \sim Q) \supset P$ DR' 1
$(PQ) \supset P$ df.

THEOREM 8. $\vdash_{HA} (P \supset Q) \supset (\sim Q \supset \sim P)$

Proof: $(Q \supset \sim\sim Q) \supset [(\sim P \vee Q) \supset (\sim P \vee \sim\sim Q)]$ P 4
$(Q \supset \sim\sim Q)$ Th. 4
$(\sim P \vee Q) \supset (\sim P \vee \sim\sim Q)$ R' 1
$(\sim P \vee \sim\sim Q) \supset (\sim\sim Q \vee \sim P)$ P 3
$(\sim P \vee Q) \supset (\sim\sim Q \vee \sim P)$ DR' 1
$(P \supset Q) \supset (\sim Q \supset \sim P)$ df.

THEOREM 9. $\vdash_{HA} [P \vee (Q \vee R)] \supset [Q \vee (P \vee R)]$

Proof: $R \supset (R \vee P)$ P 2
$(R \vee P) \supset (P \vee R)$ P 3
$R \supset (P \vee R)$ DR' 1
$[R \supset (P \vee R)] \supset \{(Q \vee R) \supset [Q \vee (P \vee R)]\}$ P 4
$(Q \vee R) \supset [Q \vee (P \vee R)]$ R' 1
$\{(Q \vee R) \supset [Q \vee (P \vee R)]\} \supset \{[P \vee (Q \vee R)] \supset$
        $\{P \vee [Q \vee (P \vee R)]\}\}$ P 4
$[P \vee (Q \vee R)] \supset \{P \vee [Q \vee (P \vee R)]\}$ R' 1
$\{P \vee [Q \vee (P \vee R)]\} \supset \{[Q \vee (P \vee R)] \vee P\}$ P 3
$[P \vee (Q \vee R)] \supset \{[Q \vee (P \vee R)] \vee P\}$ DR' 1

$(P \vee R) \supset [(P \vee R) \vee Q]$ P 2
$[(P \vee R) \vee Q] \supset [Q \vee (P \vee R)]$ P 3
$(P \vee R) \supset [Q \vee (P \vee R)]$ DR' 1
$P \supset (P \vee R)$ P 2
$P \supset [Q \vee (P \vee R)]$ DR' 1
$\{P \supset [Q \vee (P \vee R)]\} \supset \{\{[Q \vee (P \vee R)] \vee P\} \supset$
      $\{[Q \vee (P \vee R)] \vee [Q \vee (P \vee R)]\}\}$ P 4

$$\{[Q \lor (P \lor R)] \lor P\} \supset \{[Q \lor (P \lor R)] \lor [Q \lor (P \lor R)]\} \quad \text{R' 1}$$
$$\{[Q \lor (P \lor R)] \lor [Q \lor (P \lor R)]\} \supset [Q \lor (P \lor R)] \quad \text{P 1}$$
$$\{[Q \lor (P \lor R)] \lor P\} \supset [Q \lor (P \lor R)] \quad \text{DR' 1}$$

Now from this step and the ninth, we have

$$[P \lor (Q \lor R)] \supset [Q \lor (P \lor R)] \quad \text{DR' 1}$$

With the establishment of Theorem 9 of the H.A. system, we have proved it equivalent to the *Principia Mathematica*[*] 'calculus of elementary propositions'. The P.M. (*Principia Mathematica*) postulates *1.2, *1.4, *1.6 correspond exactly to P 1, P 3, P 4 of H.A., and in the presence of P 3, P.M.'s *1.3 corresponds to H.A.'s P 2. The additional (fifth) postulate *1.5 of P.M. is identical with Theorem 9 of H.A. That it can be derived as a theorem from the other four postulates shows the association of disjunction to have been an unnecessary assumption. This redundancy of the P.M. postulates was first shown by Paul Bernays.[†]

THEOREM 10. $\vdash_{\overline{\text{HA}}} (P \supset Q) \supset [\sim(QR) \supset \sim(RP)]$

Proof:
$$(\sim Q \supset \sim P) \supset [(\sim R \lor \sim Q) \supset (\sim R \lor \sim P)] \quad \text{P 4}$$
$$(P \supset Q) \supset (\sim Q \supset \sim P) \quad \text{Th. 8}$$
$$(P \supset Q) \supset [(\sim R \lor \sim Q) \supset (\sim R \lor \sim P)] \quad \text{DR' 1}$$
$$\sim(P \supset Q) \lor [\sim(\sim R \lor \sim Q) \lor (\sim R \lor \sim P)] \quad \text{df.}$$
$$\{\sim(P \supset Q) \lor [\sim(\sim R \lor \sim Q) \lor (\sim R \lor \sim P)]\} \supset$$
$$\{\sim(\sim R \lor \sim Q) \lor [\sim(P \supset Q) \lor (\sim R \lor \sim P)]\} \quad \text{Th. 9}$$
$$\sim(\sim R \lor \sim Q) \lor [\sim(P \supset Q) \lor (\sim R \lor \sim P)] \quad \text{R' 1}$$
$$(\sim R \lor \sim Q) \supset [\sim(P \supset Q) \lor (\sim R \lor \sim P)] \quad \text{df.}$$
$$(\sim Q \lor \sim R) \supset (\sim R \lor \sim Q) \quad \text{P 3}$$
$$(\sim Q \lor \sim R) \supset [\sim(P \supset Q) \lor (\sim R \lor \sim P)] \quad \text{DR' 1}$$
$$\sim(\sim Q \lor \sim R) \lor [\sim(P \supset Q) \lor (\sim R \lor \sim P)] \quad \text{df.}$$
$$\{\sim(\sim Q \lor \sim R) \lor [\sim(P \supset Q) \lor (\sim R \lor \sim P)]\} \supset$$
$$\{\sim(P \supset Q) \lor [\sim(\sim Q \lor \sim R) \lor (\sim R \lor \sim P)]\} \quad \text{Th. 9}$$
$$\sim(P \supset Q) \lor [\sim(\sim Q \lor \sim R) \lor (\sim R \lor \sim P)] \quad \text{R' 1}$$
$$(P \supset Q) \supset [(\sim Q \lor \sim R) \supset (\sim R \lor \sim P)] \quad \text{df.}$$

[*] By A. N. Whitehead and B. Russell, vol. 1, 1910, vol. 2, 1912, vol. 3, 1913, Cambridge, England. Second edition, 1925–1927.

[†] P. Bernays, 'Axiomatische Untersuchung des Aussagenkalküls der Principia Mathematica', *Mathematische Zeitschrift*, vol. 25 (1926), pp. 305–320.

$[(\sim Q \text{ v} \sim R) \supset (\sim R \text{ v} \sim P)] \supset$

$\qquad\qquad [\sim(\sim R \text{ v} \sim P) \supset \sim(\sim Q \text{ v} \sim R)]$ Th. 8

$(P \supset Q) \supset [\sim(\sim R \text{ v} \sim P) \supset \sim(\sim Q \text{ v} \sim R)]$ DR′ 1

$(P \supset Q) \supset [(RP) \supset (QR)]$ df.

$[(RP) \supset (QR)] \supset [\sim(QR) \supset \sim(RP)]$ Th. 8

$(P \supset Q) \supset [\sim(QR) \supset \sim(RP)]$ DR′ 1

There is a close analogy between Theorems 5, 7, and 10 of the Hilbert-Ackermann System and Axioms 1, 2, and 3 of R.S. But they are not identical, in spite of their identical *appearance*, because '$P \supset Q$' of R.S. is an abbreviation for '$\sim(P\sim Q)$', while '$P \supset Q$' in the Hilbert-Ackermann System is an abbreviation for '$\sim P \text{ v } Q$'. The possibility of confusion can be eliminated by writing (and then deriving) the three axioms of R.S. in their unabbreviated forms, expressing them entirely by means of the operator symbols '$\cdot$' and '$\sim$'. So expressed, they are

     Ax. 1. $\sim[P\cdot\sim(P\cdot P)]$

     Ax. 2. $\sim[(P\cdot Q)\cdot\sim P]$

     Ax. 3. $\sim\{\sim(P\cdot\sim Q)\cdot\sim\sim[\sim(Q\cdot R)\cdot\sim\sim(R\cdot P)]\}$

and these will be proved as the next three theorems in H.A.

Theorem 11. $\vdash_{\text{HA}} \sim[P\cdot\sim(P\cdot P)]$

Proof: $P \supset (P\cdot P)$ Th. 5

$(P\cdot P) \supset \sim\sim(P\cdot P)$ Th. 4

$P \supset \sim\sim(P\cdot P)$ DR′ 1

$\sim P \text{ v} \sim\sim(P\cdot P)$ df.

$[\sim P \text{ v} \sim\sim(P\cdot P)] \supset \sim\sim[\sim P \text{ v} \sim\sim(P\cdot P)]$ Th. 4

$\sim\sim[\sim P \text{ v} \sim\sim(P\cdot P)]$ R′ 1

$\sim[P\cdot\sim(P\cdot P)]$ df.

Theorem 12. $\vdash_{\text{HA}} \sim[(P\cdot Q)\cdot\sim P]$

Proof: $(P\cdot Q) \supset P$ Th. 7

$P \supset \sim\sim P$ Th. 4

$(P\cdot Q) \supset \sim\sim P$ DR′ 1

$\sim(P\cdot Q) \text{ v} \sim\sim P$ df.

$[\sim(P\cdot Q) \text{ v} \sim\sim P] \supset \sim\sim[\sim(P\cdot Q) \text{ v} \sim\sim P]$ Th. 4

$\sim\sim[\sim(P\cdot Q) \text{ v} \sim\sim P]$ R′ 1

$\sim[(P\cdot Q)\cdot\sim P]$ df.

THEOREM 13. $\vdash_{\overline{HA}}$ ~{~(P·~Q)·~~[~(Q·R)·~~(R·P)]}

Proof:

(~~Q ⊃ Q) ⊃ [(P ⊃ ~~Q) ⊃ (P ⊃ Q)]	Th. 1
~~Q ⊃ Q	Th. 6
(P ⊃ ~~Q) ⊃ (P ⊃ Q)	R′ 1
(P ⊃ Q) ⊃ [~(Q·R) ⊃ ~(R·P)]	Th. 10
(P ⊃ ~~Q) ⊃ [~(Q·R) ⊃ ~(R·P)]	DR′ 1
[~(Q·R) ⊃ ~(R·P)] ⊃ [~~(R·P) ⊃ ~~(Q·R)]	Th. 8
(P ⊃ ~~Q) ⊃ [~~(R·P) ⊃ ~~(Q·R)]	DR′ 1
(P ⊃ ~~Q) ⊃ [~~~(R·P) v ~~(Q·R)]	df.
[~~~(R·P) v ~~(Q·R)] ⊃ [~~(Q·R) v ~~~(R·P)]	P 3
(P ⊃ ~~Q) ⊃ [~~(Q·R) v ~~~(R·P)]	DR′ 1
(~P v ~~Q) ⊃ [~~(Q·R) v ~~~(R·P)]	df.
~~(~P v ~~Q) ⊃ (~P v ~~Q)	Th. 6
~~(~P v ~~Q) ⊃ [~~(Q·R) v ~~~(R·P)]	DR′ 1
[~~(Q·R) v ~~~(R·P)] ⊃ ~~[~~(Q·R) v ~~~(R·P)]	Th. 4
~~(~P v ~~Q) ⊃ ~~[~~(Q·R) v ~~~(R·P)]	DR′ 1
~~[~~(Q·R) v ~~~(R·P)] ⊃ ~~~~[~~(Q·R) v ~~~(R·P)]	Th. 4
~~(~P v ~~Q) ⊃ ~~~~[~~(Q·R) v ~~~(R·P)]	DR′ 1
~~(~P v ~~Q) v ~~~~~[~~(Q·R) v ~~~(R·P)]	df.
{~~~(~P v ~~Q) v ~~~~~[~~(Q·R) v ~~~(R·P)]} ⊃ ~~{~~~~(~P v ~~Q) v ~~~~~~[~~(Q·R) v ~~~(R·P)]}	Th. 4
~~{~~~~(~P v ~~Q) v ~~~~~~[~~(Q·R) v ~~~(R·P)]}	R′ 1
~~{~~(P·~Q) v ~~~[~(Q·R)·~~(R·P)]}	df.
~{~(P·~Q)·~~[~(Q·R)·~~(R·P)]}	df.

We have now proved that Axioms 1, 2, and 3 of R.S. can be derived from the Hilbert-Ackermann System's Postulates 1, 2, 3, and 4 by repeated applications of R′ 1. In the preceding chapter we proved that every tautology is derivable from Axioms 1, 2, and 3 of R.S. by repeated uses of R 1. If we can show that every *wff* derivable by R 1 is also derivable by R′ 1, then we shall have proved that every tautology is derivable from Postulates 1, 2, 3, and 4 of H.A. by repeated uses of R′ 1. This will complete our proof of the deductive completeness of the Hilbert-Ackermann logistic system.

For any *wff* S to follow by its use, R 1 must be applied to two *wffs* of the structure R and $\sim(R{\cdot}\sim S)$. Thus to show that every *wff* derivable from any other *wffs* by R 1 is *also* derivable from those same *wffs* by R′ 1, it will suffice to show that S follows from the *wffs* R and $\sim(R{\cdot}\sim S)$ by R′ 1. This will be stated and proved as our

THIRD DERIVED RULE (DR′ 3). $R,\ \sim(R{\cdot}\sim S) \mathrel{\vert_{\overline{\text{HA}}}} S$.

Proof:

$\sim(R{\cdot}\sim S)$	premiss
$\sim\sim(\sim R \text{ v} \sim\sim S)$	df.
$\sim\sim(\sim R \text{ v} \sim\sim S) \supset (\sim R \text{ v} \sim\sim S)$	Th. 6
$\sim R \text{ v} \sim\sim S$	R′ 1
$R \supset \sim\sim S$	df.
$\sim\sim S \supset S$	Th. 6
$R \supset S$	DR′ 1
R	premiss
S	R′ 1

We have now completed our proof that H.A. is deductively complete. And since it is also functionally complete and analytic, the Hilbert-Ackermann System is a Model System of Logic.

EXERCISES

Prove each of the following to be Model Systems of Logic:

1. The simple system S.S. has as its primitive or undefined symbols, in addition to the propositional symbols P, Q, R, S, . . . , and parentheses, the operator symbols $\sim$ and $\supset$. The axioms of S.S. are

> Ax. 1. $P \supset (Q \supset P)$
> Ax. 2. $[P \supset (Q \supset R)] \supset [(P \supset Q) \supset (P \supset R)]$
> Ax. 3. $(P \supset Q) \supset (\sim Q \supset \sim P)$
> Ax. 4. $\sim\sim P \supset P$
> Ax. 5. $P \supset \sim\sim P$
> Ax. 6. $(P \supset \sim P) \supset \sim(\sim P \supset P)$

The rule of inference for S.S. is R_8 1: If P and $P \supset Q$ then Q. The definition of a *wff* of S.S. parallels the recursive definitions used in R.S. and H.A. The definitions of $P_1, P_2, \ldots, P_n \underset{\text{s}}{\models} Q$ and of $\underset{\text{s}}{\models} Q$ parallel those for R.S. and H.A. The syntactical definitions to be used are

$$P \vee Q = \text{df} \sim P \supset Q$$
$$P \cdot Q = \text{df} \sim (P \supset \sim Q)$$

2. Frege's system F.S. has the same primitive symbols as S.S. and the same rule of inference, the same recursive definition of *wff*, the same syntactical definition of $\vee$ and $\cdot$, but the different axioms:

    Ax. 1. $P \supset (Q \supset P)$
    Ax. 2. $[P \supset (Q \supset R)] \supset [(P \supset Q) \supset (P \supset R)]$
    Ax. 3. $[P \supset (Q \supset R)] \supset [Q \supset (P \supset R)]$
    Ax. 4. $(P \supset Q) \supset (\sim Q \supset \sim P)$
    Ax. 5. $\sim\sim P \supset P$
    Ax. 6. $P \supset \sim\sim P$

The definitions of $P_1, P_2, \ldots, P_n \underset{\text{F}}{\models} Q$ and of $\underset{\text{F}}{\models} Q$ are as usual.

3. Lukasiewicz's system L.S. is similar to S.S. and F.S. in undefined symbols, rules of inference, recursive definition of *wff*, syntactical definitions of $\vee$ and $\cdot$, but with only three axioms:

    Ax. 1. $P \supset (Q \supset P)$
    Ax. 2. $[P \supset (Q \supset R)] \supset [(P \supset Q) \supset (P \supset R)]$
    Ax. 3. $(\sim P \supset \sim Q) \supset (Q \supset P)$

The definitions of $P_1, P_2, \ldots, P_n \underset{\text{L}}{\models} Q$ and of $\underset{\text{L}}{\models} Q$ are as usual.

III. THE USE OF DOTS AS BRACKETS

It has been remarked that the language of symbolic logic requires punctuation if ambiguity is to be avoided. This characteristic is one which it shares with natural languages, such as English, as well as with other artificial languages such as (ordinary) algebra. We have been using three kinds of punctuation marks in our logical language: ordinary parentheses, square brackets, and braces. In the following discussion it will be convenient to use the word 'brackets' to refer indifferently to all of these.

In even moderately complicated formulas it is necessary to use a considerable number of pairs of brackets, which often makes for difficulty in reading the formulas. Our usage, and in fact any usage of paired punctuation devices, involves a certain redundancy. Let us consider the formula

$$(P \supset Q) \vee (P \supset \sim Q)$$

in which *some* punctuation is necessary for the avoidance of ambiguity. Brackets are essential to it, but it need not contain *paired* brackets, for the outermost parentheses can be dropped without incurring any ambiguity, leaving

$$P \supset Q) \vee (P \supset \sim Q.$$

The same punctuation effect can be obtained by replacing the remaining parentheses by dots, which would give

$$P \supset Q . \vee . P \supset \sim Q.$$

There is no danger of confusing the punctuation dot with the conjunction dot because the punctuation dot can only occur adjacently to a connective symbol such as 'v', '$\supset$', or '$\equiv$', while the conjunction dot can never do so.

Dots are symmetrical in shape, in contrast to the asymmetry of brackets. Thus '(', '[', '{' are all concave on the right, which indicates that they group or 'operate toward' the right, while ')', ']', '}' are concave on and 'operate toward' the left. The symmetry of the dot notation is compensated for by introducing the convention that punctuation dots always operate *away* from the connective symbol to which they are adjacent.

There is another characteristic which the method of bracketing logical formulas shares with the method of punctuating sentences of natural languages. The latter have punctuation marks of different degrees of strength, the stronger of which 'take precedence over' or 'extend over' the weaker. For example, a period is stronger than a semicolon, and a semicolon is stronger than a comma. Of the three kinds of brackets used for punctuating our logical formulas, the unstated convention has been followed of regarding braces as stronger than square brackets, and square brackets as stronger than parentheses. That is, we have used parentheses to group symbols *within* square brackets, but not conversely, and we have used square brackets to group symbols *within* braces, but not conversely. This usage was illustrated in the statement of Theorem 13 of the Hilbert-Ackermann system:

$$\sim\{\sim(P\cdot\sim Q)\cdot\sim\sim[\sim(QR)\cdot\sim\sim(RP)]\}.$$

When this convention is adhered to, it permits the dropping of additional redundant brackets. Thus the formula

$$(P \supset Q) \supset [(R \text{ v } P) \supset (R \text{ v } Q)]$$

remains unambiguous when rewritten as

$$P \supset Q) \supset [R \text{ v } P) \supset (R \text{ v } Q.$$

If we use a single dot in place of a parenthesis, and a double dot in place of a square bracket, the preceding formula can be rewritten as

$$P \supset Q . \supset : R \text{ v } P . \supset . R \text{ v } Q$$

where the convention is that two dots bind more strongly or have greater scope than one dot. Using three dots as a punctuation mark which has greater scope than either one or two dots, the seventh formula in the proof of Theorem 9 of H.A.,

$$[P \text{ v } (Q \text{ v } R)] \supset \{P \text{ v } [Q \text{ v } (P \text{ v } R)]\}$$

can be rewritten as

$$P \text{ v } . Q \text{ v } R : \supset : . P \text{ v } : Q \text{ v } . P \text{ v } R.$$

In writing the sixth formula of that proof, we were forced to include one pair of braces within another, because we had only three kinds of brackets available. Now the use of dots permits the generation of as many different punctuation marks of different degrees of strength as may be desired, by the simple expedient of adding dots one at a time. The general convention here is that the scope of a group of n dots extends over that of any number of groups of less than n dots, and that the scope of a group of n dots extends to but not beyond the nearest group of n or more dots. The sixth formula of the proof of Theorem 9 of H.A.,

$$\{(Q \vee R) \supset [Q \vee (P \vee R)]\} \supset \{[P \vee (Q \vee R)] \supset \{P \vee [Q \vee (P \vee R)]\}\}$$

can be written as

$$Q \vee R . \supset : Q \vee . P \vee R :. \supset :: P \vee . Q \vee R : \supset :. P \vee : Q \vee . P \vee R.$$

For the sake of symmetry and greater ease of reading, one frequently adds dots which are not strictly necessary for the avoidance of ambiguity. Thus the formula

$$P \supset . Q \supset P$$

is frequently written

$$P . \supset . Q \supset P.$$

The preceding lengthy formula may be more easily read when rewritten according to this convention as

$$Q \vee R : \supset : Q . \vee . P \vee R :: \supset :: P . \vee . Q \vee R :. \supset :. P : \vee : Q . \vee . P \vee R.$$

One matter not yet discussed is the way in which bracketing by dots is to be done when two bracketed expressions are connected by the conjunction symbol, as, for example, in the formula

$$(P \supset Q) \cdot (Q \supset P).$$

Applying the technique already described, we should emerge with the awkward expression

$$P \supset Q \,\cdot\,\cdot\,\cdot\, Q \supset P.$$

For the avoidance of this kind of repetitiousness, it is customary to dispense with the special bracketing dots, and to let the conjunction dot do the work of bracketing, rewriting the formula simply as

$$P \supset Q . Q \supset P.$$

Here the single dot is to be thought of as operating in *both* directions, left and right. That this convention is satisfactory can be seen by observing that the different formulas

1. $P \supset [(Q.Q) \supset P]$
2. $[P \supset (Q.Q)] \supset P$
3. $[(P \supset Q).Q] \supset P$
4. $P \supset [Q.(Q \supset P)]$

can be written in distinguishable and unambiguous fashion as

1'. $P \supset :. Q.Q : \supset P$
2'. $P \supset : Q.Q :. \supset P$
3'. $P \supset Q.Q : \supset P$
4'. $P \supset : Q.Q \supset P$

The use of dots as brackets has the advantage of economy, and the further advantage of providing an infinite number of different punctuation marks of different degrees of strength, where the strength or scope of each may be determined by the simple expedient of counting its constituent dots.*

EXERCISES

1. Rewrite the proofs of the last five theorems of H.A. using dots instead of brackets.
2. Rewrite the proofs of the last five theorems of R.S. using dots instead of brackets.

IV. A PARENTHESIS-FREE NOTATION

A system of symbolism which dispenses with brackets entirely has been devised by the Polish logician, J. Lukasiewicz, and has been extensively used by logicians of the Polish School. Corresponding to the four most commonly used operator symbols

$$\sim \quad \supset \quad \cdot \quad \text{v}$$

they have the four symbols

$$N \quad C \quad K \quad A.$$

---

* A more extended discussion of this topic will be found in *Symbolic Logic*, by C. I. Lewis and C. H. Langford, New York, 1932, Appendix I, pp. 486–489. For more technical discussions, the reader is referred to 'On The Use of Dots as Brackets in Logical Expressions', by H. B. Curry, in *The Journal of Symbolic Logic*, vol. 2 (1937), pp. 26–28 and 'The Use of Dots as Brackets in Church's System', by A. M. Turing, *Ibid.*, vol. 7 (1942), pp. 146–156.

In writing their formulas they use lower case letters '*p*', '*q*', '*r*', '*s*', . . . instead of the capital letters '*P*', '*Q*', '*R*', '*S*', . . . which we have been accustomed to. Instead of the connective symbols '*C*', '*K*', '*A*' being written *between* the formulas they connect, they are placed directly to the left of the two formulas to be joined. Thus

$$\sim P \text{ is written } Np$$
$$P \supset Q \text{ is written } Cpq$$
$$P \cdot Q \text{ is written } Kpq$$
$$P \vee Q \text{ is written } Apq$$

That this notation is unambiguous without the use of parentheses or brackets of any kind is seen by comparing the following formulas:

$$P \supset (Q \supset R) \text{ is written } CpCqr$$
$$(P \supset Q) \supset R \text{ is written } CCpqr$$
$$P \supset (Q \cdot R) \text{ is written } CpKqr$$
$$(P \supset Q) \cdot R \text{ is written } KCpqr$$
$$(P \vee Q) \supset (R \cdot S) \text{ is written } CApqKrs$$

The axioms of R.S. translate into the Polish notation as

Ax. 1. *CpKpp*
Ax. 2. *CKpqp*
Ax. 3. *CCpqCNKqrNKrp*

And the three postulates of Lukasiewicz's own system are written in his notation as

P 1. *CpCqp*
P 2. *CCpCqrCCpqCpr*
P 3. *CCNqNpCpq*

The Polish notation has the obvious advantage of dispensing with all special punctuation marks, for the *order* in which its symbols are written suffices to make any formula unambiguous. And its use is becoming more widespread, especially in connection with computer work. *

---

* Cf. *Truth-function Evaluation Using the Polish Notation*, by Arthur W. Burks, Don W. Warren, and Jesse Wright. Published by the Engineering Research Institute of the University of Michigan.

EXERCISES

1. Translate the postulates of H.A. into the Polish notation.
2. Translate the postulates of F.S. into the Polish notation.
3. Write out the proofs of the last five theorems of H.A. in the Polish notation.
4. Write out the proofs of the last five theorems of R.S. in the Polish notation.
5. Expressing all formulas in the Polish notation, derive the six postulates of F.S. from the three postulates of L.S.

V. THE STROKE AND DAGGER OPERATORS

Any of the following pairs of operators will provide a functionally complete logic: $\sim$ and $\cdot$, $\sim$ and v, $\sim$ and $\supset$, or $\supset$ and $+$. It is possible to obtain a functionally complete system of logic containing just a single operator, and we can do it in either of two ways.

The first of these ways is by adopting as the single primitive operator the so-called 'stroke function'. This operator symbol, called 'alternative denial' by Quine,* operates on or connects two formulas and is written '$P|Q$'. Its standard interpretation is that of denying that both of the formulas P and Q are true, which is the same as affirming that at least one is false. It is defined by the truth table

P	Q	$P|Q$
T	T	F
T	F	T
F	T	T
F	F	T

The other operators, $\sim$, $\cdot$, v, and $\supset$ can all be defined in terms of the stroke function. That the following definitions preserve the standard interpretations of the symbols being defined is

---

* Cf. pp. 48–49 of *Mathematical Logic*, by W. V. O. Quine, Harvard University Press, 1947. The stroke function is frequently referred to as the 'Sheffer stroke function' after Professor H. M. Sheffer, although it was first discovered by C. S. Peirce.

easily verified by the method of truth tables:

$$\sim P = \mathrm{df}\ P|P$$
$$P.Q = \mathrm{df}\ P|Q.|.P|Q$$
$$P \vee Q = \mathrm{df}\ P|P.|.Q|Q$$
$$P \supset Q = \mathrm{df}\ P.|.Q|Q$$

The other operator which suffices for a functionally complete logic is that of 'joint denial', symbolized by a dagger with its point down. Written '$P{\downarrow}Q$', its standard interpretation is that of denying that either of the formulas P or Q is true, which is the same as affirming that they are both false. It is defined by the truth table

P	Q	$P{\downarrow}Q$
T	T	F
T	F	F
F	T	F
F	F	T

The other operators can all be defined in terms of the dagger function alone. That the following definitions preserve the standard interpretations of the symbols being defined is easily verified by the method of the truth tables:

$$\sim P = \mathrm{df}\ P{\downarrow}P$$
$$P.Q = \mathrm{df}\ P{\downarrow}P.{\downarrow}.Q{\downarrow}Q$$
$$P \vee Q = \mathrm{df}\ P{\downarrow}Q.{\downarrow}.P{\downarrow}Q$$
$$P \supset Q = \mathrm{df}\ P{\downarrow}P.{\downarrow}.Q:{\downarrow}:P{\downarrow}P.{\downarrow}.Q$$

Thus we see that functionally complete systems of logic based on only one operator can be constructed in terms either of the stroke or the dagger. It is interesting to note the parallelism between the definition of the stroke function in terms of the dagger and the definition of the dagger function in terms of the stroke. These are

$$P{\downarrow}Q = \mathrm{df}\ P|P.|.Q|Q:|:P|P.|.Q|Q$$
$$P|Q = \mathrm{df}\ P{\downarrow}P.{\downarrow}.Q{\downarrow}Q:{\downarrow}:P{\downarrow}P.{\downarrow}.Q{\downarrow}Q$$

as may easily be verified.

EXERCISES

1. Express the three axioms of R.S. in terms of the stroke function alone.
2. Express the six postulates of F.S. in terms of the stroke function alone.
3. Express the four postulates of H.A. in terms of the dagger function alone.
4. Express the three postulates of L.S. in terms of the dagger function alone.

VI. THE NICOD SYSTEM

Thus far in the text and exercises, a number of alternative Model Systems of Logic have been set forth. Each of them is based on two primitive operator symbols, and the number of their axioms or postulates ranges from three (for R.S. and L.S.) to six (for S.S. and F.S.). A system that is more economical both in primitive operators and postulates is due to J. G. P. Nicod.[*] The Nicod System can be set forth as follows.

The primitive symbols are infinitely many propositional symbols P, Q, R, S, T, with and without subscripts, parentheses (or dots), and the single operator symbol '$|$'. The recursive rule for well formed formulas in N may be stated as:

1. Any single letter of N is a *wff*.
2. If P and Q are *wffs*, then $(P)|(Q)$ is a *wff*.
(No formula of N will be regarded as being a *wff* unless its being so follows from this definition.)

It should be noted that even the recursive rule for well formed formulas is simpler in the Nicod System, needing only two rather than three clauses. We have here the first fruit of using only one operator symbol.

[*] 'A Reduction in the Number of the Primitive Propositions of Logic', by J. G. P. Nicod, *Proceedings of the Cambridge Philosophical Society*, vol. 19 (1916), pp. 32–40. Cf. also

A Treatise of Formal Logic, by J. Jørgensen, London, 1931, vol. 2, pp. 149–172.

'A Note on Nicod's Postulate', by W. V. Quine, *Mind*, n.s. vol. 41 (1932), pp. 345–350.

'Remark on Nicod's Reduction of *Principia Mathematica*', by B. A. Bernstein, *The Journal of Symbolic Logic*, vol. 2 (1937), pp. 165–166.

The single axiom required (or rather, the single pattern for infinitely many axioms of the object logic) is stated in our metalanguage, in which we use dots for brackets, as

$$\text{Ax. } P.|.Q|R:|::T.|.T|T:.|::S|Q:|:P|S.|.P|S$$

The single rule of inference required may be stated as

Rule. If P and $P.|.R|Q$ then Q.

The definition of 'valid argument in N' and of 'theorem of N', that is, of

$$P_1, P_2, \ldots, P_n \underset{\text{N}}{\Vdash} Q \qquad \text{and} \qquad \underset{\text{N}}{\Vdash} P$$

are strictly analogous to those given for '$\underset{\text{RS}}{\Vdash}$', '$\underset{\text{HA}}{\Vdash}$', '$\underset{\text{S}}{\Vdash}$', '$\underset{\text{F}}{\Vdash}$', and '$\underset{\text{L}}{\Vdash}$'.

Although more economical in the respects indicated, the Nicod System can scarcely be said to be *simpler* than such systems as R.S., H.A., F.S. and L.S. There is only one axiom for N, but it is more complicated than any axiom or postulate of any of the other systems. Not only is it longer, but it involves five distinct propositional symbols, 'P', 'Q', 'R', 'S', and 'T', whereas the entire set of axioms for any of the other systems can be stated in terms of only three distinct propositional symbols. The situation is similar with respect to the rules of inference of the several systems. The Nicod Rule is not *modus ponens*, but a more powerful instrument for deduction. *Modus ponens*, which may be stated as

$$\text{if } P \text{ and } P.|.Q|Q \text{ then } Q$$

is simply a special case of the Nicod Rule, in which 'R' and 'Q' denote identically the same well formed formula of the object language. Nicod's Rule as well as his axiom is more complicated than those required in less economical systems of logic.

That the Nicod System is functionally complete has already been indicated in our discussion of the stroke function in Section V. The analyticity of N is simply enough shown by establishing via truth tables that the Axiom is tautologous, and that the Rule can lead only to tautologies from tautologies. The deductive completeness of N remains to be proved to complete the proof that the Nicod System is a Model Logic. When this is attempted we find that for all the economy of its single axiom and the greater deductive strength of its Rule, it is very difficult indeed to derive theorems in the Nicod system. Nevertheless it is interesting from the point of view of seeing how far one can go in the direction of reducing the number of postulates and still have a deductively complete system of logic.

We shall develop seventeen theorems of the Nicod system, and one derived rule. The last four theorems will be the four axioms of the Hilbert-Ackermann System, and the derived rule will be the Hilbert-Ackermann System's rule R′ 1. Of course these must be stated in their unabbreviated form, and then expressed in the Nicod System's notation. The Hilbert-Ackermann axioms, expressed in terms of that system's primitive symbols $\sim$ and v are

1. $\sim(P \text{ v } P) \text{ v } P$
2. $\sim P \text{ v } (P \text{ v } Q)$
3. $\sim(P \text{ v } Q) \text{ v } (Q \text{ v } P)$
4. $\sim(\sim P \text{ v } Q) \text{ v } [\sim(R \text{ v } P) \text{ v } (R \text{ v } Q)]$

The Hilbert-Ackermann rule, similarly unabbreviated, is

$$\text{If } P \text{ and } \sim P \text{ v } Q \text{ then } Q.$$

These, expressed in the Nicod System's notation, in which '$\sim P$' is written '$P|P$', and '$P \text{ v } Q$' is written '$P|P.|.Q|Q$', are

1. $P|P.|.P|P:|:P|P.|.P|P:.|:.P|P.|.P|P:|:P|P.|.P|P::|::P|P.$
2. $P|P.|.P|P:.|:.P|P.|.Q|Q:|:P|P.|.Q|Q.$
3. $P|P.|.Q|Q:|:P|P.|.Q|Q:.|:.P|P.|.Q|Q:|:P|P.|.Q|Q::|::Q|Q.|.P|P:|:Q|Q.|.$
   $P|P.$
4. $P|P.|.P|P:|:Q|Q:.|:.P|P.|.P|P:|:Q|Q::|::P|P.|.P|P:|:Q|Q:.|:.P|P.|.$
   $P|P:|:Q|Q:::|:::R|R.|.P|P:|:R|R.|.P|P:.|:.R|R.|.P|P:|:R|R.|.P|P::|::$
   $R|R.|.Q|Q:|:R|R.|.Q|Q:.|:.R|R.|.P|P:|:R|R.|.P|P:.|:.R|R.|.P|P:|:R|R.|.$
   $P|P::|::R|R.|.Q|Q:|:R|R.|.Q|Q.$

R′ 1. If P and $P|P.|.P|P:|:Q|Q$ then Q.

Our development of the Nicod system will be entirely in terms of the stroke function. Since the formulas of the proofs are of almost intolerable length, they will be *described* rather than written out. Our descriptions, however, will be sufficiently complete to permit the reader to write them out for himself.

Theorem 1. $\vdash_{\overline{N}}$ $Q{:.}|{:.}T.|.T|T{:}|{:}S{::.}|{::.}S{:}|{:}T.|.T|T{:.}|{:.}Q{::}|{::}S{:}|{:}T.|.$ $T|T{:.}|{:.}Q.$

Proof: Step 1 is the Nicod Axiom with T in place of P, of Q, and of R. Step 2 is the Nicod Axiom with $T.|.T|T$ in place of P and of Q, and with $S|T{:}|{:}T|S.|.T|S$ in place of R. Step 3 is the result of applying the Nicod Rule to steps 1 and 2. Step 4 is the Nicod Axiom with $S{:}|{:}T.|.T|T$ in place of P, with $T.|.T|T{:}|{:}S$ in place of Q and of R, and with Q in place of S. Step 5 is the result of applying the Nicod Rule to steps 3 and 4.

Theorem 2. $\vdash_{\overline{N}}$ $T.|.T|T.$

Proof: Step 1 is Theorem 1 with $T.|.T|T$ in place of Q, and with $S|T{:}|{:}T|S.|.T|S$ in place of S. Step 2 is the Nicod Axiom with $T.|.T|T{::}|{::}T.|.T|T{:.}|{:.}S|T{:}|{:}T|S.|.T|S$ in place of P, with $S|T{:}|{:}T|S.|.T|S{:.}|{:.}T.|.T|T{::}|{::}T.|.T|T$ in place of Q and of R, and with $S|T{:::}|{:::}S|T{:}|{:}T|S.|.T|S{:.}|{:.}T.|.$ $T|T{::}|{::}S{::.}|{::.}S|T{:}|{:}T|S.|.T|S{:.}|{:.}T.|.T|T{::}|{::}S{:::.}|{:::.}$ $T.|.T|T$ in place of S. Step 3 is the result of applying the Nicod Rule to steps 1 and 2. Step 4 is the Nicod Axiom with $S|T{:}|{:}T|S.|.T|S{:.}|{:.}T.|.T|T$ in place of P, with T in place of Q, and with $T|T$ in place of R. Step 5 is Theorem 1 with $S|T{:}|{:}T|S.|.T|S{:.}|{:.}T.|.T|T{::}|{::}T.|.T|T$ in place of Q and with $S|T{:::}|{:::}S|T{:}|{:}T|S.|.T|S{:.}|{:.}T.|.T|T{::}|{::}S{::.}$ $|{::.}S|T{:}|{:}T|S.|.T|S{:.}|{:.}T.|.T|T{::}|{::}S$ in place of S. Step 6 is the result of applying the Nicod Rule to steps 4 and 5. Step 7 is the result of applying the Nicod Rule to steps 3 and 6. Step 8 is the Nicod Axiom with T in place of P, of Q, and of R. Step 9 is the result of applying the Nicod Rule to steps 7 and 8.

THEOREM 3. $\vdash_{\text{N}}$ $S|P:|:P|S.|.P|S$.

Proof: Step 1 is the Nicod Axiom with P in place of Q and of R. Step 2 is Theorem 2 with P in place of T. Step 3 is the result of applying the Nicod Rule to steps 1 and 2.

THEOREM 4. $\vdash_{\text{N}}$ $P|P.|.P$

Proof: Step 1 is Theorem 3 with $P|P$ in place of P and with P in place of S. Step 2 is Theorem 2 with P in place of T. Step 3 is the result of applying the Nicod Rule to steps 1 and 2.

THEOREM 5. $\vdash_{\text{N}}$ $P|P:|:S|P.|.S|P$

Proof: Step 1 is Theorem 3 with $P|S$ in place of S and with $S|P.|.S|P$ in place of P. Step 2 is Theorem 3 with P in place of S and S in place of P. Step 3 is the result of applying the Nicod Rule to steps 1 and 2. Step 4 is the Nicod Axiom with $S|P.|.S|P$ in place of P, with P in place of Q, with S in place of R, and with $P|P$ in place of S. Step 5 is the result of applying the Nicod Rule to steps 3 and 4. Step 6 is Theorem 4. Step 7 is the result of applying the Nicod Rule to steps 5 and 6. Step 8 is Theorem 3 with $S|P.|.S|P$ in place of S, and with $P|P$ in place of P. Step 9 is the result of applying the Nicod Rule to steps 7 and 8.

THEOREM 6. $\vdash_{\text{N}}$ $P.|.Q|R::|:::S|Q:|:P|S.|.P|S:.|:..S|Q:|:P|S.|.P|S$

Proof: Step 1 is the Nicod Axiom with $S|Q:|:P|S.|.P|S:.|:..S|Q:|:P|S.|.P|S$ in place of P, with $T.|.T|T:.|:..S|Q:|:P|S.|.P|S$ in place of Q and of R, and with $P.|.Q|R$ in place of S. Step 2 is Theorem 5 with $S|Q:|:P|S.|.P|S$ in place of P, and with $T.|.T|T$ in place of S. Step 3 is the result of applying the Nicod Rule to steps 1 and 2. Step 4 is the Nicod Axiom. Step 5 is the result of applying the Nicod Rule to steps 3 and 4. Step 6 is Theorem 3 with $S|Q:|:P|S.|.P|S:.|:..S|Q:|:P|S.|.P|S$ in place of S, and with $P.|.Q|R$ in place of P. Step 7 is the result of applying the Nicod Rule to steps 5 and 6.

THEOREM 7. $\vdash_{\overline{N}}$ $Q|S.|.U:|:Q|S.|.U:.|:.S|Q.|.U$

Proof: Step 1 is Theorem 6 with $Q|S$ in place of P, with $S|Q$ in place of Q and of R, and with U in place of S. Step 2 is Theorem 3 with Q in place of S and with S in place of P. Step 3 is the result of applying the Nicod Rule to steps 1 and 2. Step 4 is Theorem 3 with $U.|.S|Q$ in place of S and with $Q|S.|.U:|:Q|S.|.U$ in place of P. Step 5 is the result of applying the Nicod Rule to steps 3 and 4. Step 6 is Theorem 6 with $S|Q.|.U$ in place of P, with $U.|.S|Q$ in place of Q and of R, and with $Q|S.|.U:|:Q|S.|.U$ in place of S. Step 7 is Theorem 3 with $S|Q$ in place of S and with U in place of P. Step 8 is the result of applying the Nicod Rule to steps 6 and 7. Step 9 is the result of applying the Nicod Rule to steps 5 and 8. Step 10 is Theorem 3 with $S|Q.|.U$ in place of S, and with $Q|S.|.U:|:Q|S.|.U$ in place of P. Step 11 is the result of applying the Nicod Rule to steps 9 and 10.

THEOREM 8. $\vdash_{\overline{N}}$ $P.|.Q|R::|:::Q|S:|:P|S.|.P|S:.|:.Q|S:|:P|S.|.P|S$

Proof: Step 1 is Theorem 6 with $P.|.Q|R$ in place of P, with $S|Q:|:P|S.|.P|S$ in place of Q and of R, and with $Q|S:|:P|S.|.P|S:.|:.Q|S:|:P|S.|.P|S$ in place of S. Step 2 is Theorem 6. Step 3 is the result of applying the Nicod Rule to steps 1 and 2. Step 4 is Theorem 7 with $P|S.|.P|S$ in place of U. Step 5 is the result of applying the Nicod Rule to steps 3 and 4.

THEOREM 9. $\vdash_{\overline{N}}$ $S:.|:.P.|.S|S:|:P.|.S|S$

Proof: Step 1 is Theorem 3 with $S|S.|.P$ in place of S, and with $P.|.S|S:|:P.|.S|S$ in place of P. Step 2 is Theorem 1 with $S|S$ in place of S. Step 3 is the result of applying the Nicod Rule to steps 1 and 2. Step 4 is the Nicod Axiom with $P.|.S|S:|:P.|.S|S$ in place of P, with $S|S$ in place of Q, and with P in place of R. Step 5 is the result of applying the Nicod Rule to steps 3 and 4. Step 6 is Theorem 2 with S in place of T. Step 7 is the result of applying the Nicod Rule to steps 5 and 6. Step 8 is Theorem 3 with $P.|.S|S:|:P.|.S|S$ in place of S, and with S in place of P. Step 9 is the result of applying the Nicod Rule to steps 7 and 8.

THEOREM 10. $\vdash_{\overline{N}}$ $Q|Q:|:Q|S.|.Q|S$

Proof: Step 1 is Theorem 8 with $Q|Q$ in place of P, with $S|Q$ in place of Q and of R, and with $Q|S.|.Q|S$ in place of S. Step 2 is Theorem 5 with Q in place of P. Step 3 is the result of applying the Nicod Rule to steps 1 and 2. Step 4 is Theorem 3 with Q in place of P. Step 5 is the result of applying the Nicod Rule to steps 3 and 4.

THEOREM 11. $\vdash_{\overline{N}}$ $Q:.|:.Q|P.|.P:|:Q|P.|.P$

Proof: Step 1 is Theorem 8 with Q in place of R and with P in place of S. Step 2 is Theorem 9 with Q in place of S. Step 3 is Theorem 8 with Q in place of P, with $P.|.Q|Q$ in place of Q and of R, and with $Q|P:|:P|P.|.P|P:.|:.Q|P:|:P|P.|.P|P$ in place of S. Step 4 is the result of applying the Nicod Rule to steps 2 and 3. Step 5 is the result of applying the Nicod Rule to steps 1 and 4. Step 6 is Theorem 9 with $P|P.|.P$ in place of S and with Q in place of P. Step 7 is Theorem 4. Step 8 is the result of applying the Nicod Rule to steps 6 and 7. Step 9 is Theorem 8 with $Q|P$ in place of P, with $P|P$ in place of Q and of R, and with P in place of S. Step 10 is Theorem 8 with Q in place of P, with $Q|P:|:P|P.|.P|P$ in place of Q and of R, and with $P|P.|.P:.|$ $:.Q|P.|.P:|:Q|P.|.P::|:::P|P.|.P:.|:.Q|P.|.P:|:Q|P.|.P$ in place of S. Step 11 is the result of applying the Nicod Rule to steps 5 and 10. Step 12 is the result of applying the Nicod Rule to steps 9 and 11. Step 13 is Theorem 8 with Q in place of P, with $P|P.|.P$ in place of Q and of R, and with $Q|P.|.P:|:Q|P.|.P$ in place of S. Step 14 is the result of applying the Nicod Rule to steps 8 and 13. Step 15 is Theorem 8 with Q in place of P, with $P|P.|.P:.|:.Q|P.|.$ $P:|:Q|P.|.P$ in place of Q and of R, and with $Q:.|:.Q|P.|.$ $P:|:Q|P.|.P::|:::Q:.|:.Q|P.|.P:|:Q|P.|.P$ in place of S. Step 16 is the result of applying the Nicod Rule to steps 12 and 15. Step 17 is the result of applying the Nicod Rule to steps 14 and 16. Step 18 is Theorem 10 with $Q|P.|.P:|:Q|P.|.P$ in place of S. Step 19 is Theorem 3 with $Q|Q$ in place of S, and with $Q:.|:.Q|P.|.P:|:Q|P.|.P::|::Q:.|:.Q|P.|.P:|:Q|P.|.P$ in place of P. Step 20 is the result of applying the Nicod Rule to steps 18 and 19. Step 21 is Theorem 8 with $Q:.|:.Q|P.|.P:|:Q|P.|.P::|::Q:.|:.Q|P.|.P:|:Q|P.|.P$ in place of P and of S, and with Q in place of R. Step 22 is the result of applying the Nicod Rule to steps 20 and 21. Step 23 is the result of applying the Nicod Rule to steps 17 and 22. Step 24 is Theorem 4 with $Q:.|:.Q|P.|.P:|:Q|P.|.P::|::Q:.|:.Q|P.|.P:|:Q|P.|.P$ in place of P. Step 25 is the result of applying the Nicod Rule to steps 23 and 24.

Theorem 12. $\vdash_{\text{N}} P:|:Q|R.|.Q|R::|::Q:|:P|R.|.P|R::.|:.Q:|:P|R.|.P|R$

Proof: Step 1 is Theorem 8 with Q in place of P, with $Q|R.|.R$ in place of Q and of R, and with $P|R.|.P|R$ in place of S. Step 2 is Theorem 11 with R in place of P. Step 3 is the result of applying the Nicod Rule to steps 1 and 2. Step 4 is Theorem 8 with $P:|:Q|R.|.Q|R$ in place of P, with $Q|R.|.R:|:P|R.|.P|R$ in place of Q and of R, and with $Q:|:P|R.|.P|R:.|:.Q:|:P|R.|.P|R$ in place of S. Step 5 is Theorem 8 with $Q|R$ in place of Q and of R, and with R in place of S. Step 6 is the result of applying the Nicod Rule to steps 4 and 5. Step 7 is the result of applying the Nicod Rule to steps 3 and 6.

Theorem 13. $\vdash_{\text{N}} P.|.Q|Q::.|::.R|R.|.P|P::.|:.R|R.|.Q|Q:|:R|R.|.Q|Q::|:::R|R.|.P|P::.|:.R|R.|.Q|Q:|:R|R.|.Q|Q$

Proof: Step 1 is Theorem 12 with $R|R.|.P|P$ in place of P, with $P.|.Q|Q$ in place of Q, and with $R|R.|.Q|Q:|:R|R.|.Q|Q$ in place of R. Step 2 is Theorem 8 with $R|R$ in place of P, with P in place of Q and of R, and with $Q|Q$ in place of S. Step 3 is the result of applying the Nicod Rule to steps 1 and 2.

THEOREM 14. $\underset{\text{N}}{\vdash}$ $P|P.|.P|P:|:P|P.|.P|P:.|:.P|P.|.P|P:|:P|P.|.P|P::|:::P|P$
(Ax. 1 of H.A.)

Proof: Step 1 is Theorem 4 with $P|P.|.P|P:|:P|P.|.P|P$ in place of
P. Step 2 is Theorem 4 with $P|P$ in place of P. Step 3 is
Theorem 8 with $P|P.|.P|P:|:P|P.|.P|P:.|:.P|P.|.P|P:|:P|P.|.$
$P|P$ in place of P, with $P|P.|.P|P$ in place of Q and of R,
and with $P|P$ in place of S. Step 4 is the result of applying
the Nicod Rule to steps 1 and 3. Step 5 is the result of
applying the Nicod Rule to steps 2 and 4.

THEOREM 15. $\underset{\text{N}}{\vdash}$ $P|P.|.P|P:.|:.P|P.|.Q|Q:|:P|P.|.Q|Q$ (Ax. 2 of H.A.)

Proof: Step 1 is Theorem 10 with $P|P$ in place of Q, and with
$Q|Q$ in place of S.

THEOREM 16. $\underset{\text{N}}{\vdash}$ $P|P.|.Q|Q:|:P|P.|.Q|Q:.|:.P|P.|.Q|Q:|:P|P.|.Q|Q::|:::Q|$
$Q.|.P|P:|:Q|Q.|.P|P$ (Ax. 3 of H.A.)

Proof: Step 1 is Theorem 3 with $P|P$ in place of S, and with $Q|Q$
in place of P. Step 2 is Theorem 4 with $P|P.|.Q|Q:|:P|P.|.$
$Q|Q$ in place of P. Step 3 is Theorem 8 with $P|P.|.Q|Q:|:$
$P|P.|.Q|Q:.|:.P|P.|.Q|Q:|:P|P.|.Q|Q$ in place of P, with
$P|P.|.Q|Q$ in place of Q and of R, and with $Q|Q.|.P|P:|:$
$Q|Q.|.P|P$ in place of S. Step 4 is the result of applying
the Nicod Rule to steps 2 and 3. Step 5 is the result of
applying the Nicod Rule to steps 1 and 4.

THEOREM 17. $\underset{\text{N}}{\vdash}$ $P|P.|.P|P:|:Q|Q:.|:.P|P.|.P|P:|:Q|Q::|:::P|P.|.P|P:|:$
$Q|Q:.|:.P|P.|.P|P:|:Q|Q:::|::::R|R.|.P|P:|:R|R.|.P|P:.|:.R|R.|.P|P:|:$
$R|R.|.P|P::|:::R|R.|.Q|Q:|:R|R.|.Q|Q::.|:::R|R.|.P|P:|:R|R.|.P|P:.|:.$
$R|R.|.P|P:|:R|R.|.P|P::|:::R|R.|.Q|Q:|:R|R.|.Q|Q$ (Ax. 4 of H.A.)

Proof: Step 1 is Theorem 4 with $P|P.|.P|P:|:Q|Q:.|:.P|P.|.P|P:|:$
$Q|Q$ in place of P. Step 2 is Theorem 9 with P for S
and $P|P$ for P. Step 3 is Theorem 8 with $P|P.|.P|P$ in place
of Q and of R, and with $Q|Q$ in place of S. Step 4 is the
result of applying the Nicod Rule to steps 2 and 3. Step 5
is Theorem 8 with $P|P.|.P|P:|:Q|Q:.|:.P|P.|.P|P:|:Q|Q::|:::$
$P|P.|.P|P:|:Q|Q:.|:.P|P.|.P|P:|:Q|Q$ in place of P, with
$P|P.|.P|P:|:Q|Q$ in place of Q and of R, and with $P.|.Q|Q:|:$
$P.|.Q|Q$ in place of S. Step 6 is the result of applying the

Nicod Rule to steps 1 and 5. Step 7 is the result of applying the Nicod Rule to steps 4 and 6. Step 8 is Theorem 13. Step 9 is Theorem 4 with $R|R.|.P|P:|:R|R.|.P|P$ in place of P. Step 10 is Theorem 8 with $R|R.|.P|P:|:R|R.|.P|P:.|:.R|R.|.P|P:|:R|R.|.P|P$ in place of P, with $R|R.|.P|P$ in place of Q and of R, and with $R|R.|.Q|Q:|:R|R.|.Q|Q$ in place of S. Step 11 is the result of applying the Nicod Rule to steps 9 and 10. Step 12 is Theorem 8 with $P.|.Q|Q$ in place of P, with $R|R.|.P|P:.|:.R|R.|.Q|Q:|:R|R.|.Q|Q$ in place of Q and of R, and with $R|R.|.P|P:|:R|R.|.P|P:.|:.R|R.|.P|P:|:R|R.|.P|P:|::R|R.|.Q|Q:|:R|R.|.Q|Q:.|::.R|R.|.P|P:|:R|R.|.P|P:.|:.R|R.|.P|P:|:R|R.|.P|P::|::R|R.|.Q|Q:|:R|R.|.Q|Q$ in place of S. Step 13 is the result of applying the Nicod Rule to steps 8 and 12. Step 14 is the result of applying the Nicod Rule to steps 11 and 13. Step 15 is Theorem 8 with $P|P.|.P|P:|:Q|Q:.|:.P|P.|.P|P:|:Q|Q::|:::P|P.|.P|P:|:Q|Q:.|:.P|P.|.P|P:|:Q|Q$ in place of P, with $P.|.Q|Q$ in place of Q and of R, and with $R|R.|.P|P:|:R|R.|.P|P:.|:.R|R.|.P|P:|:R|R.|.P|P::|:::R|R.|.Q|Q:|:R|R.|.Q|Q::|:::R|R.|.P|P:|:R|R.|.P|P:.|:.R|R.|.P|P:|:R|R.|.P|P::|:::R|R.|.Q|Q:|:R|R.|.Q|Q$ in place of S. Step 16 is the result of applying the Nicod Rule to steps 7 and 15. Step 17 is the result of applying the Nicod Rule to steps 14 and 16.

DR 1. $P,\ P|P.|.P|P:|:Q|Q \ \vdash_{\overline{N}}\ Q$ (R′ 1 of H.A).

Proof: Step 1 is Theorem 9 with P in place of S, and with $P|P$ in place of P. Step 2 is the premiss P. Step 3 is the result of applying the Nicod Rule to steps 1 and 2. Step 4 is the premiss $P|P.|.P|P:|:Q|Q$. Step 5 is the result of applying the Nicod Rule to steps 3 and 4.

Deriving all tautologies from a single axiom (axiom form) by a single rule in terms of a single operator is thus seen to be possible. But it is a tedious business. As Dr. Samuel Johnson is said to have remarked about a woman preaching, it is ' . . . like a dog's walking on his hind legs. It is not done well; but you are surprised to find it done at all.'

CHAPTER NINE

A First-Order
Function Calculus

I. THE NEW LOGISTIC SYSTEM RS₁

In Chapter Four and the first four sections of Chapter Five we *used* certain logical rules or principles governing the quantification of individual variables in validating arguments and in demonstrating logical truths. An axiomatic development of those principles is called a 'first-order function calculus', or, alternatively, a 'lower' or 'restricted' function calculus. In this chapter we shall set up such a logistic system, develop some of its theorems, and prove that it has certain (desirable) properties such as consistency and completeness—of a sort. Again our meta-language will be ordinary English plus some very elementary arithmetic, and some special symbols which will be introduced and defined as needed. Our object language or object logic is the new system RS_1 which will now be described.

The logistic system RS_1 contains infinitely many primitive symbols, of the following categories.

1. Infinitely many capital letters from the first part of the alphabet, with and without subscripts:

$$A, B, C, A_1, B_1, C_1, A_2, B_2, C_2, \ldots$$

These will be referred to as *propositional constants*, and on the system's intended interpretation will express non-compound propositions.

2. Infinitely many capital letters from the middle part of the alphabet, with and without subscripts:

$$P, Q, R, P_1, Q_1, R_1, P_2, Q_2, R_2, \ldots$$

These will be referred to as *propositional variables*, and on the system's intended interpretation will be statement variables of the kind discussed in Section III of Chapter Two. Symbols of the first two categories will be referred to as *propositional symbols*.

3. Infinitely many capital letters from the first part of the alphabet, with and without subscripts, having right hand superscripts '1', '2', '3'. . . .

$$A^1, B^1, C^1, A_1^1, B_1^1, C_1^1, A_2^1, B_2^1, C_2^1, \ldots$$
$$A^2, B^2, C^2, A_1^2, B_1^2, C_1^2, A_2^2, B_2^2, C_2^2, \ldots$$
$$A^3, B^3, C^3, A_1^3, B_1^3, C_1^3, A_2^3, B_2^3, C_2^3, \ldots$$
$$\cdot \cdot \cdot \cdot \cdot \cdot \cdot \cdot \cdot \cdot \cdot \cdot \cdot \cdot \cdot \cdot \cdot \cdot \cdot \cdot \cdot \cdot$$
$$\cdot \cdot \cdot \cdot \cdot \cdot \cdot \cdot \cdot \cdot \cdot \cdot \cdot \cdot \cdot \cdot \cdot \cdot \cdot \cdot \cdot \cdot$$

These will be referred to as *predicate constants*, and on the system's intended interpretation each of them will designate a particular property or dyadic relation or triadic relation . . . or n-adic relation according as its right superscript is '1' or '2' or '3' or . . . or 'n'.

4. Infinitely many capital letters from the middle part of the alphabet, with and without subscripts, having right hand superscripts '1', '2', '3', . . .

$$P^1, Q^1, R^1, P_1^1, Q_1^1, R_1^1, P_2^1, Q_2^1, R_2^1, \ldots$$
$$P^2, Q^2, R^2, P_1^2, Q_1^2, R_1^2, P_2^2, Q_2^2, R_2^2, \ldots$$
$$P^3, Q^3, R^3, P_1^3, Q_1^3, R_1^3, P_2^3, Q_2^3, R_2^3, \ldots$$
$$\cdot \cdot \cdot \cdot \cdot \cdot \cdot \cdot \cdot \cdot \cdot \cdot \cdot \cdot \cdot \cdot \cdot \cdot \cdot \cdot \cdot \cdot$$
$$\cdot \cdot \cdot \cdot \cdot \cdot \cdot \cdot \cdot \cdot \cdot \cdot \cdot \cdot \cdot \cdot \cdot \cdot \cdot \cdot \cdot \cdot$$

These will be referred to as *predicate variables*, and on the system's intended interpretation will be symbols for which names of particular properties, dyadic relations, etc., can be substituted. Symbols of the third and fourth categories will be referred to as *predicate symbols*.

5. Infinitely many lower case letters from the first part of the alphabet, with and without subscripts:

$$a, \ b, \ c, \ a_1, \ b_1, \ c_1, \ a_2, \ b_2, \ c_2, \ \cdots$$

These will be referred to as *individual constants*, and on the system's intended interpretation will be proper names of particular individuals.

6. Infinitely many lower case letters from the latter part of the alphabet, with and without subscripts:

$$x, \ y, \ z, \ x_1, \ y_1, \ z_1, \ x_2, \ y_2, \ z_2, \ \cdots$$

These will be referred to as individual variables, and on the system's intended interpretation will be individual variables of the kind discussed in Chapter Four. Symbols of the fifth and sixth categories will be referred to as *individual symbols*.

7. Just four additional symbols complete the list of primitive symbols of RS₁; these are the tilde, the dot, and left and right hand parentheses:

$$\sim, \ \cdot, \ (, \ ).$$

In addition to the primitive symbols we shall introduce some defined symbols into our object language RS₁. Before doing so, however, we must indicate the usage of certain special symbols of our metalanguage. As in Chapter Seven, we introduce the special symbols '$\sim$', '$\cdot$', '(', and ')' to denote the symbols '$\sim$', '$\cdot$', '(', and ')' of the object language, and we shall also use square brackets and braces to denote the object language's parentheses when that is conducive to easier reading. Capital letters, with and without subscripts, will be used in the metalanguage as syntactical variables, that is, as symbols for which designations of any symbols or sequences of symbols of the object language can be substituted. And lower case letters, with and without subscripts, will be used as syntactical individual variables, that is, symbols for which designations of individual symbols of the object language can be substituted. Finally, we adopt the convention that the juxtaposition of two symbols of the object language will be denoted in the metalanguage by the juxtaposition of their names. Thus in any context where 'F' denotes 'A^1' and 'x' denotes 'x', '$F(x)$' will denote '$A^1(x)$'. We shall also find it convenient to insert commas into any sequence of symbols of the metalanguage which designate individual symbols of the object language. Thus where 'F' denotes 'B^3' and 'x_1', 'x_2', and 'x_3' denote 'a_1', 'a_2', and 'a_3', respectively, we shall use '$F(x_1, x_2, x_3)$' to denote '$B^3(a_1a_2a_3)$'.

We introduce the symbols '$\mathbf{v}$', '$\mathbf{\supset}$', '$\mathbf{\equiv}$', and '$\mathbf{\exists}$' into the object language *by definition*, and shall denote them in the metalanguage by the symbols 'v', '$\supset$', '$\equiv$', and '$\exists$'. The new symbols of the object language are introduced as definitional abbreviations:

How reconcile with p. 193 sup.?

Df. $P \text{ v } Q$ is defined to be an abbreviation of $\sim(\sim P \cdot \sim Q)$.
Df. $P \supset Q$ is defined to be an abbreviation of $\sim(P \cdot \sim Q)$.
Df. $P \equiv Q$ is defined to be an abbreviation of $(P \supset Q) \cdot (Q \supset P)$.
Df. $(\exists x)P$ is defined to be an abbreviation of $\sim(x)\sim P$.

We shall feel free to drop parentheses (in the metalanguage), retaining only so many as may be required to avoid ambiguity, or which may make for greater ease of interpretation. We shall also, on occasion, write '$P \cdot Q$' as 'PQ'. Although we shall not always take advantage of the following convention by dropping unnecessary parentheses, we set up the following *order of precedence* among the symbols (of our metalanguage), each symbol having precedence over any that lies in a column to its right:

$$\equiv \quad \supset \quad v \quad \cdot \quad \sim$$
$$(x) \text{ where not immediately preceded by a predicate symbol}$$
$$(\exists x)$$

This convention dictates that an expression such as

$$P \equiv (x)Q \text{ v } \sim RS \supset (\exists x) T \cdot U$$

is understood to denote the same formulas of the object language that are denoted by

$$\{P\} \equiv \{\{[(x)Q] \lor [(\sim R)\cdot(S)]\} \supset \{[(\exists x)T]\cdot[U]\}\}.$$

We define *formula of* RS₁ as any finite sequence of symbols of RS₁. Among these are included such sequences as

$$)\sim)($$
$$(x)(A^1(x))$$
$$((\exists y)(B^2(xy))) \supset (C^1(a))$$
$$(\exists \lor \sim \equiv$$
$$Q^3(ab)$$

of which we shall want to include only the second and third as *well formed*, that is, as meaningful on the system's intended or normal interpretation.

Now we define *well formed formula of* RS₁ by the following recursive rules:

α) 1. If F is a propositional symbol then F is a *wff*.
   2. If F is an n-adic predicate symbol (where $n = 1, 2, 3, \ldots$) then $F(x_1, x_2, \ldots, x_n)$ is a *wff*.

β) 1. If F is a *wff* then $\sim(F)$ is a *wff*.
   2. If F is a *wff* and G is a *wff* then $(F)\cdot(G)$ is a *wff*.
   3. If F is a *wff* and x is an individual variable then $(x)(F)$ is a *wff*.

No formula of RS₁ is a *wff* unless its being so follows from these rules, or from these rules together with the definitions of the defined symbols which were stated above.

Now that we have an effective criterion for *wff*, we shall restrict our discussion in the remainder of this chapter to *wffs*, which alone interest us.

It is convenient at this point to introduce and define some additional special terms. (There is no loss of generality in phrasing our definitions in terms of undefined symbols only, for defined symbols are always eliminable.)

Df. If x is an individual variable, then (x), when not immediately preceded by a predicate symbol, is the *universal quantifier* of x.

Df. An occurrence of a variable x in a *wff* P will be called a *bound* occurrence of x in P if it is in a well formed part of P of the form $(x)Q$.

Df. An occurrence of a variable x in a *wff* P will be called a *free occurrence* if it is not bound.

We assume infinitely many postulates for our object logic. Every *wff* of any of the five following patterns is a postulate:

P 1. $P \supset (P \cdot P)$

P 2. $(P \cdot Q) \supset P$

P 3. $(P \supset Q) \supset [\sim(Q \cdot R) \supset \sim(R \cdot P)]$

P 4. $(x)(P \supset Q) \supset [P \supset (x)Q]$, where x is any individual variable, P is any *wff* containing no free occurrences of x, and Q is any *wff*.

P 5. $(x)P \supset Q$, where x is any individual variable, y is any individual variable or constant, P is any *wff*, Q is the result of replacing each free occurrence of x in P by y, and if y is a variable then no bound occurrence of y in Q is the result of replacing a free occurrence of x in P by y.

The restrictions on P 4 and P 5 serve to prevent the inclusion of such manifest falsehoods (on the intended interpretation, of course) as

$$(x)[(x = 1) \supset (x + x = 2)] \supset [(x = 1) \supset (x)(x + x = 2)]$$

which has a true antecedent and a false consequent, but which is *not* an instance of P 4 since x occurs free in $(x = 1)$. Also prevented is such a patent falsehood as

$$(x)[(\exists y)(y \neq x)] \supset [(\exists y)(y \neq y)]$$

which is *not* an instance of P 5 since there is a bound occurrence of the variable y in $(\exists y)(y \neq y)$ which is the result of replacing a free occurrence of the variable x in $(\exists y)(y \neq x)$ by y.

We assume *two* rules of inference for RS_1:

R 1. If P and $P \supset Q$ then Q.

R 2. If P then $(x)P$.

Next we define 'demonstration' for RS₁. Formally,

$$P_1, P_2, \ldots, P_n \vdash Q$$

asserts that there is a finite sequence of *wffs* $S_1, S_2, \ldots, S_t$ such that for every $S_j (1 \leq j \leq t)$ either:

a) S_j is one of the Postulates P 1–P 5; or
b) S_j is one of the premisses $P_i (1 \leq i \leq n)$; or
c) S_j is the result of applying R 1 to two earlier S's of the sequence, say S_i and S_k where $i < j$ and $k < j$; or
d) S_j is the result of applying R 2 to an earlier S_i of the sequence, so that S_j is $(x)S_i$ where $i < j$;

and S_t is Q.

Informally, we regard $P_1, P_2, \ldots, P_n \vdash Q$ as asserting that Q is validly inferred from $P_1, P_2, \ldots, P_n$ in RS₁.

Next we define 'theorem of RS₁' as any *wff* Q such that $\vdash Q$. It should be noted that '$\vdash$' is a special symbol of our meta-language, and does not occur in RS₁ itself.

We can now establish the *consistency* of RS₁, following the proof given by Hilbert and Ackermann in 1928. We begin by stating the following definitions:

Df. A *quantifier-free formula* of RS₁ is a *wff* of RS₁ which contains no quantifiers.

Df. Where F is any *wff* of RS₁ the *associated quantifier-free formula* of F (symbolized F') is the result of crossing out (erasing) all occurrences of quantifiers in F and all parentheses whose presence was required by the occurrence of those quantifiers.

Examples:

a) where F is itself a quantifier-free formula, $F = F'$.
b) where F is $((x)((A^1(y)) \supset (B^1(x)))) \supset ((A^1(y)) \supset ((x)(B^1(x))))$
   F' is $((A^1(y)) \supset (B^1(x))) \supset ((A^1(y)) \supset (B^1(x)))$

Df. Where F is any *wff* of RS₁ its *associated propositional formula* (abbreviated to 'a.f.p.' for 'associated formula of the Propositional Calculus', and symbolized $F°$) is any result of replacing every well formed part of F' which is of the form $P^n(x_1, x_2, \ldots, x_n)$ by a propositional symbol—where different well formed parts beginning with different P^n's are replaced by different propositional symbols, but where different well formed parts beginning with the same P^n are replaced by the same propositional symbol regardless of differences among the individual symbols $x_1, x_2, \ldots, x_n$ which follow them.

Example: where F is

$$((x_1)((x_2)(A^2(x_1 x_2)))) \supset (((x_1)(B^1(x_1)))\cdot((x_2)(B^1(x_2))))$$

F' is

$$(A^2(x_1 x_2)) \supset ((B^1(x_1))\cdot(B^1(x_2)))$$

and $F°$ is any of the formulas

$$(A) \supset ((B)\cdot(B)), \quad (A) \supset ((C)\cdot(C)), \quad (A) \supset ((A_1)\cdot(A_1)), \ldots$$
$$(A_1) \supset ((B)\cdot(B)), \quad (A_1) \supset ((C)\cdot(C)), \quad (A_1) \supset ((A)\cdot(A)), \ldots$$
$$\ldots \ldots \ldots \ldots \ldots \ldots \ldots \ldots \ldots \ldots$$

Next we state and prove the following:

LEMMA: If $\vdash F$ then $F°$ is a (truth-table) tautology.

Proof: 1. First we show that every postulate of RS$_1$ has only tautologies for its a.f.P.'s. Any a.f.P. of any instance of P 1 is of the form $P° \supset (P°\cdot P°)$, which is a tautology. Similarly for P 2 and P 3. Every a.f.P. of any instance of P 4 has the form $(P° \supset Q°) \supset (P° \supset Q°)$ which is a tautology. In P 5, since Q differs from P only in the individual symbols they contain, their a.f.P.'s are identical, so that every a.f.P. of any instance of P 5 has the form $P° \supset P°$ which is a tautology.

2. Next we show that any *wff* obtained by applying the rules of RS$_1$ to *wffs* which have only tautologies for their a.f.P's has itself the property that all its a.f.P.'s are tautologies. By R 2 we derive $(x)P$ from P. But $(x)P$ and P have identically the same a.f.P.'s, so if all

of P's are tautologies, all of $(x)P$'s are also. By R 1 we derive Q from P and $P \supset Q$. Let $Q°$ be *any* a.f.P. of Q, and select $P°$ so that $P° \supset Q°$ is an a.f.P. of $P \supset Q$. (It is obvious that this can always be done since there are infinitely many distinct propositional symbols.) Now if all a.f.P.'s of P and $P \supset Q$ are tautologies, $P°$ and $P° \supset Q°$ are, and hence $Q°$ is also—regardless of which a.f.P. of Q we took for $Q°$.

Since all theorems of RS_1 follow by the rules from the postulates, all theorems of RS_1 have only tautologies as their a.f.P.'s. And this completes our proof of the lemma.

The consistency of RS_1 will be stated as

METATHEOREM I: RS_1 is consistent.

Proof: (Here we use Post's criterion for consistency: a system is consistent if it contains a *wff* which is not a theorem.) The formula '$(A)·(\sim(A))$' is a *wff* of RS_1 which has an a.f.P. (itself) which is not a tautology. Hence by our lemma it is not a theorem of RS_1, so RS_1 is consistent.

II. DEVELOPMENT OF RS_1

In developing the present system we shall borrow freely from the results obtained in Chapter Seven, in which it was established that every tautology can be demonstrated as a theorem in a Propositional Calculus based on P 1, P 2, P 3, and R 1. We shall state this in the following theorem and derived rule.

THEOREM O. All tautologies are theorems, and if in any tautology T which contains the propositional symbols P_1, P_2, . . . , P_n we replace all occurrences of P_1, P_2, . . . , P_n respectively by any *wffs* F_1, F_2, . . . , F_n of RS_1, the result is a theorem F of RS_1.

Proof: By the completeness of the Propositional Calculus based on P 1, P 2, P 3, and R 1, there is a demonstration in RS_1 for every tautology. If in every step of that demonstration we replace all occurrences of P_1, P_2, . . . , P_n by F_1, F_2, . . . , F_n we obtain a demonstration in RS_1 of F, since making the indicated substitutions in the postulates P 1, P 2, P 3 give us simply other instances of those postulates.

DERIVED RULE O. All tautologically valid argument forms are demonstrable in RS_1, and if in any tautologically valid derived rule $S_1, S_2, . . . , S_m \vdash T$ which contains the propositional symbols P_1, P_2, . . . , P_n we replace all occurrences of P_1, P_2, . . . , P_n respectively by any *wffs* F_1, F_2, . . . , F_n of RS_1, the result is a demonstrably valid derived rule G_1, G_2, . . . , $G_m \vdash H$ of RS_1.

Proof: Exactly parallels the proof of Theorem O.

In any *proof* in RS_1, any step which is justified by Th. O or DR O will be noted simply by ℗ (for 'Propositional Calculus').

At this point we proceed to establish the first few derived rules and theorems of RS_1.

DR 1. $(x)[F(x) \supset G(x)]$, $(x)F(x) \vdash (x)G(x)$

Demonstration:

S_1: $(x)[F(x) \supset G(x)]$	premiss
S_2: $(x)[F(x) \supset G(x)] \supset [F(x) \supset G(x)]$	P 5
S_3: $F(x) \supset G(x)$	R 1
S_4: $(x)F(x)$	premiss
S_5: $(x)F(x) \supset F(x)$	P 5
S_6: $F(x)$	R 1
S_7: $G(x)$	R 1
S_8: $(x)G(x)$	R 2

DR 2. $(x)(P \cdot Q) \vdash (x)P \cdot (x)Q$

Proof:

$(x)(P \cdot Q)$	premiss
$(x)(P \cdot Q) \supset P \cdot Q$	P 5
$P \cdot Q$	R 1
P	℗
$(x)P$	R 2
Q	℗
$(x)Q$	R 2
$(x)P \cdot (x)Q$	℗

DR 3. $(x)(P \equiv Q) \vdash (x)P \equiv (x)Q$

Proof:

$(x)(P \equiv Q)$	premiss
$(x)(P \equiv Q) \supset (P \equiv Q)$	P 5
$P \equiv Q$	R 1
$P \supset Q$	℗
$(x)P \supset P$	P 5
$(x)P \supset Q$	℗
$(x)[(x)P \supset Q]$	R 2
$(x)[(x)P \supset Q] \supset [(x)P \supset (x)Q]$	P 4
$(x)P \supset (x)Q$	R 1
$Q \supset P$	℗
$(x)Q \supset Q$	P 5
$(x)Q \supset P$	℗
$(x)[(x)Q \supset P]$	R 2
$(x)[(x)Q \supset P] \supset [(x)Q \supset (x)P]$	P 4
$(x)Q \supset (x)P$	R 1
$[(x)P \supset (x)Q]\cdot[(x)Q \supset (x)P]$	℗
$(x)P \equiv (x)Q$	df.

Tн. 1. $\vdash (x)(P\cdot Q) \equiv (x)P\cdot(x)Q$

Proof: First we establish A: $\vdash (x)(P\cdot Q) \supset (x)P\cdot(x)Q$

$\vdash (x)(P\cdot Q) \supset P\cdot Q$	P 5
$\vdash P\cdot Q \supset P$	P 2
$\vdash (x)(P\cdot Q) \supset P$	℗
$\vdash (x)[(x)(P\cdot Q) \supset P]$	R 2
$\vdash (x)[(x)(P\cdot Q) \supset P] \supset$ $[(x)(P\cdot Q) \supset (x)P]$	P 4
$\vdash (x)(P\cdot Q) \supset (x)P$	R 1

By steps similar to the above we obtain:

$\vdash (x)(P\cdot Q) \supset (x)Q$	
$\vdash (x)(P\cdot Q) \supset (x)P\cdot(x)Q$	℗

Next we establish B: $\vdash (x)P\cdot(x)Q \supset (x)(P\cdot Q)$

$\vdash (x)P\cdot(x)Q \supset (x)P$	P 2
$\vdash (x)P \supset P$	P 5
$\vdash (x)P\cdot(x)Q \supset P$	℗
$\vdash (x)P\cdot(x)Q \supset (x)Q$	℗
$\vdash (x)Q \supset Q$	P 5
$\vdash (x)P\cdot(x)Q \supset Q$	℗
$\vdash (x)P\cdot(x)Q \supset P\cdot Q$	℗

$$\vdash (x)[(x)P \cdot (x)Q \supset P \cdot Q] \qquad \text{R 2}$$
$$\vdash (x)[(x)P \cdot (x)Q \supset P \cdot Q] \supset$$
$$\qquad [(x)P \cdot (x)Q \supset (x)(P \cdot Q)] \qquad \text{P 4}$$
$$\vdash (x)P \cdot (x)Q \supset (x)(P \cdot Q) \qquad \text{R 1}$$

Now from A and B,

$$\vdash [(x)(P \cdot Q) \supset (x)P \cdot (x)Q] \cdot$$
$$\qquad [(x)P \cdot (x)Q \supset (x)(P \cdot Q)] \qquad \text{\textcircled{P}}$$
$$\vdash (x)(P \cdot Q) \equiv (x)P \cdot (x)Q \qquad \text{df.}$$

Th. 2. $\vdash (x)(P \supset Q) \supset [(x)P \supset (x)Q]$

Proof:
$$\vdash [(x)(P \supset Q) \cdot (x)P] \supset (x)(P \supset Q) \qquad \text{P 2}$$
$$\vdash [(x)(P \supset Q) \cdot (x)P] \supset (x)P \qquad \text{\textcircled{P}}$$
$$\vdash (x)(P \supset Q) \supset (P \supset Q) \qquad \text{P 5}$$
$$\vdash (x)P \supset P \qquad \text{P 5}$$
$$\vdash [(x)(P \supset Q) \cdot (x)P] \supset [(P \supset Q) \cdot P] \qquad \text{\textcircled{P}}$$
$$\vdash [(P \supset Q) \cdot P] \supset Q \qquad \text{\textcircled{P}}$$
$$\vdash [(x)(P \supset Q) \cdot (x)P] \supset Q \qquad \text{\textcircled{P}}$$
$$\vdash (x)\{[(x)(P \supset Q) \cdot (x)P] \supset Q\} \qquad \text{R 2}$$
$$\vdash (x)\{[(x)(P \supset Q) \cdot (x)P] \supset Q\} \supset$$
$$\qquad \{[(x)(P \supset Q) \cdot (x)P] \supset (x)Q\} \qquad \text{P 4}$$
$$\vdash [(x)(P \supset Q) \cdot (x)P] \supset (x)Q \qquad \text{R 1}$$
$$\vdash (x)(P \supset Q) \supset [(x)P \supset (x)Q] \qquad \text{\textcircled{P}}$$

Next we state and prove the Deduction Theorem for RS_1, which corresponds to the strengthened method of Conditional Proof used in Chapters Four and Five.

METATHEOREM II. (The Deduction Theorem—D.T.) If there is a demonstration that $P_1, P_2, \ldots, P_{n-1}, P_n \vdash Q$ in which no variable occurring free in P_n is ever quantified by R 2, then there is a demonstration that $P_1, P_2, \ldots, P_{n-1} \vdash P_n \supset Q$ in which exactly those variables are quantified by R 2 which were quantified by R 2 in the original demonstration.

Proof: We assume that there is a sequence of *wffs* $S_1, S_2, \ldots, S_t$ such that every $S_j (1 \leq j \leq t)$ is (a) one of the Postulates P 1–P 5, or (b) one of the P_i's $(1 \leq i \leq n)$, or (c) results from applying R 1 to two earlier S's of the sequence, or (d) results from applying R 2 to an earlier S; and S_t is Q. Now consider the sequence of *wffs:* $P_n \supset S_1, P_n \supset S_2,$

. . . , $P_n \supset S_t$. If we can 'fill in' *wffs* before each $P_n \supset S_j$ in such a way that the resulting total sequence is a demonstration from $P_1, P_2, \ldots, P_{n-1}$, that is, so that each step of the resulting total sequence is either (a) one of the Postulates P 1–P 5, or (b) one of the P_i's $(1 \leq i \leq n - 1)$, or (c) results from applying R 1 to two earlier steps of the sequence, or (d) results from applying R 2 to an earlier step of the sequence, then since the last step $P_n \supset S_t$ is $P_n \supset Q$ we shall have a demonstration that $P_1, P_2, \ldots, P_{n-1} \vdash P_n \supset Q$.

The proof proceeds by weak induction on the number of steps (t) in the original demonstration.

α) In case $t = 1$ we have only the formula $P_n \supset S_1$ to consider. We wish to show that $P_1, P_2, \ldots, P_{n-1} \vdash P_n \supset S_1$. By assumption, S_1 is either a Postulate P 1–P 5 or a $P_i(1 \leq i \leq n)$.

CASE 1. S_1 is a Postulate. Here we fill in with the demonstration of $S_1 \supset (P_n \supset S_1)$ and S_1 itself. From these we have $P_n \supset S_1$ by R 1, so that the total sequence up to and including $P_n \supset S_1$ is a demonstration that $\vdash P_n \supset S_1$ and hence that $P_1, P_2, \ldots, P_{n-1} \vdash P_n \supset S_1$.

CASE 2. S_1 is a $P_i(1 \leq i \leq n)$.

Sub-case A: S_1 is P_n. Here we fill in with the demonstration of $S_1 \supset S_1$, which is a demonstration that $\vdash P_n \supset S_1$, and hence that $P_1, P_2, \ldots, P_{n-1} \vdash P_n \supset S_1$.

Sub-case B: S_1 is $P_i(1 \leq i \leq n - 1)$. Here we fill in with the demonstration of $S_1 \supset (P_n \supset S_1)$ and S_1 itself, from which we have $P_n \supset S_1$ by R 1. Here the total sequence is a demonstration that $S_1 \vdash P_n \supset S_1$, and since S_1 is a $P_i(1 \leq i \leq n - 1)$ it is a demonstration that $P_1, P_2, \ldots, P_{n-1} \vdash P_n \supset S_1$.

β) Now suppose we have filled in for all steps $P_n \supset S_1$, $P_n \supset S_2$, . . . , up to and including $P_n \supset S_{k-1}$, so that we have a sequence of *wffs* which is a demonstration that $P_1, P_2, \ldots, P_{n-1} \vdash P_n \supset S_{k-1}$. Under this assumption we show how to fill in so as to include $P_n \supset S_k$ in the sequence so that it becomes a demonstration that $P_1, P_2, \ldots, P_{n-1} \vdash P_n \supset S_k$. By our original assumption, S_k is either a postulate, a $P_i(1 \leq i \leq n)$, results from applying R 1 to two earlier S's, or results from applying R 2 to an earlier S.

CASE 1. S_k is a Postulate. Fill in as in the α-case.

CASE 2. S_k is a $P_i(1 \leq i \leq n)$. Fill in as in the α-case.

CASE 3. S_k results from applying R 1 to two previous S's, say S_i and S_j where S_j is $S_i \supset S_k$. By the β-case assumption, since $i < k$, $j < k$ we already have $P_n \supset S_i$ and $P_n \supset S_j$, that is, $P_n \supset (S_i \supset S_k)$. Here we insert the demonstration of $[P_n \supset (S_i \supset S_k)] \supset [(P_n \supset S_i) \supset (P_n \supset S_k)]$ (a tautology), and $P_n \supset S_k$ follows by two applications of R 1.

CASE 4. S_k results from applying R 2 to an earlier S, say S_j where $j < k$. By the β-case assumption we already have $P_n \supset S_j$. S_k is $(x)S_j$ where x, by our original assumption, is not free in P_n. Hence by R 2, $(x)(P_n \supset S_j)$, and by P 4, $(x)(P_n \supset S_j) \supset (P_n \supset (x)S_j)$. Now R 1 will give $P_n \supset (x)S_j$ which is $P_n \supset S_k$.

From α, β by weak induction we can thus fill in for *any* number of steps S_j of the original demonstration. Moreover, no variable is quantified in the 'filled in' sequence which was not quantified in the original sequence. This proves Metatheorem II (D.T.).

MT II. COROLLARY: The D.T. as stated above holds for *any* system of logic which has only rules R 1 and R 2 and which contains demonstrations for

$P \supset P, P \supset (Q \supset P), (P \supset Q) \supset \{[P \supset (Q \supset R)] \supset (P \supset R)\}$, and
$(x)(P \supset Q) \supset (P \supset (x)Q)$ where no free x's occur in P.

Proof: Obvious.

We can illustrate the *use* of the D.T. by using it to prove DR 4:

DR 4. $(x)[F(x) \supset G(x)] \vdash (x)F(x) \supset (x)G(x)$
Proof: $(x)[F(x) \supset G(x)], (x)F(x) \vdash (x)G(x)$ DR 1
$(x)[F(x) \supset G(x)] \vdash (x)F(x) \supset (x)G(x)$ D.T.

Some additional theorems which can be established quite easily using the Deduction Theorem are

TH. 3. $\vdash (x)(P \equiv Q) \supset [(x)P \equiv (x)Q]$.
TH. 4. $\vdash (x)(P \supset Q) \supset [(\exists x)P \supset (\exists x)Q]$.

Their proofs will be left as exercises for the reader. We now proceed to some theorems which state equivalences. Since $(\exists x)$ was introduced as an abbreviation for $\sim(x)\sim$, the next theorem,

TH. 5. $\vdash (\exists x)P \equiv \sim(x)\sim P$

follows immediately from $\vdash \sim(x)\sim P \equiv \sim(x)\sim P(\text{ⓟ})$ by definition.

The following theorems, however, require proofs which are simple but not quite so simple as that of Th. 5.

TH. 6. $\vdash (x)P \equiv \sim(\exists x)\sim P$
TH. 7. $\vdash \sim(x)P \equiv (\exists x)\sim P$
TH. 8. $\vdash \sim(\exists x)P \equiv (x)\sim P$

The proofs of these will also be left as exercises.

The next theorem provides for the permutation of universal quantifiers:

TH. 9. $\vdash (x)(y)P \equiv (y)(x)P$
Proof: $\vdash (y)P \supset P$ P 5
$\vdash (x)[(y)P \supset P]$ R 2
$\vdash (x)(y)P \supset (x)P$ DR 4
$\vdash (y)[(x)(y)P \supset (x)P]$ R 2
$\vdash (y)[(x)(y)P \supset (x)P] \supset [(x)(y)P \supset (y)(x)P]$ P 4
$\vdash (x)(y)P \supset (y)(x)P$ R 1

We obtain $\vdash (y)(x)P \supset (x)(y)P$ in the same fashion, and then have

$$\vdash (x)(y)P \equiv (y)(x)P \qquad \text{by ℗}$$

Another theorem which can be proved quite simply is

Tн. 10. $\vdash [(x)P \lor (x)Q] \supset (x)(P \lor Q)$

Proof: $\vdash (x)P \supset P$ P 5

$\vdash (x)Q \supset Q$ P 5

$\vdash [(x)P \lor (x)Q] \supset (P \lor Q)$ ℗

$\vdash (x)\{[(x)P \lor (x)Q] \supset (P \lor Q)\}$ R 2

$\vdash (x)\{[(x)P \lor (x)Q] \supset (P \lor Q)\} \supset$
$\qquad\qquad\qquad \{[(x)P \lor (x)Q] \supset (x)(P \lor Q)\}$ P 4

$\vdash [(x)P \lor (x)Q] \supset (x)(P \lor Q)$ R 1

Having derived a number of equivalences as theorems, it will be convenient to establish a substitution rule which will permit the interchange of equivalent formulas in any context. This will be proved as the next Metatheorem.

Metatheorem III. (The Substitution Theorem—S.T.) Let $P_1, P_2, \ldots, P_n, A, B$ be any *wffs*, and let W be any *wff* which contains no symbols other than the P_i's $(1 \leq i \leq n)$, $A, \cdot, \sim, (x)$, and parentheses.* Let W^* be the result of replacing any number of the occurrences of A in W by B's. Then $A \equiv B \vdash W \equiv W^*$.

Proof: We use strong induction on the number of symbols in W, counting each occurrence of $P_i(1 \leq i \leq n)$, $A, B, \sim, \cdot, (x)$, as a single symbol.

α) In case W contains a single symbol, W is either a P_i or A.

case 1. W is P_i (and P_i is not A). Here W^* is P_i, and since $\vdash P_i \equiv P_i$ we have $\vdash W \equiv W^*$ and so $A \equiv B$ $\vdash W \equiv W^*$.

---

* The last restriction does not limit the generality of the Metatheorem since all occurrences of the defined symbols $\lor$, $\supset$, $\equiv$, and $\exists$ can be replaced by undefined symbols.

CASE 2. W is A. Here W^* is either A or B.

Sub-case A: W^* is A. Since $\vdash A \equiv A$ we have $\vdash W \equiv W^*$ and so $A \equiv B \vdash W \equiv W^*$.

Sub-case B: W^* is B. Since $A \equiv B \vdash A \equiv B$ we have $A \equiv B \vdash W \equiv W^*$.

β) Now suppose the Metatheorem true for any *wff* W which contains k or less symbols, and consider a *wff* W which has $k + 1$ symbols. W must have the structure $\sim L$, $(x)L$, or $M \cdot N$.

CASE 1. W is $\sim L$. L must have just k symbols, so by the β-case assumption $A \equiv B \vdash L \equiv L^*$. But $(L \equiv L^*) \supset (\sim L \equiv \sim L^*)$ is provable so that $A \equiv B \vdash \sim L \equiv \sim L^*$ which is $A \equiv B \vdash W \equiv W^*$.

CASE 2. W is $(x)L$. Again L has just k symbols so by the β-case assumption $A \equiv B \vdash L \equiv L^*$. Hence by R 2 we have $A \equiv B \vdash (x)(L \equiv L^*)$ and by DR 3 we have $(x)(L \equiv L^*) \vdash (x)L \equiv (x)L^*$ so that $A \equiv B \vdash W \equiv W^*$.

CASE 3. W is $M \cdot N$. Since M and N each has less than k symbols, by the β-case assumption $A \equiv B \vdash M \equiv M^*$ and $A \equiv B \vdash N \equiv N^*$. Since $\vdash [(M \equiv M^*) \cdot (N \equiv N^*)] \supset [M \cdot N \equiv M^* \cdot N^*]$, and $M^* \cdot N^*$ is W^*, we have $A \equiv B \vdash W \equiv W^*$.

This completes the induction and finishes the proof.

MT III. COROLLARY: If W and W^* are as in MT III, then $A \equiv B$, $W \vdash W^*$. The proof is quite obvious.

III. DUALITY

We begin our discussion of duality with a quite complicated definition:

Df. Let W be any *wff* which contains no occurrences of $\supset$ or $\equiv$ (any *wff* can be made into such a W by rewriting every well formed part of the form $P \supset Q$ as $\sim P$ v Q and every well formed part of the form $P \equiv Q$ as $(\sim P$ v $Q) \cdot (\sim Q$ v $P))$. Where $P_1, \ldots, P_n$ are propositional symbols or composed of predicate symbols followed by the appropriate number of individual symbols, W will be constructed out of P_1, P_2, $\ldots, P_n$, $\cdot$, $\sim$, v, (x), $(\exists x)$ exclusively. Then the *dual* of W (written W^Δ) is formed by

replacing every occurrence of P_i	in W by $\sim P_i$,*
" " " " $\sim P_i$ " " " P_i,
" " " " (x) " " " $(\exists x)$,
" " " " $(\exists x)$ " " " (x),
" " " " $\cdot$ " " " v,
" " " " v " " " $\cdot$.

Examples (where P, Q, R, S are P_i's):
1. W: $P \cdot Q$
   W^Δ: $\sim P$ v $\sim Q$
2. W: $(x)(P$ v $Q)$
   W^Δ: $(\exists x)(\sim P \cdot \sim Q)$
3. W: $(y)(\exists z)[P$ v $(\sim Q$ v $R \cdot S)]$
   W^Δ: $(\exists y)(z)[\sim P \cdot Q \cdot (\sim R$ v $\sim S)]$

There are several immediate consequences of our definition: First, where W is any *wff* which contains no part of the form $\sim\sim P_i$:

1. $W = W^{\Delta\Delta}$

Where W and U are any *wffs* whatever:

2. $(W \cdot U)^\Delta = W^\Delta$ v U^Δ
3. $(W$ v $U)^\Delta = W^\Delta \cdot U^\Delta$
4. $((x)W)^\Delta = (\exists x)W^\Delta$
5. $((\exists x)W)^\Delta = (x)W^\Delta$
6. $(\sim W)^\Delta$ $\begin{cases} \text{a. If } W \text{ is a } P_i \text{ then } (\sim W)^\Delta \text{ is } P_i. \\ \text{b. If } W \text{ contains at least two symbols then } (\sim W)^\Delta = \\ \quad \sim(W^\Delta). \end{cases}$

*Except those occurrences of P_i in well formed parts of the form $\sim P_i$.

We can now establish a general duality result.

METATHEOREM IV. (Duality Theorem) If W^Δ is the dual of W then $\vdash \sim W \equiv W^\Delta$.

Proof: We use strong induction on the structure of W (i.e., the number of symbols it contains, counting each P_i as a single symbol).

α) If W contains just one symbol, W is a P_i. Here W^Δ is $\sim P_i$, and since $\vdash \sim P_i \equiv \sim P_i$ by ⓟ, we have $\vdash \sim W \equiv W^\Delta$.

β) Assume the Metatheorem true for any W containing k or less symbols. Now consider any W containing $k + 1$ symbols.

  CASE 1. W is $\sim R$.
  Sub-case A: R contains more than one symbol. Then $(\sim R)^\Delta$ is $\sim R^\Delta$. By the β-case assumption, $\vdash \sim R \equiv R^\Delta$, hence by ⓟ $\vdash \sim\sim R \equiv \sim R^\Delta$. But this is $\vdash \sim W \equiv W^\Delta$.
  Sub-case B: R contains just one symbol, i.e., R is a P_i. Then W is $\sim P_i$ and W^Δ is P_i. But by ⓟ $\vdash \sim\sim P_i \equiv P_i$, so that $\vdash \sim W \equiv W^\Delta$.

  CASE 2. W is $(x)R$. By β we have $\vdash \sim R \equiv R^\Delta$. We also have, by S.T., $\vdash \sim(x)R \equiv \sim(x)\sim\sim R$, so, by S.T., $\vdash \sim(x)R \equiv \sim(x)\sim R^\Delta$ which (by definition) is $\vdash \sim(x)R \equiv (\exists x)R^\Delta$ or $\vdash \sim W \equiv W^\Delta$.

  CASE 3. W is $(\exists x)R$. By β, $\vdash \sim R \equiv R^\Delta$. We also have (Theorem 8) $\vdash \sim(\exists x)R \equiv (x)\sim R$. By S.T. we have $\vdash \sim(\exists x)R \equiv (x)R^\Delta$ which is $\vdash \sim W \equiv W^\Delta$.

  CASE 4. W is $A \cdot B$. By β, $\vdash \sim A \equiv A^\Delta$ and $\vdash \sim B \equiv B^\Delta$. By ⓟ, $\vdash \sim(A \cdot B) \equiv \sim A \text{ v } \sim B$, so by S.T., $\vdash \sim(A \cdot B) \equiv A^\Delta \text{ v } B^\Delta$ which is $\vdash \sim W \equiv W^\Delta$.

  CASE 5. W is $A \text{ v } B$. By β, $\vdash \sim A \equiv A^\Delta$ and $\vdash \sim B \equiv B^\Delta$. By ⓟ, $\vdash \sim(A \text{ v } B) \equiv \sim A \cdot \sim B$, so by S.T., $\vdash \sim(A \text{ v } B) \equiv A^\Delta \cdot B^\Delta$ which is $\vdash \sim W \equiv W^\Delta$.

MT IV. Corollary: $\vdash (W \equiv U) \supset (W^\Delta \equiv U^\Delta)$
The proof of the corollary is obvious.

Duality has many uses. The traditional 'Square of Opposition'* which displays *I* and *O* propositions as the contradictories or denials of *E* and *A* propositions, respectively, is clearly a special case of the duality result established above:

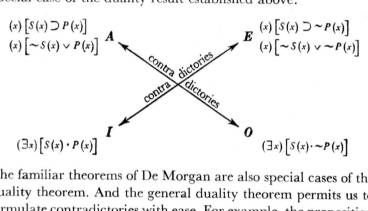

$$(x)\big[S(x) \supset P(x)\big]$$
$$(x)\big[\sim S(x) \vee P(x)\big] \quad A$$

$$E \quad (x)\big[S(x) \supset \sim P(x)\big]$$
$$(x)\big[\sim S(x) \vee \sim P(x)\big]$$

contradictories

contradictories

$$I$$
$$(\exists x)\big[S(x) \cdot P(x)\big]$$

$$O$$
$$(\exists x)\big[S(x) \cdot \sim P(x)\big]$$

The familiar theorems of De Morgan are also special cases of the duality theorem. And the general duality theorem permits us to formulate contradictories with ease. For example, the proposition

> There is a course which all students take.

may be symbolized as

$$(\exists x)\{C^1(x) \cdot (y)[S^1(y) \supset T^2(y,x)]\}$$

and may have its implication sign deleted to become

$$(\exists x)\{C^1(x) \cdot (y)[\sim S^1(y) \vee T^2(y,x)]\}.$$

The dual (and hence the contradictory or denial) of this formula is

$$(x)\{\sim C^1(x) \vee (\exists y)[S^1(y) \cdot \sim T^2(y,x)]\}$$

which is most 'naturally' written with the implication sign as

$$(x)\{C^1(x) \supset (\exists y)[S^1(y) \cdot \sim T^2(y,x)]\}$$

and is the symbolic translation of the English sentence

> For every course there is some student who doesn't take it.

---

* Discussed in Chapter Four, pp. 70–73.

Having established the Substitution and Duality results, some additional theorems are very easily proved.

Tн. 11. $\vdash (\exists x)(P \lor Q) \equiv (\exists x)P \lor (\exists x)Q$
Proof: $\vdash (x)(\sim P \cdot \sim Q) \equiv (x)\sim P \cdot (x)\sim Q$ Th. 1
$ \vdash (\exists x)(P \lor Q) \equiv (\exists x)P \lor (\exists x)Q$ Duality Theorem and S.T.

The proofs of the next two theorems are equally simple, and may be left as exercises.

Tн. 12. $\vdash (\exists x)(\exists y)P \equiv (\exists y)(\exists x)P$
Tн. 13. $\vdash (\exists x)(P \cdot Q) \supset (\exists x)P \cdot (\exists x)Q$

Now that we have the Substitution Theorem, it is desirable to augment our supply of equivalences. For the next ten theorems (Th. 14 through Th. 23) and the next derived rule (DR 5) we make the blanket assumption that *there are no free occurrences* of x in Q. We shall give proofs of some of these next results, and leave others as exercises for the reader:

Tн. 14. $\vdash (x)Q \equiv Q$
Proof: $\vdash (x)Q \supset Q$ P 5
$ \vdash Q \supset Q$ $\mathbf{(P)}$
$ \vdash (x)(Q \supset Q)$ R 2
$ \vdash (x)(Q \supset Q) \supset (Q \supset (x)Q)$ P 4
$ \vdash Q \supset (x)Q$ R 1
$ \vdash (x)Q \equiv Q$ $\mathbf{(P)}$
Tн. 15. $\vdash (\exists x)Q \equiv Q$
Tн. 16. $\vdash (x)(P \cdot Q) \equiv (x)P \cdot Q$
Proof: $\vdash (x)(P \cdot Q) \equiv (x)P \cdot (x)Q$ Th. 1
$ \vdash (x)Q \equiv Q$ Th. 14
$ \vdash (x)(P \cdot Q) \equiv (x)P \cdot Q$ S.T.
Tн. 17. $\vdash (\exists x)(P \lor Q) \equiv (\exists x)P \lor Q$
Proof: $\vdash (x)(\sim P \cdot \sim Q) \equiv (x)\sim P \cdot \sim Q$ Th. 16
$ \vdash (\exists x)(P \lor Q) \equiv (\exists x)P \lor Q$ Duality Theorem and S.T.
Tн. 18. $\vdash (\exists x)(P \supset Q) \equiv (x)P \supset Q$
Tн. 19. $\vdash (\exists x)(Q \supset P) \equiv Q \supset (\exists x)P$
Tн. 20. $\vdash (x)(Q \supset P) \equiv Q \supset (x)P$
Tн. 21. $\vdash (x)(P \supset Q) \equiv (\exists x)P \supset Q$
Tн. 22. $\vdash (x)(P \lor Q) \equiv (x)P \lor Q$
Tн. 23. $\vdash (\exists x)(P \cdot Q) \equiv (\exists x)P \cdot Q$
DR 5. $P \supset Q \vdash (\exists x)P \supset Q$

The next theorem requires no such restriction on free occurrences of variables in the formulas it contains:

TH. 24. $\vdash (\exists x)(y)P \supset (y)(\exists x)P$

Proof: $(y)P \vdash (y)P \supset P$ $\qquad\qquad\qquad\qquad$ P 5

$\qquad(y)P \vdash (y)P$ $\qquad\qquad\qquad\qquad\qquad$ premiss

$\qquad(y)P \vdash P$ $\qquad\qquad\qquad\qquad\qquad\qquad$ R 1

$\qquad(y)P \vdash (x)\sim P \supset \sim P$ $\qquad\qquad\qquad$ P 5

$\qquad(y)P \vdash \sim\sim P \supset \sim(x)\sim P$ $\qquad\qquad$ ℗

$\qquad(y)P \vdash P \supset \sim(x)\sim P$ $\qquad\qquad\quad$ ℗

$\qquad(y)P \vdash \sim(x)\sim P$ $\qquad\qquad\qquad\qquad$ R 1

$\qquad(y)P \vdash (\exists x)P$ $\qquad\qquad\qquad\qquad\quad$ df.

$\qquad(y)P \vdash (y)(\exists x)P$ $\qquad\qquad\qquad\qquad$ R 2

$\qquad\vdash (y)P \supset (y)(\exists x)P$ $\qquad\qquad\qquad$ D.T.

$\qquad\vdash (\exists x)(y)P \supset (y)(\exists x)P$ $\qquad\qquad$ DR 5

For the next two theorems we make the general assumptions that x and y are any two individual variables, that $F(y)$ is the result of replacing all free x's in $F(x)$ by y's, and that $F(x)$ is the result of replacing all free y's in $F(y)$ by x's:

TH. 25. $\vdash (x)F(x) \equiv (y)F(y)$

Proof: $\vdash (x)F(x) \supset F(y)$ $\qquad\qquad\qquad\qquad\qquad$ P 5

$\qquad\vdash (y)[(x)F(x) \supset F(y)]$ $\qquad\qquad\qquad\quad$ R 2

$\qquad\vdash (y)[(x)F(x) \supset F(y)] \supset [(x)F(x) \supset (y)F(y)]$ $\quad$ P 4

$\qquad\vdash (x)F(x) \supset (y)F(y)$ $\qquad\qquad\qquad\qquad$ R 1

We obtain $\vdash (y)F(y) \supset (x)F(x)$ the same way, and then have

$\qquad\vdash (x)F(x) \equiv (y)F(y)$ $\qquad\qquad\qquad\qquad$ by ℗

TH. 26. $\vdash (\exists x)F(x) \equiv (\exists y)F(y)$

Proof: $\vdash (x)\sim F(x) \equiv (y)\sim F(y)$ $\qquad\qquad\qquad$ Th. 25

$\qquad\vdash \sim(x)\sim F(x) \equiv \sim(y)\sim F(y)$ $\qquad\qquad$ ℗

$\qquad\vdash (\exists x)F(x) \equiv (\exists y)F(y)$ $\qquad\qquad\qquad$ df.

Theorems 25 and 26, together with the Substitution Theorem, permit the 'interchange of bound variables'—subject to the restrictions mentioned in the statement of the theorems.

We end the present group of theorems with

TH. 27. If P and Q are as in P 5, then $Q \supset (\exists x)P$.

Proof: $\vdash (x)\sim P \supset \sim Q$ $\qquad\qquad\qquad\qquad\qquad$ P 5

$\qquad\vdash \sim\sim Q \supset \sim(x)\sim P$ $\qquad\qquad\qquad\quad$ ℗

$\qquad\vdash Q \supset \sim(x)\sim P$ $\qquad\qquad\qquad\qquad\quad$ ℗

$\qquad\vdash Q \supset (\exists x)P$ $\qquad\qquad\qquad\qquad\qquad$ df.

IV. RS₁ AND THE 'NATURAL DEDUCTION' TECHNIQUES

We wish now to show that RS_1 *is* an axiomatization of the logic we *used* in validating inferences by our list of Elementary Valid Argument Forms, the strengthened method of Conditional Proof, and the four Quantification Rules set forth in Chapter Four. That RS_1 contains all the Elementary Valid Argument Forms has been shown by our completeness proof for the system of logic based on P 1, P 2, P 3, and R 1, and our discussion in connection with Th. 0 and DR 0. In a sense, the Deduction Theorem for RS_1 corresponds to the strengthened method of Conditional Proof.

In the presence of R 1, P 5 corresponds to **UI**. The restrictions on **UI** are exactly the same as the restrictions on P 5. We may establish **UI** as a derived rule of RS_1:

DR 6. If P and Q are as in P 5 then $(x)P \vdash Q$.
Proof: $(x)P \vdash (x)P$ premiss
$ (x)P \vdash (x)P \supset Q$ P 5
$ (x)P \vdash Q$ R 1

Again in the presence of R 1, **EG** follows directly from P 5. The restrictions on **EG** are exactly the same as those on P 5. We may establish **EG** as a derived rule of RS_1:

DR 7. If P and Q are as in P 5 then $Q \vdash (\exists x)P$.
Proof: $Q \vdash Q$ premiss
$ Q \vdash Q \supset (\exists x)P$ Th. 27
$ Q \vdash (\exists x)P$ R 1

The rule **UG** corresponds roughly to R 2. The various restrictions on **UG** had to do with **EI** and with assumptions of limited scope made in the course of a Conditional Proof. The latter restriction is here made on that method itself in our statement of the Deduction Theorem—which does not permit going from $F(x) \vdash (x)F(x)$ to $\vdash F(x) \supset (x)F(x)$ where R 2 is used on a variable occurring free in the premiss. The restrictions pertaining to **EI** will be stated in connection with that rule itself, permitting us to state **UG** in its strongest form.

DR 8. $P \vdash (\acute{x})P$

> The proof is directly by R 2. It is clear that R 2 permits us to go from $F(x,y)$ to either $(x)F(x,y)$ or $(y)F(x,y)$. To get to $(x)F(x,x)$ or $(y)F(y,y)$—which are equivalent by Th. 25—we can proceed from $(x)F(x,y) \supset F(y,y)$ by P 5 to $F(y,y)$ by R 1 and thence to $(y)F(y,y)$ by R 2 (or DR 8) again. Thus we can do everything in RS_1 by DR 8 that we could informally by **UG**.

Having stated **UG** quite freely in RS_1 we must attach sufficient restrictions on **EI** to prevent any unwanted consequences. These unwanted consequences may be listed as follows:

1. We do not want $(\exists x)(x \neq y) \vdash y \neq y$. Hence we permit going by **EI** from $(\exists x)F(x)$ to $F(y)$ only if the free y's in $F(y)$ correspond to the free x's in $F(x)$.

2. We do not want to be able by using **EI** to get from $(x)(\exists y)$ $F(x,y)$ to $(\exists y)(x)F(x,y)$. This *could* be done by the sequence

$$
\begin{array}{ll}
(x)(\exists y)F(x,y) \vdash (\exists y)F(x,y) & \text{P 5, R 1} \\
(x)(\exists y)F(x,y) \vdash F(x,y) & \text{`EI'} \\
(x)(\exists y)F(x,y) \vdash (x)F(x,y) & \text{R 2} \\
(x)(\exists y)F(x,y) \vdash (\exists y)(x)F(x,y) & \text{DR 7 (EG)}
\end{array}
$$

We avoid this danger by permitting the use of **EI** only with the restriction that R 2 will not be used to quantify any variable which has a free occurrence in a step inferred by **EI**.

3. We do not want to be able by using **EI** to go from $(\exists x)$ $F(x) \cdot (\exists x)G(x)$ to $(\exists x)[F(x) \cdot G(x)]$. This *could* be done by the sequence

$$
\begin{array}{ll}
(\exists x)F(x) \cdot (\exists x)G(x) \vdash (\exists x)F(x) & \text{\textcircled{P}} \\
(\exists x)F(x) \cdot (\exists x)G(x) \vdash F(z) & \text{`EI'} \\
(\exists x)F(x) \cdot (\exists x)G(x) \vdash (\exists x)G(x) & \text{\textcircled{P}} \\
(\exists x)F(x) \cdot (\exists x)G(x) \vdash G(z) & \text{`EI'} \\
(\exists x)F(x) \cdot (\exists x)G(x) \vdash F(z) \cdot G(z) & \text{\textcircled{P}} \\
(\exists x)F(x) \cdot (\exists x)G(x) \vdash (\exists x)[F(x) \cdot G(x)] & \text{DR 7 (EG)}
\end{array}
$$

We avoid this particular danger by the (familiar) restriction that every use of **EI** must be with respect to a new individual variable.

4. We do not want to be able by using **EI** to prove anything like $(\exists x)F(x) \vdash F(y)$ where this could be used subsequently as a

derived rule not subject to the kind of restriction mentioned under 2 above. Hence in a proof that $P_1, P_2, \ldots, P_n \vdash Q$, **EI** must not be used to introduce any variable which occurs free in Q.

Instead of attempting to formulate a derived rule corresponding to **EI**, we shall prove a Metatheorem which will legitimize any use of **EI** in a proof subject to the aforementioned restrictions.

METATHEOREM V. (The legitimacy of **EI**) If there is a sequence of *wffs* which constitutes a demonstration that $P_1, P_2, \ldots, P_n \vdash Q$ *except* that some *wffs* follow from preceding ones by **EI** (here construed simply as the rule that $F(y)$ follows from $(\exists x)F(x)$), such that

1. There are m uses of **EI** of which the ith $(1 \leq i \leq m)$ use is to go from $(\exists x_i)F_i(x_i)$ to $F_i(y_i)$ where the free x_i's in $F_i(x_i)$ correspond exactly to the free y_i's in $F_i(y_i)$;
2. No variable which occurs free in any $F_i(y_i)$ is ever quantified by R 2;
3. No y_i occurs free either in any P_j or in any *wff* of the 'demonstration' which precedes $F_i(y_i)$;
4. No y_i occurs free in Q;

then there is a demonstration that $P_1, P_2, \ldots, P_n \vdash Q$ (which contains no use of **EI**). And in the latter (genuine) demonstration there are no uses of R 2 to quantify variables free in $P_1, P_2, \ldots, P_n$ which were not quantified by R 2 in the original 'demonstration'.

Proof: Any such 'demonstration' will be of the form

.
.
.

$(\exists x_1)F_1(x_1)$
.

.
.

$F_1(y_1)$ $\qquad\qquad\qquad\qquad$ 1ˢᵗ use of **EI**
.
.
.

$$(\exists x_2)F_2(x_2)$$

.

.

.

$$F_2(y_2) \qquad\qquad\qquad 2^{nd} \text{ use of } \mathbf{EI}$$

.

.

.

.

.

$$(\exists x_{m-1})F_{m-1}(x_{m-1})$$

.

.

$$F_{m-1}(y_{m-1}) \qquad\qquad (m-1)^{st} \text{ use of } \mathbf{EI}$$
.

.

$$(\exists x_m)F_m(x_m)$$

.

.

$$F_m(y_m) \qquad\qquad\qquad m^{th} \text{ and last use of } \mathbf{EI}$$
.

.

.

$$Q$$

With the exception of the m *wffs* $F_1(y_1), F_2(y_2), \ldots, F_{m-1}(y_{m-1})$, $F_m(y_m)$ every step of the preceding sequence is either an axiom or a P_j or follows from earlier steps by R 1 or R 2. Hence the preceding sequence is a genuine demonstration that

$$P_1, \ldots, P_n, F_1(y_1), F_2(y_2), \ldots, F_{m-1}(y_{m-1}), F_m(y_m) \vdash Q.$$

By condition 2 of the Metatheorem, no variable occurring free in any $F_i(y_i)$ is ever quantified by R 2. Hence we can use the Deduction Theorem to obtain a demonstration that

$$P_1, \ldots, P_n, F_1(y_1), F_2(y_2), \ldots, F_{m-1}(y_{m-1}) \vdash F_m(y_m) \supset Q$$

in which no variable occurring free in any $F_i(y_i)$ is ever quantified by R 2. We *now* apply R 2 to obtain

$$P_1, \ldots, P_n, F_1(y_1), F_2(y_2), \ldots, F_{m-1}(y_{m-1}) \vdash (y_m)[F_m(y_m) \supset Q].$$

By condition 4, y_m has no free occurrence in Q, so we can use Th. 21 and the Substitution Theorem to obtain

$$P_1, \ldots, P_n, F_1(y_1), F_2(y_2), \ldots, F_{m-1}(y_{m-1}) \vdash (\exists y_m)F_m(y_m) \supset Q.$$

By condition 1, the free x_m's in $F_m(x_m)$ correspond exactly to the free y_m's in $F_m(y_m)$, so by Th. 26 and the Substitution Theorem we obtain

$$P_1, \ldots, P_n, F_1(y_1), F_2(y_2), \ldots, F_{m-1}(y_{m-1}) \vdash (\exists x_m)F_m(x_m) \supset Q.$$

Since $(\exists x_m)F_m(x_m)$ preceded $F_m(y_m)$ in our original 'demonstration,' we know that

$$P_1, \ldots, P_n, F_1(y_1), F_2(y_2), \ldots, F_{m-1}(y_{m-1}) \vdash (\exists x_m)F_m(x_m).$$

Hence by R 1 we obtain

(1) $\qquad P_1, \ldots, P_n, F_1(y_1), F_2(y_2), \ldots, F_{m-1}(y_{m-1}) \vdash Q.$

In the preceding steps y_m was the only variable quantified by R 2. Now by condition 3 of the Metatheorem, y_m does not occur free either in any P_j or in any *wff* which precedes $F_m(y_m)$. Hence in the demonstration of (1), R 2 is never used to quantify any variable which occurs free in any P_j or in any *wff* which precedes $F_m(y_m)$.

Consequently all four conditions of the Metatheorem still hold, and we can repeat the preceding argument m times to obtain successively

(2) $\quad P_1, \ldots, P_n, F_1(y_1), F_2(y_2), \ldots, F_{m-3}(y_{m-3}), F_{m-2}(y_{m-2}) \vdash Q$

(3) $\quad P_1, \ldots, P_n, F_1(y_1), F_2(y_2), \ldots, F_{m-3}(y_{m-3}) \vdash Q$

and finally

(m) $\quad P_1, \ldots, P_n \vdash Q$

which completes our proof of Metatheorem V.

The preceding discussion suffices to show that our first-order function calculus RS_1 *is* an axiomatization of the logic *used* in Chapter Four and the first four sections of Chapter Five. That it contains no *more* than was used there can be shown by giving demonstrations (in the earlier sense of 'demonstration') of the postulates of RS_1. The rules of RS_1 are obviously equivalent to *modus ponens* and **UG** (the restriction on **UG** being shifted to **EI** within the formal system).

The question naturally arises as to *how much* logic is contained in RS_1. We shall present a proof that RS_1 is deductively complete in the sense that all logically true propositions involving quantification of individual variables only are provable as theorems within it. This sense will be specified more precisely in Section VI. Before proving the completeness of our first-order function calculus, however, we shall develop some notions and Metatheorems concerning the subject of 'Normal Forms.'

V. NORMAL FORMS

We begin by defining the notion of 'prenex normal form'. A *wff* is in *prenex normal form* if and only if it has the structure $(Qx_1)(Qx_2) \ldots (Qx_n)G$ where $x_1, x_2, \ldots, x_n$ are distinct individual variables, (Qx_i) is either $(\exists x_i)$ or (x_i), and G is a quantifier-free *wff* containing at least one occurrence of each of the x_i's. Some examples of formulas of RS_1 which are in prenex normal form are

$$(x)(A^1(x))$$
$$(\exists x)((B^1(x)) \supset (C^2(xy)))$$
$$(y)((\exists z)(\sim(A^3(xyz))))$$

We now define the term 'scope' as follows: If $(Qx)B$ is a well formed part (i.e., a *wff* which is a part) of a *wff* A then the scope of that particular occurrence of (Qx) in A is the particular occurrence of B which immediately follows (Qx). * And we define the phrase 'initially placed' in this way: A quantifier is initially placed in a *wff* F if it either stands at the beginning of F or is

---

* This definition provides a more precise formulation of the notion of scope which was discussed informally in Section IV of Chapter Four. Cf. pp. 93ff.

preceded only by other quantifiers, and its scope extends to the end of F. It should be clear that an equivalent definition of 'prenex normal form' can be stated as: A *wff* is in *prenex normal form* if and only if all its quantifiers are initially placed, no two quantifiers are the same variable, and every variable occurring in a quantifier occurs also at least once within the *scope* of that quantifier.

We can now state and prove our next Metatheorem.

METATHEOREM VI. Given any *wff* F of RS_1, a formula P in prenex normal form can be found such that $\vdash F \equiv P$.

Proof: CASE 1. F is in prenex normal form. Here P is F and $\vdash F \equiv P$ by Ⓟ.

    CASE 2. F is not in prenex normal form. Such an F must either: (a) contain a quantifier which is not initially placed, or (b) contain two quantifiers on the same variable, or (c) contain a variable which occurs *only* in a quantifier.

    Sub-case 1: All quantifiers in F are initially placed.

        Sub-sub-case 1.*i*: At least two quantifiers are on the same variable. Here we have F of the form

$$(Qx_1)(Qx_2) \ldots (Qx_i) \ldots (Qx_i) \ldots (Qx_n)G.$$

If we denote all of F which immediately follows the first (Qx_i) by A, then x_i does not occur free in A, and by Th. 14 or Th. 15, $\vdash (Qx_i)A \equiv A$. Hence by the Substitution Theorem the first of any initially placed quantifiers on the same variable can be simply dropped out to yield an equivalent formula. So if all quantifiers of F are initially placed, then there is an equivalent formula all of whose quantifiers are initially placed and which has not more than one quantifier on any one variable.

        Sub-sub-case 1.*ii*: There is a variable in F which occurs only in a quantifier. Here we have F of the form

$$(Qx_1) \ldots (Qx_i) \ldots (Qx_n)G$$

where x_i does not occur free in G. If we denote all of F which immediately follows (Qx_i) by A, then x_i does not occur free in A and by Th. 14 or Th. 15, $\vdash (Qx_i)A \equiv A$. Hence by the Substitution Theorem any initially placed quantifier on a variable which has no occurrence outside of that quantifier may be simply dropped out to yield an equivalent formula. So if all quantifiers of F are initially placed then there is an equivalent formula all of whose quantifiers are initially placed and which contains no variables whose only occurrences are in quantifiers.

Sub-case 2: Some quantifiers in F are not initially placed. In this sub-case it is convenient to write F in unabbreviated form, so the only propositional calculus symbols in it are $\cdot$ and $\sim$. Next we consider a *wff* G such that no two quantifiers in G are on the same variable, no variable in G has both free and bound occurrences, and $\vdash F \equiv G$. If F is such a *wff*, let F be G; otherwise G is obtained from F by interchanging bound variables according to Theorems 25 and 26 and the Substitution Theorem.

Apart from parentheses, each symbol other than a quantifier that occurs to the left of a given quantifier (Qx_j) in a *wff* G can be counted as a "reason" why (Qx_j) is not initially placed in G, and each symbol that occurs to the right of (Qx_j) in G and does not lie within its scope can also be counted as a "reason" why (Qx_j) is not initially placed in G. It is obvious that any quantifier (Qx_j) occurring in a *wff* G is initially placed in G if and only if there are no "reasons" why that quantifier is not initially placed in G.

Given any such *wff* G in which the quantifier on x_j is not initially placed and all quantifiers in G preceding the quantifier on x_j are initially placed in G, we can construct a *wff* G_1 such that: every initially placed quantifier in G is initially placed in G_1 also, all quantifiers in G_1 preceding the quantifier on x_j are initially placed, $\vdash G \equiv G_1$, and there are fewer "reasons" why the quantifier on x_j is not initially placed in G_1 than there were "reasons" why the quantifier on x_j was not initially placed in G. The construction of G_1 proceeds as follows.

If (Qx_j) is the first quantifier in G that is not initially placed in G, then it can occur in only one of the following wf parts of G: $((Qx_j)(A))\cdot(B)$ or $(B)\cdot((Qx_j)(A))$ or $\sim((Qx_j)(A))$.

In the first case, since x_j has no occurrence in B, we replace the wf part $((Qx_j(A))\cdot(B)$ by $(Qx_j)((A)\cdot(B))$, using Theorem 16 or Theorem 23 and the Substitution Theorem, to obtain the *wff* G_1.

In the second case, we first use ⓟ to replace the wf part $(B)\cdot((Qx_j)(A))$ by $((Qx_j)(A))\cdot(B)$, and then replace that as in the preceding case by $(Qx_j)((A)\cdot(B))$ to obtain the *wff* G_1.

In the third case we obtain the *wff* G_1 using Theorem 7 or Theorem 8 and the Substitution Theorem to replace the wf part $\sim((Qx_j)(A))$ by $(Q^*x_j)(\sim(A))$, where (Q^*x_j) is either (x_j) or $(\exists x_j)$ according as (Qx_j) is $(\exists x_j)$ or (x_j).

If the quantifier on x_j is not initially placed in G_1, we repeat the construction just described to obtain G_2, in which there are still fewer "reasons" why the quantifier on x_j is not initially placed. Since each *wff* contains only finitely many symbols, in any *wff* there can be only finitely many "reasons" why any quantifier in it is not initially placed. Hence the construction described need be iterated only finitely many times to produce a *wff* G_k in which the quantifier on x_j is initially placed.

A new series of such constructions can be used for each quantifier that is not initially placed in the original *wff* F, until finally a *wff* G_K is obtained in which all quantifiers are initially placed and such that $\vdash F \equiv G_K$. And to G_K there is an equivalent *wff* in prenex normal form by Sub-case 1.

We define two new terms at this point: In any *wff* in prenex normal form

$$(Qx_1)(Qx_2) \ . \ . \ . \ (Qx_n)G$$

the group of quantifiers $(Qx_1)(Qx_2) \ . \ . \ . \ (Qx_n)$ is the *prefix* and the quantifier-free formula G is the *matrix*.

EXERCISES

Find a prenex normal form for

1. $(x)(\exists y)(\exists x)(y)[(z)G(z){\cdot}F(x) \supset (\exists z)H(z){\cdot}F(z)]$
2. $[(x)G(x) \text{ v } H(y)] \equiv [(y)(z)F(y,z)]$
3. $(x)[F(x) \supset G(x)] \supset [(x)F(x) \supset (x)G(x)]$
4. $(y)(\exists x)F(x,y) \supset (\exists x)(y)F(x,y)$
5. $(x_1)(\exists x_2)(x_3)(\exists x_4)(x_5)[P^6(x_1, \ . \ . \ . \ , x_6) \supset (z_1)(\exists x)(\exists z)H(x_1,z)]$

A *wff* which is in prenex normal form may contain free variables. We wish to be able, without any loss in generality, to confine our attention to *wffs* which contain no free variables. These will be referred to as *closed wffs* (abbreviated *cwffs*). To legitimize our concentrating on *cwffs*, we state and prove the following:

Metatheorem VII. For any *wff* F a *cwff* G may be found which is in prenex normal form such that $\vdash F$ if and only if $\vdash G$.

Proof: By Metatheorem VI we can always find the prenex normal form P for any *wff* F such that $\vdash F \equiv P$.

case 1. If P is a *cwff* then G is the same as P, and since $\vdash F \equiv G$, $\vdash F$ if and only if $\vdash G$.

case 2. If P contains n free variables $x_1, x_2, \ . \ . \ . \ , x_n$, then G is the *cwff* $(x_1)(x_2) \ . \ . \ . \ (x_n)P$. For if $\vdash F$ then $\vdash P$, and by R 2, $\vdash (x_n)P$, and by n uses of R 2 we have $\vdash G$. And if $\vdash G$, that is, $\vdash (x_1)(x_2) \ldots (x_n)P$, then since $\vdash (x_1)(x_2) \ldots (x_n)P \supset (x_2) \ldots (x_n)P$ by P 5, R 1 gives $\vdash (x_2) \ldots (x_n)P$, and by n uses of P 5 and R 1, we have $\vdash P$, and hence $\vdash F$.

We prove now a further result which gives for any *wff* a still more specialized normal form *wff* which is a theorem if and only if the original *wff* is a theorem.

METATHEOREM VIII. For any *wff* F a *cwff* R may be found which is in prenex normal form and begins with an existential quantifier, such that $\vdash F$ if and only if $\vdash R$.

Proof: By Metatheorem VII, for any *wff* F there is a *cwff* G in prenex normal form such that $\vdash F$ if and only if $\vdash G$. Let $D(t)$ be a function of one variable t such that neither D nor t occurs in G. Then by ℗, $\vdash G \equiv \{G \cdot [D(t) \supset D(t)]\}$. Hence

$\vdash G \supset \{G \cdot [D(t) \supset D(t)]\}$	by ℗
$\vdash (\exists t)\{G \supset \{G \cdot [D(t) \supset D(t)]\}\}$	by DR 7, (**EG**)
$\vdash G \supset (\exists t)\{G \cdot [D(t) \supset D(t)]\}$	by Th. 19, R 1

We also have

$\vdash \{G \cdot [D(t) \supset D(t)]\} \supset G$	P 2
$\vdash (t)\{\{G \cdot [D(t) \supset D(t)]\} \supset G\}$	R 2
$\vdash (\exists t)\{G \cdot (D(t) \supset D(t))\} \supset G$	Th. 21, R 1

Hence

$\vdash (\exists t)\{G \cdot [D(t) \supset D(t)]\} \equiv G$	by ℗

Now the prenex normal form of $(\exists t)\{G \cdot [D(t) \supset D(t)]\}$ is the formula *of type* R that was desired, for it is closed, is in prenex normal form, begins with an existential quantifier, and $\vdash F$ if and only if $\vdash R$. Where G is $(Qx_1)(Qx_2) \ldots (Qx_n)G'$, then

$\vdash (\exists t)\{G \cdot [D(t) \supset D(t)]\}$ or
$\vdash (\exists t)\{[(Qx_1)(Qx_2) \ldots (Qx_n)G'] \cdot \sim [D(t) \cdot \sim D(t)]\}$

has as its prenex normal form

$$\vdash (\exists t)(Qx_1)(Qx_2) \ldots (Qx_n)\{G' \cdot \sim [D(t) \cdot \sim D(t)]\}$$

by repeated uses of Th. 16 or Th. 23 and the Substitution Theorem.

By definition, any *cwff* in prenex normal form which begins with an existential quantifier will be said to be *of type R*.

EXERCISES

For each of the following *wffs* construct a logically equivalent formula *of type R:*

1. $(x)(y)(z)\{[H(x) \vee H(y)] \vee H(z)\}$
2. $F(x_1, x_2, \ldots, x_n) \supset G(z)$
3. $(\exists x)G(x,y) \vee F(z)$
4. $(\exists z)F(z,z) \supset (x)G(x,y)$
5. $(x)F(x,y) \supset G(z)$

Next we present three new definitions, of which the third defines the 'Skolem normal form', which is a still more specialized type of well formed formula, about which we shall establish a further Metatheorem.

Df. The *rank of an occurrence of an existential quantifier* in a formula *of type R* is the number of universal quantifiers which precede that existential quantifier in the prefix.

Df. The *rank of a formula of type R* is the greatest of the ranks of the occurrences of the existential quantifiers of its prefix.

Df. A *wff F* is in *Skolem normal form* if and only if it is *of type R* and of rank 0.

METATHEOREM IX. Given any *wff F* we can find a formula F_0 in Skolem normal form such that $\vdash F$ if and only if $\vdash F_0$.

Proof: For any *wff F* we can construct a formula *of type R*, call it F_1, such that $\vdash F$ if and only if $\vdash F_1$. (If *F* is already *of type R* then $F = F_1$.) If F_1 is of rank 0, then it is in the desired Skolem normal form. If F_1 is of rank $k > 0$, then we show how to construct a formula *of type R* of rank less than k, call it F_2, such that $\vdash F_1$ if and only if $\vdash F_2$. We thus embark on a process which will yield formulas F_3, F_4, F_5, . . . all *of type R* and of decreasing rank. Ultimately, then, we arrive at a formula *of type R* and of rank 0, F_0, such that $\vdash F$ if and only if $\vdash F_0$.

If F_1 is not in Skolem normal form, then its rank is greater than 0, that is, F_1 has the structure

$$(\exists x_1)(\exists x_2) \ldots (\exists x_n)(y)(Qz_1)(Qz_2) \ldots (Qz_m)G$$

where $(Qz_1)(Qz_2)$, . . . , (Qz_m) are quantifiers of which at least one is an existential quantifier. We now introduce the following notations:

1. $B(x_1, x_2, \ldots, x_n, y) = \mathrm{df}\ (Qz_1)(Qz_2) \ldots (Qz_m)G$. This we shall abbreviate as A.
2. $H(y) = \mathrm{df}\ H(x_1, x_2, \ldots, x_n, y)$ where H is any function of $x_1, x_2, \ldots, x_n, y$ such that H does not occur in G.
3. $H(t) = \mathrm{df}\ H(x_1, x_2, \ldots, x_n, t)$ where t is a variable which does not occur in G.
4. $C = \mathrm{df}\ (\exists x_1)(\exists x_2) \ldots (\exists x_n)\{(y)[(Qz_1)(Qz_2) \ldots (Qz_m)G \supset H(y)] \supset (t)H(t)\}$

First we want to show that $\vdash F_1$ if and only if $\vdash C$. The two implications are

(i) If $\vdash F_1$ then $\vdash C$. Here we prove that $\vdash F_1 \supset C$.

$\vdash A \supset \{[A \supset H(y)] \supset H(y)\}$	ⓟ
$\vdash (y)\{A \supset \{[A \supset H(y)] \supset H(y)\}\}$	R 2
$\vdash (y)A \supset (y)\{[A \supset H(y)] \supset H(y)\}$	DR 4
$\vdash (y)A \supset \{(y)[A \supset H(y)] \supset (y)H(y)\}$	Th. 2, ⓟ
$\vdash (y)A \supset \{(y)[A \supset H(y)] \supset (t)H(t)\}$	Th. 25, Substitution
$\vdash (x_n)\{(y)A \supset \{(y)[A \supset H(y)] \supset (t)H(t)\}\}$	R 2
$\vdash (\exists x_n)(y)A \supset (\exists x_n)\{(y)[A \supset H(y)] \supset (t)H(t)\}$	
	Th. 4, R 1

. . . .

. . . .

$\vdash (\exists x_1)(\exists x_2) \ldots (\exists x_n)(y)A \supset (\exists x_1)(\exists x_2) \ldots$
$\quad (\exists x_n)\{(y)[A \supset H(y)] \supset (t)H(t)\}$ by n uses of R 2, Th. 4, R 1
$\vdash F_1 \supset C.$ df.

Hence if $\vdash F_1$ then $\vdash C$.

(ii) If $\vdash C$ then $\vdash F_1$. Here we must assume that $\vdash C$ and derive $\vdash F_1$.

$\vdash (\exists x_1) \ldots (\exists x_n)\{(y)[Qz_1) \ldots (Qz_m)G \supset$
$\qquad\qquad\qquad\qquad\qquad H(y)] \supset (t)H(t)\}$ C
$\vdash (\exists x_1) \ldots (\exists x_n)\{(y)[B(x_1, \ldots, x_n, y) \supset$
$\quad H(x_1, \ldots, x_n, y)] \supset (t)H(x_1, \ldots, x_n, t)\}$ df.
$\vdash (\exists x_2) \ldots (\exists x_n)\{(y)[B(x'_1, \ldots, x_n, y) \supset$
$\quad H(x'_1, \ldots, x_n, y)] \supset (t)H(x'_1, \ldots, x_n, t)\}$ **EI**

$\cdots \cdots \cdots \cdots \cdots \cdots \cdots \cdots$

$\vdash (y)[B(x'_1, \ldots, x'_n, y) \supset H(x'_1, \ldots, x'_n, y)] \supset$
$\qquad\qquad\qquad\qquad (t)H(x'_1, \ldots, x'_n, t)$ n uses of **EI**

Now we take $H(x'_1, \ldots, x'_n, y)$ to be $B(x'_1, \ldots, x'_n, y)$, which is legitimate since H was *any* function.[7]

$\vdash (y)[B(x'_1, \ldots, x'_n, y) \supset B(x'_1, \ldots, x'_n, y)] \supset$
$\qquad\qquad\qquad (t)B(x'_1, \ldots, x'_n, t)$
$\vdash (y)[B(x'_1, \ldots, x'_n, y) \supset B(x'_1, \ldots, x'_n, y)] \supset$
$\qquad\qquad\qquad (y)B(x'_1, \ldots, x'_n, y)$
$\qquad\qquad\qquad\qquad\qquad$ Th. 25, Substitution
$\vdash B(x'_1, \ldots, x'_n, y) \supset B(x'_1, \ldots, x'_n, y)$ ⓟ
$\vdash (y)[B(x'_1, \ldots, x'_n, y) \supset B(x'_1, \ldots, x'_n, y)]$ R 2
$\vdash (y)B(x'_1, \ldots, x'_n, y)$ R 1
$\vdash (\exists x_n)(y)B(x'_1, \ldots x_n, y)$ DR 7, (**EG**)

$\cdots \cdots \cdots \cdots \cdots \cdots \cdots \cdots$

$\vdash (\exists x_1) \ldots (\exists x_n)(y)B(x_1, \ldots, x_n, y)$ n uses of **EG**
$\vdash (\exists x_1) \ldots (\exists x_n)(y)(Qz_1) \ldots (Qz_m)G$ df.
$\vdash F_1$ df.

Hence if $\vdash C$ then $\vdash F_1$.

C is not in prenex normal form. Its prenex normal form is constructed as follows, using the notation Q* defined as follows:

fn 7 in 2nd ed.

If (Qz_i) is (z_i) then (Q^*z_i) is $(\exists z_i)$;
If (Qz_i) is $(\exists z_i)$ then (Q^*z_i) is (z_i).

$$C \equiv (\exists x_1) \ \ldots \ (\exists x_n)\{(y)[(Qz_1)(Qz_2) \ \ldots$$
$$(Qz_m)G \supset H(y)] \supset (t)H(t)\}$$

Since $H(y)$ does not contain any free z_i's,

$$\vdash (Qz_1) \ \ldots \ (Qz_m)G \supset H(y) \equiv (Q^*z_1) \ \ldots \ (Q^*z_m)[G \supset H(y)]$$

by m uses of Th. 18 or Th. 21. Hence by Substitution,

$$C \equiv (\exists x_1) \ \ldots \ (\exists x_n)\{(y)(Q^*z_1) \ \ldots \ (Q^*z_m)[G \supset H(y)] \supset (t)H(t)\}$$

Since $(t)H(t)$ does not contain any free z_i's,

$$\vdash \{(y)(Q^*z_1) \ \ldots \ (Q^*z_m)[G \supset H(y)] \supset (t)H(t)\} \equiv$$
$$\{(\exists y)(Qz_1) \ \ldots \ (Qz_m)[[G \supset H(y)] \supset (t)H(t)]\}$$

by $m + 1$ uses of Th. 18 or Th. 21. Hence by Substitution,

$$C \equiv (\exists x_1) \ \ldots \ (\exists x_n)(\exists y)(Qz_1) \ \ldots \ (Qz_m)[[G \supset H(y)] \supset (t)H(t)]$$

Since t is not free in $G \supset H(y)$, by Th. 20,

$$\vdash [[G \supset H(y)] \supset (t)H(t)] \equiv (t)[[G \supset H(y)] \supset H(t)],$$

hence by Substitution,

$$C \equiv (\exists x_1) \ \ldots \ (\exists x_n)(\exists y)(Qz_1) \ \ldots \ (Qz_m)(t)[[G \supset H(y)] \supset H(t)].$$

The right hand formula is the formula F_2 *of type R* such that $\vdash F$ if and only if $\vdash F_2$. Now the rank of F_2 is lower than the rank of F_1, for their prefixes are the same except that F_2 has an additional universal quantifier in the final position, which does not affect the rank, and one of the universal quantifiers $((y))$ which preceded an existential quantifier has been replaced by an existential quantifier, which lowers the rank by one. If F_2 has rank 0 then it is the Skolem normal form of F. If it is not, then the argument can be repeated to obtain a formula F_3 *of type R* of still lower rank. Hence we can ultimately arrive at a formula *of type R* of rank 0, which is the desired Skolem normal form.

EXERCISES

Find a Skolem normal form for

1. $(\exists x)(y)(\exists z)[F(x,y) \vee G(z)]$
2. $(x)(\exists y)F(x,y)$
3. $(\exists x_1)(x_2)(x_3)(\exists x_4)F(x_1, x_2, x_3, x_4)$

VI. COMPLETENESS OF RS_1

We turn now to the problem of proving our first-order function calculus complete. There are several different senses of the term 'complete' which must be distinguished. A very strong kind of completeness is possessed by a system *all* of whose well formed formulas are provable as theorems. But this kind of completeness amounts to inconsistency, and is of course undesirable. Our first Metatheorem, which established the consistency of our system, proved it to lack *this* kind of completeness. A somewhat weaker kind of completeness is possessed by a system each of whose *wffs* is either provable as a theorem or else has its denial provable as a theorem; that is, for every *wff* F either $\vdash F$ or $\vdash \sim F$. This kind of completeness is not desirable either, for on their normal interpretations, each of the following *wffs*

N_1: $(\exists x)F(x) \supset (x)F(x)$
N_2: $(\exists x)(\exists y)\{F(x)\cdot F(y)\cdot[G(x) \equiv \sim G(y)]\} \supset (x)F(x)$
N_3: $(\exists x)(\exists y)(\exists z)\{F(x)\cdot F(y)\cdot F(z)\cdot[G(x) \equiv \sim G(y)].$
       $[H(y) \equiv \sim H(z)]\cdot[I(x) \equiv \sim I(z)]\} \supset (x)F(x)$
. . . .
. . . .

asserts (respectively) that there is at most one individual, that there are at most two individuals, that there are at most three individuals, . . . But if we want our logical system to be applicable to *any* non-empty universe *regardless* of the exact number of individuals it contains, there is no N_i such that we want either N_i or $\sim N_i$ to be provable as theorems. A different kind of completeness was proved for the propositional calculus presented in Chapter Seven. That logistic system was proved to be complete in the sense that every *wff* which (on its normal interpretation) is a truth table tautology is provable as a theorem in the system. That kind of completeness is admirably suited for a propositional calculus, but it will not do for a functional calculus. A first-order function calculus which did not have the *wff*

$$(\exists x)(y)F(x,y) \supset (y)(\exists x)F(x,y)$$

provable as a theorem within it would be woefully unsatisfactory and 'incomplete', even though the formula in question is *not* a truth table tautology. The reason for regarding as unsatisfactory a logic in which the given expression is a *wff* but not provable is that (on its normal interpretation) the formula expresses a logical truth—where a 'logical truth' is a proposition which is true in (or of) *every possible non-empty universe*. The kind of completeness desired for our first-order function calculus can be expressed loosely by saying that every logical truth which can be expressed in the system is provable as a theorem within it. This notion, however, must be expressed much more precisely before it can be used in any proof of completeness.*

Instead of continuing to speak of 'possible universes' we shall talk about *models*, where a model is any (non-empty) collection of elements each of which is thought of as an *individual*. And instead of speaking of our system of logic as being 'applied' to a 'possible universe', we shall speak of a model as constituting an 'interpretation' of our formal system. This last term will be given a precise meaning presently. With any given set of individuals which may be intended to serve as a *model*, we assume that we are given also the properties which may belong to the individual elements, and

---

* The following discussion and proof of completeness is an adaptation to RS₁ of the completeness proof for an alternative first-order function calculus given by Leon Henkin in his article 'The Completeness of the First-Order Functional Calculus', *The Journal of Symbolic Logic*, vol. 14 (1949), pp. 159–166. The respect in which the following is a simplification of the published proof is due to Professor Henkin himself, who communicated it to the present writer in the spring of 1951. It is reproduced here with his kind permission.

The first proof of completeness for a first-order function calculus was published by Kurt Gödel, 'Die Vollstandigkeit der Axiome der logischen Funktionenkalkuls', *Monatshefte für Mathematik und Physik*, vol. 37 (1930), pp. 349–360.

the relations (dyadic, triadic, etc.) which may hold between (or among) them. Now we define '*interpretation of a wff S with respect to a given model*' as an assignment of meanings such that

1. To each propositional symbol in S we assign a truth value, either **T** or **F**.
2. To each individual constant, and to each variable with free occurrence in S, we assign an element of the model.
3. To each predicate symbol we assign a property or a dyadic or triadic or n-adic relation according as it is of degree (has right superscript) 1, 2, 3, or n

This notion of interpretation of a *wff* with respect to a given model is incomplete, however, because no mention is made of what to do with the logical symbols $\sim$, $\cdot$, and the quantifier symbol (x). Our intended or *normal* interpretation of a *wff S* with respect to a given model is defined as an interpretation of S with respect to that model, subject to the following conditions:

a. Any well formed part $\sim W$ is assigned the truth value **T** or **F** according as the well formed part W is assigned the truth value **F** or **T**.
b. Any well formed part of the form $X \cdot Y$ is assigned the truth value **T** if and only if both X and Y are assigned the truth value **T**.
c. Any well formed part $(x)R$ is assigned the truth value **T** if and only if R is assigned the value **T** regardless of which element of the model is assigned to all free occurrences of x in R.
d. Any well formed part $P^n(x_1, x_2, \ldots, x_n)$ is assigned the truth value **T** if and only if the elements of the model assigned to x_1, $x_2, \ldots, x_n$, in that order, stand to each other in the n-adic relation assigned to P^n.

So far we have defined 'interpretation' and 'normal interpretation' only for a *wff* with respect to a given model. An *interpretation of a system with respect to a given model* is an assignment of meanings which provides interpretations for *all wffs* of the system, and a *normal interpretation of a system with respect to a given model* is an assignment of meanings which provides *normal* interpretations for all *wffs* of the system.

There are many interpretations, and even many normal interpretations of a formal system with respect to a given model. On some of these the value **T** may be assigned a *wff* which on another interpretation is assigned the truth value **F**. The postulates of our first-order function calculus, however, will be assigned the truth value **T** on *any* normal interpretation of the system with respect to *any* given model.* A particular normal interpretation of a *wff* S with respect to a given model will be said to *satisfy* S with respect to that model if by it S is assigned the truth value **T**. A *wff* S will be said to be *satisfiable with respect to a given model* if there is a normal interpretation of S with respect to that model which assigns the truth value **T** to S. And a *wff* S will be said to be *satisfiable* if there is at least one model such that there is a normal interpretation of S with respect to it which assigns the truth value **T** to S. Another term which it is important to introduce in this connection is 'valid'. A *wff* S is *valid with respect to a given model* if every normal interpretation of S with respect to that model assigns the truth value **T** to S. It follows immediately from the definitions that the *wff* S is *valid* with respect to a given model if and only if every normal interpretation of S with respect to that model *satisfies* S. Finally we define the term 'valid' by itself: a *wff* S is *valid* if it is valid with respect to every model. It follows immediately from the definitions that for any *wff* S either S is valid or $\sim S$ is satisfiable.

In the notion of a *model* we have a precise formulation of our informal notion of a possible universe, and *normal interpretation* is what ought to be signified by the looser phrase 'intended application'. Consequently, the *validity* of a *wff* is a precise notion which serves the purpose suggested by the phrase 'logically true'. The completeness we wish to prove for our first-order function calculus RS₁ can now be defined precisely. A first-order function calculus is *complete* if and only if every valid *wff* is provable in it as a theorem.

---

* This is too obvious to require formal proof.

A First-Order Function Calculus

In establishing the completeness of RS_1 it will be sufficient to confine our attention to *wffs* which contain no free individual variables, for it is easily demonstrated that to every *wff* S which contains free individual variables there corresponds a *wff* S^c (called the *closure* of S) containing no free individual variables, such that ⊢S if and only if ⊢S^c, and such that S is valid if and only if S^c is valid. Where S contains exactly n free variables, say $x_1, x_2, \ldots, x_{n-1}, x_n$ (in the order of their occurrence), then S^c will be $(x_1)(x_2) \ldots (x_{n-1})(x_n)S$. Now if ⊢S then ⊢$(x_n)S$ by R 2, and another application of R 2 gives ⊢$(x_{n-1})(x_n)S$; finally we have ⊢S^c by n uses of R 2. Conversely, if ⊢S^c, that is, ⊢(x_1) $(x_2) \ldots (x_{n-1})(x_n)S$, then applying R 1 to it and the instance of P 5 which is $(x_1)(x_2) \ldots (x_{n-1})(x_n)S \supset (x_2) \ldots (x_{n-1})(x_n)S$ will give ⊢$(x_2) \ldots (x_{n-1})(x_n)S$; so that by n uses of R 1 and P 5 we obtain ⊢S. If S is valid, every normal interpretation of S with respect to any model assigns to S the value **T** regardless of which elements of the model its free individual variables $x_1, x_2, \ldots, x_n$ are taken to denote. From this it follows that $(x_n)S$ is valid, and $(x_{n-1})(x_n)S$ is valid, $\ldots$, and finally that S^c is valid. On the other hand, if S^c is valid, $(x_2)(x_3) \ldots (x_n)S$ is assigned the value **T** regardless of which elements of the model x_1 is taken to denote, from which it follows that $(x_3) \ldots (x_n)S$ is assigned the value **T** regardless of which elements x_1 and x_2 are taken to denote, from which it follows $\ldots$ finally that S is assigned the value **T** regardless of which elements of the model the free individual variables $x_1, x_2 \ldots, x_n$ are taken to denote, which means that S is valid. Hence with no real loss in generality we can confine our attention to closed *wffs* (*wffs* containing no free variables), which we shall refer to as *cwffs*.

To prove our system complete it is necessary to introduce and use the notion of a *set* of *cwffs*. We shall use the capital Greek letters *Gamma* and *Lambda*, with and without subscripts, to denote *sets* of *cwffs* of RS_1. We shall also make use of braces to represent sets of *cwffs*: for example, the set whose only member is the *cwff* S will be written {S}, the set whose only two members are the *cwffs* S_1 and S_2 will be written {S_1, S_2}, and so on. To assert that

But for any wff S either S is valid or ~S is satisfiable ∴ if S is not valid, ~S is satisfiable. So want to show

For any cwffs of ~⊢S, then ~S is satisfiable.

By means of 1) If any wff S is ~⊢ then S has property φ

there is a demonstration of the *wff* Q from the closed well formed premises $P_1, P_2, \ldots, P_n$ we may write *either*

2) If any cwff S has φ, then ~S is satisfiable

$$P_1, P_2, \ldots, P_n \vdash Q$$

or

$$\{P_1, P_2, \ldots, P_n\} \vdash Q.$$

If Γ is a set of *cwffs* and S is a *cwff* not belonging to Γ, then the new set containing all members of Γ *and* S will be written as $\{\Gamma, S\}$. To assert that there is a demonstration of Q from premises belonging to $\{\Gamma, S\}$ we may write either

$$\{\Gamma, S\} \vdash Q \qquad \text{or} \qquad \Gamma, S \vdash Q.$$

An alternative statement of the Deduction Theorem makes use of this new notation:

$$\text{If } \Gamma, P \vdash Q \qquad \text{then} \qquad \Gamma \vdash P \supset Q.$$

If there is a demonstration of the *wff* Q from the premises $P_1, P_2, \ldots, P_n$, then there is, of course, a demonstration of Q from any set of *cwffs* Γ which contains $\{P_1, P_2, \ldots, P_n\}$ as a subset (which will be written $\{P_1, P_2, \ldots, P_n\} \subset \Gamma$), no matter what other *cwffs* Γ may contain. The set Γ may even be infinite: there is nothing in our proof of the Deduction Theorem that requires any revision to accommodate this possibility. Of course in any demonstration of Q from an infinite set of premises only a finite number of them will actually be *used*, for a demonstration is always a *finite* sequence of *wffs*. *2 extra paras in 2nd d*

We define the two properties *consistency* and *inconsistency* for sets of *cwffs* in a purely formal fashion. A set Λ of (one or more) *cwffs* is called *inconsistent* if $\Lambda \vdash \sim P \cdot P$, otherwise Λ is *consistent*. It is easily seen that *any wff* can be inferred from an inconsistent set, for where S is any *wff*, $\sim P \cdot P \vdash (\sim P \cdot P) \vee S$ by ℗ (DR 22 of Chapter Seven), which is, by definition, the same as $\sim P \cdot P \vdash \sim (\sim P \cdot P) \supset S$. Since $\vdash \sim (\sim P \cdot P)$ by ℗ (Theorem 1 of Chapter Seven), by R 1 we have $\sim P \cdot P \vdash S$, whence $\Lambda \vdash S$ where Λ is any inconsistent set of *cwffs* and S is any *wff* whatever.

Our next preliminary task is to prove the following:

LEMMA. If N is a *cwff* which is not a theorem, then $\{\sim N\}$ is a consistent set.

Proof: We establish the lemma by proving that for any *cwff* N, if $\{\sim N\}$ is *not* a consistent set then N *is* a theorem. Let N be any *cwff* such that $\{\sim N\}$ is not consistent. Since $\{\sim N\}$ is not consistent, it must be inconsistent, and by definition this means that

$$\sim N \vdash \sim P \cdot P$$

By the Deduction Theorem we have

$$\vdash \sim N \supset \sim P \cdot P$$

from which we have

$$\vdash \sim (\sim P \cdot P) \supset \sim \sim N$$

by ℗. We already have

$$\vdash \sim (\sim P \cdot P)$$

by ℗, so by R 1 we obtain

$$\vdash \sim \sim N$$

which by ℗ gives us

$$\vdash N$$

which is the desired result.

The system RS_1 is complete if every valid *cwff* is provable as a theorem. That is, the completeness of RS_1 will be established if it can be proved that every *cwff* N which is *not* provable as a theorem is *not* valid. It has already been noted that a *cwff* N is valid if and only if $\sim N$ is not satisfiable; hence RS_1 is proved complete by showing that every *cwff* N which is not provable as a theorem is such that $\sim N$ is satisfiable. It has been established by the preceding lemma that every *cwff* N which is not provable as a theorem is such that $\{\sim N\}$ is a consistent set. Therefore, the completeness of RS_1 can be demonstrated by proving of every *cwff* $\sim N$ that if $\{\sim N\}$ is a consistent set, then $\sim N$ is satisfiable and hence N is not valid.

We shall prove a somewhat more general result, for the statement of which the term 'simultaneously satisfiable' must be defined. The definition is this: A set Λ of *cwffs* of a formal system is *simultaneously satisfiable* by a given model if and only if there is a normal interpretation of all formulas of Λ with respect to that model which satisfies all the *wffs* of Λ. Now we state and prove

METATHEOREM X. Any consistent set of *cwffs* of RS₁ is simultaneously satisfiable.

Proof: Our proof of the simultaneous satisfiability of any arbitrary consistent set Λ proceeds by constructing a larger set of *cwffs* which includes Λ as a subset, and then proving that this larger set is simultaneously satisfiable. This will of course establish the desired result for Λ.

We begin by considering a set of distinct symbols u_1, u_2, u_3, . . . which are different from any of those contained in RS₁. We denote by 'RS₁*' the formal system obtained from RS₁ by adding to it the symbols u_1, u_2, u_3, . . . which serve as individual constants. The only difference between RS₁ and RS₁* is that the latter has a larger number of primitive symbols: their rules for *wffs*, postulates, and theorems are identically the same. We assume—for definiteness—that all *cwffs* of RS₁* have been ordered in a sequence, so that we can refer to them as the first, the second, the third, and so on (there are many alternative ways of accomplishing this, of course).

Starting with any arbitrary consistent set Λ of *cwffs* of RS₁, we enlarge it by adding *cwffs* to it one at a time. The first *cwff* to be added is $(\exists x)Q_1 \supset Q_1{}^*$, where $(\exists x)Q_1$ is the first *cwff* of RS₁* which begins with an existential quantifier, and $Q_1{}^*$ is the result of replacing all free occurrences of x in Q_1 by u_{i_j}, where u_{i_j} is the first u_i which has no occurrence in Q_1. We may call the resulting set 'Λ_1', where $\Lambda_1 = \mathrm{df}\ \{\Lambda,\ (\exists x)Q_1 \supset Q_1{}^*\}$, and can easily prove it to be consistent. For if Λ_1 were inconsistent, we should have $\Lambda, (\exists x)Q_1 \supset Q_1{}^* \vdash \sim P \cdot P$, and by the Deduction Theorem, $\Lambda \vdash [(\exists x)Q_1 \supset Q_1{}^*] \supset \sim P \cdot P$. Since Λ contains no occurrences of u_1 nor any free individual variables, in the derivation of $[(\exists x)Q_1 \supset Q_1{}^*] \supset \sim P \cdot P$ from Λ we could replace all occurrences of u_1 by the free individual variable x to obtain $\Lambda \vdash [(\exists x)Q_1 \supset Q_1] \supset \sim P \cdot P$. From that we could successively obtain

$\Lambda \vdash (x)\{[(\exists x)Q_1 \supset Q_1] \supset \sim P \cdot P\}$ by R 2

$\Lambda \vdash (\exists x)[(\exists x)Q_1 \supset Q_1] \supset \sim P \cdot P$ by Th. 21 and Substitution

$\Lambda \vdash [(\exists x)Q_1 \supset (\exists x)Q_1] \supset \sim P \cdot P$ by Th. 19 and Substitution

$\Lambda \vdash [(\exists x)Q_1 \supset (\exists x)Q_1]$ by ⓟ

and finally $\Lambda \vdash \sim P \cdot P$

which is contrary to the assumption that Λ is consistent. Hence Λ_1 is a consistent set.

The next *cwff* to be added is $(\exists x)Q_2 \supset Q_2{}^*$, where $(\exists x)Q_2$ is the second *cwff* of $RS_1{}^*$ which begins with an existential quantifier, and $Q_2{}^*$ is the result of replacing all free occurrences of x in Q_2 by u_{i_2}, where u_{i_2} is the first u_i not in either Q_2 or Λ_1. We now define Λ_2 as $\{\Lambda_1, (\exists x)Q_2 \supset Q_2{}^*\}$, and it can be proved to be consistent in exactly the same way that Λ_1 was. We continue to add *cwffs* one at a time: to Λ_{j-1} we add $(\exists x)Q_j \supset Q_j{}^*$ where $(\exists x)Q_j$ is the jth *cwff* of $RS_1{}^*$ which begins with an existential quantifier, and $Q_j{}^*$ is the result of replacing all free occurrences of x in Q_j by u_{i_j}, where u_{i_j} is the first u_i not present either in Q_j or in Λ_{j-1}. Each Λ_j is consistent, each of them contains Λ as a subset, and each set is contained in all of the later sets of the sequence.

Next we define the set Λ_ω as the sum or union of all sets in the preceding sequence. Any *cwff* of $RS_1{}^*$ is a member of Λ_ω provided that it is a member of any of the sets Λ_i of the sequence. It is clear that $\Lambda \subset \Lambda_\omega$, and easily proved that Λ_ω is consistent. For if Λ_ω were inconsistent, there would be a demonstration of $\sim P \cdot P$ from a finite number of formulas of Λ_ω. Each of these would have to occur in Λ or some Λ_i for the first time and in every Λ_j thereafter, for Λ_ω contains no formulas except those which occur in Λ or Λ_1 or Λ_2 or Λ_3 or . . . , and we have observed that $\Lambda \subset \Lambda_1 \subset \Lambda_2 \subset \Lambda_3 \subset$ . . . Since there can be only a finite number of premisses used in any demonstration, there would have to be a first set Λ_i which contains all the premisses actually used in the alleged proof that $\Lambda_\omega \vdash \sim P \cdot P$. But that proof, then, would equally well be a proof that $\Lambda_i \vdash \sim P \cdot P$, which is contrary to the fact that each Λ_i is consistent. Hence Λ_ω is consistent.

Now we proceed to enlarge Λ_ω until we obtain a *maximal* consistent set Γ of *cwffs* of RS₁*. Our method of 'enlarging' Λ_ω is by successively adding to it each *cwff* of RS₁* which is consistent with the formulas of Λ_ω together with those previously added to it. The resulting set Γ will be consistent, since any demonstration that $\Gamma \vdash \sim P \cdot P$ would make use of only a finite number of formulas of Γ, the last of which (in the order of their addition) could *not* have been added if the directions for adding formulas had been followed. From our definition of Γ it follows for any *cwff* of RS₁* which is not in Γ that its addition to Γ would result in an inconsistent set; hence we call Γ a *maximal* consistent set.

It is obvious that Γ contains all the postulates of RS₁* that are closed and the closures of those that are not, and also all theorems of RS₁* that are closed, because if S is a *cwff* such that $\Gamma \vdash S$ then S is contained in Γ. For since Γ is maximal, the addition to it of any *cwff* S not already contained in it results in an inconsistent set, that is, for any *cwff* S not belonging to Γ, we have $\Gamma, S \vdash \sim P \cdot P$. From this, by the Deduction Theorem, we have $\Gamma \vdash S \supset \sim P \cdot P$. Now if we were also to have $\Gamma \vdash S$ then by R 1 we should have $\Gamma \vdash \sim P \cdot P$, contrary to the fact that Γ is consistent. It should also be observed that where S is any *cwff* of RS_1^*, either $\Gamma \vdash S$ or $\Gamma \vdash \sim S$. This follows from the fact that every *cwff* S of RS_1^* either is or is not contained in Γ. If S is in Γ then obviously $\Gamma \vdash S$. While if S is not in Γ then $\Gamma, S \vdash \sim P \cdot P$ and by the Deduction Theorem, $\Gamma \vdash S \supset \sim P \cdot P$. From this, by $\circledP$, we have $\Gamma \vdash \sim(\sim P \cdot P) \supset \sim S$, and since we also have by $\circledP$ that $\Gamma \vdash \sim(\sim P \cdot P)$, by R 1 we have $\Gamma \vdash \sim S$. From the preceding remarks it follows that for any *cwff* S either S belongs to Γ or $\sim S$ belongs to Γ.

To show that the formulas of Γ, and hence certainly those of Λ, are simultaneously satisfiable, we take as our model the set I of all individual constants of RS_1^*, regarded as *individuals*. These are all the individual constants of RS_1, $a, b, c, a_1, b_1, c_1, a_2, b_2, c_2, \ldots$, together with all the symbols $u_1, u_2, u_3, u_4, \ldots$. Our interpretation of the *cwffs* of Γ consists of the following assignment of meanings:

$$\leqslant K_o$$

1. To each propositional symbol of RS_1^* we assign the truth value **T** if it belongs to Γ; otherwise it is assigned the truth value **F**. This clearly assigns a definite truth value to every propositional symbol which is a component of any *cwff* of Γ.
2. To each individual constant of RS_1^* (considered as a symbol in an interpreted system) we assign itself (considered as an individual which belongs to the model I). There are no free individual variables in any *wff* of Γ, since these are all *cwffs*; consequently no attention need be paid to them here.
3. To each predicate symbol P^n we assign the n-adic relation (or property, if $n = 1$) among n individuals of I of having their names, adjoined in that order to P^n, constitute a *cwff* of Γ.

The interpretation is completed and made normal by adding the conditions *a.* Any *cwff* $\sim S$ is assigned the truth value **T** or **F** according as the *cwff* S is assigned the truth value **F** or **T**.

b. Any *cwff* $X \cdot Y$ is assigned the truth value **T** if both X and Y are assigned the truth value **T**; otherwise it is assigned **F**.

c. Any *cwff* $(x)R$ is assigned the truth value **T** if the truth value **T** is assigned to every result of replacing all free occurrences of x in R by an individual constant of RS$_1$*; otherwise it is assigned **F**.

d. Every *cwff* $P^n(a_1, a_2, \ldots, a_n)$ is assigned the truth value **T** if the elements of the model assigned to a_1, $a_2, \ldots, a_n$, in that order, stand to each other in the n-adic relation assigned to P^n, otherwise it is assigned **F**.

We now can prove that all *wffs* of Γ are satisfied on this interpretation. What we shall actually prove is the stronger result that every *cwff* S of RS$_1$* is assigned the truth value **T** or **F** according as S belongs or does not belong to Γ. Our proof is by strong induction on the number of symbols in S, counting each propositional symbol, each *cwff* of the form $P^n(a_1, a_2, \ldots, a_n)$, each universal quantifier (x), and each occurrence of $\cdot$ and $\sim$ as a single symbol.

α) In case $n = 1$, S is either a propositional symbol or a *cwff* of the form $P^n(a_1, a_2, \ldots, a_n)$. If S is a propositional symbol, by paragraph 1 of the original assignment of meanings, S is assigned the truth value **T** or **F** according as it is contained or not contained in Γ. If S is the *cwff* $P^n(a_1, a_2, \ldots, a_n)$ then by paragraph 3 and condition *d*, S is assigned the truth value **T** or **F** according as it is contained or not contained in Γ.

β) Here we assume that every *cwff* of RS$_1$* which contains less than k symbols is assigned the truth value **T** or **F** according as it is contained or not contained in Γ. Now we consider any *cwff* S of RS_1* which contains exactly k symbols. S must be of the form $\sim W$ or $X \cdot Y$ or $(x)R$.

CASE 1. S is $\sim W$. If $\sim W$ is in Γ then since Γ is a maximal consistent set, W is not in Γ. Here, by the β-case assumption, since W contains less than k symbols, W is assigned the truth value **F**. By condition a, $\sim W$ must be assigned **T**. Hence if S is in Γ it is assigned the truth value **T**. If $\sim W$ is not in Γ then W is in Γ. Here W is assigned **T**, so that $\sim W$ must be assigned **F**. Hence if S is not in Γ it is assigned the truth value **F**.

CASE 2. S is $X \cdot Y$. If $X \cdot Y$ is in Γ then by ⓟ $\Gamma \vdash X$ and $\Gamma \vdash Y$ so that X and Y are both in Γ. Since each contains less than k symbols, by the β-case assumption they are both assigned the truth value **T**, and by condition b, S is also. If $X \cdot Y$ is not in Γ then not both X and Y can be in Γ (for if they were, then by ⓟ $\Gamma \vdash X \cdot Y$ and $X \cdot Y$ would have to be contained in Γ), so not both X and Y are assigned the truth value **T**, and by condition b, S is assigned the truth value **F**.

CASE 3. S is $(x)R$. If $(x)R$ is in Γ then where Q is any result of replacing all free occurrences of x in R by an individual constant, $\vdash (x)R \supset Q$ by P 5, and by R 1, $\Gamma \vdash Q$. Since Γ is a maximal consistent set, every such Q is contained in Γ, and since each of them contains less than k symbols, they are all assigned the truth value **T** by the β-case assumption, and by condition c, $(x)R$ is assigned **T** also. Hence if $(x)R$ is in Γ it is assigned the truth value **T**. If $(x)R$ is not in Γ, then $\Gamma \vdash \sim(x)R$, which is, by Th. 7 and the Substitution Theorem, $\Gamma \vdash (\exists x)\sim R$. Since Γ is a maximal consistent set, it must contain $(\exists x)\sim R$. But $(\exists x)\sim R$ is a *cwff* of RS_1* which begins with an existential quantifier, and so the formula $(\exists x)\sim R \supset \sim R$* must have been added to some Λ_{j-1} to form Λ_j—where

$\sim R^*$ is the result of replacing all free occurrences of x in $\sim R$ by u_{i_j}. Since the cwff $(\exists x)\sim R \supset \sim R^*$ belongs to some such Λ_j it must belong to Γ. Hence, by R 1, $\Gamma \vdash \sim R^*$, so that $\sim R^*$ belongs to Γ also. Since Γ is consistent, R^* does *not* belong to Γ, and since it contains less than k symbols, by the β-case assumption it is assigned the truth value **F**. Hence by condition c, $(x)R$ is assigned the truth value **F**.

This completes the induction, and proves that all formulas of Γ, and hence all those of Λ, are simultaneously satisfiable. Metatheorem X, together with the discussion which preceded it, constitutes a proof of

METATHEOREM XI. RS_1 is complete.

In the preceding section we showed that RS_1 is logically equivalent to the natural deduction techniques developed in Chapter Four. Hence our proof of Metatheorem XI validates the claim made at the end of Chapter Four that the natural deduction techniques there developed 'permit the demonstration of all logically true propositions constructed out of truth-functional connectives and the quantifications of individual variables'.

A more complicated logistic system is required for the formalization of the logical principles involved in appraising arguments which concern properties of properties or of relations, or relations among properties and relations, or the notions of *all* or *some* properties or relations. Such logistic systems are generally called *extended function calculi*, and if they are consistent, they are demonstrably incomplete.* But these more advanced parts of symbolic logic lie beyond the scope of the present book.

* Proved by Kurt Gödel in 'Über formal unentscheidbare Sätze der Principia Mathematica und verwandter Systeme', *Monatshefte für Mathematik und Physik*, vol. 38 (1931), pp. 173–198.

The Algebra
of Classes

The four traditional types of subject-predicate propositions discussed in Section I of Chapter Four can be interpreted as assertions about classes. On this interpretation, these categorical propositions (as they have been traditionally called) are understood to affirm or to deny that one class is included in another, either in whole or in part. Thus the *A* proposition 'All humans are mortal' is taken to assert that the whole of the class of humans is contained in the class of mortal beings, and the *I* proposition 'Some humans are mortal' asserts that *part* of the class of humans is contained in the class of mortals. Their respective negations, the *O* and *E* propositions, simply deny these inclusions.

On the class interpretation of categorical propositions both their subject and predicate terms designate classes, where a class is any collection of distinct objects. In treating of classes, we permit, and shall later discuss, a class which contains no members at all. In this appendix we shall use lower case letters of the Greek alphabet to designate classes. Given the classes $\alpha, \beta, \gamma, \ldots$ certain further classes can be defined in terms of them. Thus we can define the class of all objects which belong *either* to α *or* to β: this class formed by the *addition* of α and β, is called the *sum* or *union* of α and β, and is symbolized as '$\alpha \cup \beta$'. And we can define the class of all objects which belong *both* to α *and* to β: this class, formed by the *multiplication* of α and β, is called the *product* or *intersection* of α and β, and is symbolized sometimes as '$\alpha \cap \beta$', more often simply as '$\alpha\beta$'. Given any class α we can define the *complement* of α, symbolized as '$\bar{\alpha}$', to be the class of all objects which do *not* belong to α.

Many statements about classes can be formulated using the ordinary equals sign: '$\alpha = \beta$' asserts that all members of α, if any, are also members of β, *and* that all members of β, if any, are also members of α. Many of the properties of the sum, product, and complement of classes can be expressed by means of equations. It is clear, for example, that the operations of forming the sum and forming the product of two classes are commutative: symbolically, we have

$$(\alpha \cup \beta) = (\beta \cup \alpha) \qquad \text{and} \qquad \alpha\beta = \beta\alpha.$$

They are also associative:

$$(\alpha \cup \beta) \cup \gamma = \alpha \cup (\beta \cup \gamma) \qquad \text{and} \qquad (\alpha\beta)\gamma = \alpha(\beta\gamma).$$

Two principles of distribution also hold for class sums and products. Any object which belongs either to α or to both β and γ must belong either to α or to β and must also belong either to α or to γ, and conversely. In other words, for classes, addition is distributive with respect to multiplication, which may be expressed symbolically as

$$\alpha \cup (\beta\gamma) = (\alpha \cup \beta)(\alpha \cup \gamma).$$

Moreover, any object which belongs both to α and to either β or γ must belong either to both α and β or to both α and γ. For classes, then, multiplication is distributive with respect to addition, which is expressed symbolically as

$$\alpha(\beta \cup \gamma) = \alpha\beta \cup \alpha\gamma.$$

Two principles which resemble the tautology principle for statements (cf. p. 32) are immediate consequences of the definitions of the sum and the product of classes:

$$\alpha = \alpha \cup \alpha \qquad \text{and} \qquad \alpha = \alpha\alpha.$$

Another immediate consequence of those definitions is the so-called Law of Absorption:

$$\alpha = \alpha \cup \alpha\beta$$

Turning now to the notion of class complement, we observe that since anything belongs to a given class if and only if it does not belong to the class of all things which do not belong to the given class, the complement of the complement of a class is the class itself. We thus have a sort of double negative rule for complementation, which can be expressed in symbols as

$$\alpha = \bar{\bar{\alpha}}.$$

An object which does not belong to the sum of two classes belongs to neither of them, and must therefore belong to both of their complements. And an object which does not belong to the product of two classes must belong to the class complement of at least one of them. These two propositions, and their converses, which are also true, can be expressed symbolically as

$$\overline{\alpha \cup \beta} = \bar{\alpha}\bar{\beta} \qquad \text{and} \qquad \overline{\alpha\beta} = \bar{\alpha} \cup \bar{\beta},$$

which are versions of De Morgan's theorems applying to classes.

Two special classes are the null class, which has no members, and the *universal* class, to which all objects belong. The null class (also called the *empty* class) is symbolized as '0' (sometimes as 'Λ'), and the universal class is symbolized as '1' (sometimes as 'V'). It is clear that the null class is the complement of the universal class:

$$\bar{1} = 0.$$

The following two equations are immediate consequences of the preceding definitions:

$$\alpha \cup \bar{\alpha} = 1 \qquad \text{and} \qquad \alpha\bar{\alpha} = 0.$$

Further immediate consequences are these:

$$\alpha\cup 0 = \alpha, \ \alpha 1 = \alpha, \ \alpha 0 = 0, \quad \text{and} \quad \alpha\cup 1 = 1.$$

It is easily shown that any class can be designated by infinitely many different *class-expressions*. Thus the class designated by 'α' can also be designated by '$\alpha(\beta\cup\bar\beta)$' (since $\beta\cup\bar\beta = 1$ and $\alpha 1 = \alpha$), and by '$[\alpha(\beta\cup\bar\beta)](\gamma\cup\bar\gamma)$', and so on. By this 'Law of Expansion' we can always introduce any class symbol we choose into a given class expression in such a way that the original and the expanded class expressions designate the same class.

By the principle of distribution, the class $\alpha(\beta\cup\bar\beta)$ is the same as $\alpha\beta\cup\alpha\bar\beta$. To aid in describing the form of the latter expression, let us use the phrase 'simple class term' to refer to the class symbols 'α', 'β', 'γ', . . . , in contrast to other class expressions such as sums and products. Now we can describe the expression '$\alpha\beta\cup\alpha\bar\beta$' as a sum of distinct products, such that in each product appear only simple class terms or their complements, and such that any simple class term which appears anywhere in the entire expression appears exactly once in every product. Any such expression is said to be a Boolean Expansion or Boolean normal form.* By means of the equations presented thus far, any class expression can be transformed into a Boolean Expansion which designates the same class. Thus $\overline{\alpha(\bar\alpha\cup\beta)}$ is equal by De Morgan's Theorem to $\bar\alpha\cup\overline{(\bar\alpha\cup\beta)}$ which is equal, again by De Morgan's Theorem, to $\bar\alpha\cup\bar{\bar\alpha}\bar\beta$, which by double negation is equal to $\bar\alpha\cup\alpha\bar\beta$, which is equal by Expansion to $\bar\alpha(\beta\cup\bar\beta)\cup\alpha\bar\beta$, which by distribution is equal to the Boolean Expansion $\bar\alpha\beta\cup\bar\alpha\bar\beta\cup\alpha\bar\beta$. (Our association principle, $(\alpha\cup\beta)\cup\gamma = \alpha\cup(\beta\cup\gamma)$, permits us to drop parentheses and write either simply as $\alpha\cup\beta\cup\gamma$.)

Any class whatever will divide the universal class into two subdivisions or subclasses which are mutually exclusive and jointly exhaustive. That is, for any class α: $1 = \alpha\cup\bar\alpha$ and $\alpha\bar\alpha = 0$. Any two classes will divide the universal class into *four* subclasses which are exclusive and exhaustive. Thus for any classes α and β: $1 = \alpha\beta\cup\alpha\bar\beta\cup\bar\alpha\beta\cup\bar\alpha\bar\beta$, and the product of any two of those four

---

* Compare these with the Boolean Expansions for statements discussed in Section V of Chapter Two.

products is the null class. Similarly, any n classes will divide the universal class into 2^n subclasses which are exclusive and exhaustive. The class expression which symbolizes such a division of the universal class, it should be observed, is a Boolean Expansion. A Boolean Expansion containing n different simple class terms designates the universal class if it is the sum of 2^n distinct products (where a mere difference in the order of their terms does not make two products distinct). Boolean Expansions thus provide us with a method for deciding whether or not any class expression designates the universal class regardless of what classes are designated by the simple class terms which it contains. Given any class expression, we need only construct its Boolean Expansion and count the number of products of which it is the sum.

The Boolean Expansions discussed above are often called *disjunctive* Boolean Expansions, to contrast them with *conjunctive* Boolean Expansions. A conjunctive Boolean Expansion is a product of distinct sums of simple class terms or their complements, where any simple class term which occurs anywhere in the expression will occur exactly once in every sum. By De Morgan's Theorem and the other equivalences already mentioned, the complement of any disjunctive Boolean Expansion can be transformed into a conjunctive Boolean Expansion which involves the same simple class terms and which is the product of as many sums as the disjunctive Boolean Expansion is the sum of products. Since the complement of 1 is 0, a conjunctive Boolean expansion containing n different simple class terms designates the null class if it is the product of 2^n distinct sums. Hence we have a method for deciding whether or not any class expression designates the null class regardless of what classes are designated by the simple class terms which it contains.

The notations introduced thus far permit the symbolization of the A and E subject-predicate propositions. The E proposition: *No α is β,* asserts that the classes α and β have no members in common, which means that their product is null. The E proposition is therefore symbolized as

$$\alpha\beta = 0.$$

The *A* proposition: *All α is β*, asserts that there is nothing which belongs to α but not to β, which means that the product of α and the complement of β is null. The *A* proposition is therefore symbolized as

$$\alpha\bar{\beta} = 0.$$

To symbolize the *I* and *O* categorical propositions we must introduce the inequality sign '$\neq$', where '$\alpha \neq \beta$' asserts that either α contains an object which is not a member of β or β contains an object which is not a member of α. The *I* proposition: *Some α is β*, asserts that there is at least one member of α which is also a member of β, i.e., that the product of α and β is not null. In symbols, the *I* propositions appears as

$$\alpha\beta \neq 0.$$

The *O* proposition: *Some α is not β*, asserts that there is at least one member of α which is not a member of β, i.e., that the product of α and $\bar{\beta}$ is not null. In symbols, the *O* proposition is expressed as

$$\alpha\bar{\beta} \neq 0.$$

When formulated in our class notation it is completely obvious that the *A* and *O* propositions are contradictories, as are the *E* and *I* propositions.

Some of the traditional 'immediate inferences' involving categorical propositions are already contained in the notation of the class algebra. Thus every proposition has exactly the same symbolization as its obverse, e.g., '$\alpha\bar{\beta} = 0$' symbolizes both *All α is β* and *No α is non-β*. And conversion, where it is valid, is an immediate consequence of the principle of commutation, e.g., *Some α is β* and *Some β is α* are symbolized by '$\alpha\beta \neq 0$' and '$\beta\alpha \neq 0$', respectively, which are obviously equivalent since $\alpha\beta = \beta\alpha$ by commutation.

When we turn to the 'mediate inferences' of the traditional catagorical syllogism, we can divide all categorical syllogisms into two kinds: those which contain only universal propositions (*A* and *E*), and those which contain at least one existential proposition (I or O). It is easily shown that all valid syllogisms of the first kind have the form

$$\alpha\bar{\beta} = 0,\ \beta\bar{\gamma} = 0\ \therefore\ \alpha\bar{\gamma} = 0.$$

The validity of this form can be derived within the algebra of classes by appealing to the results already set forth in this appendix. Since $\bar{\gamma}0 = 0$, and $\alpha\bar{\beta} = 0$ is a premiss, we have $\bar{\gamma}(\alpha\bar{\beta})$ $= 0$, which by association and commutation yields $(\alpha\bar{\gamma})\bar{\beta} = 0$. Now $\alpha 0 = 0$, and $\beta\bar{\gamma} = 0$ is a premiss, so we have $\alpha(\beta\bar{\gamma}) = 0$, which by association and commutation yields $(\alpha\bar{\gamma})\beta = 0$. Hence $(\alpha\bar{\gamma})\beta \cup (\alpha\bar{\gamma})\bar{\beta} = 0$, which by distribution yields $(\alpha\bar{\gamma})(\beta\cup\bar{\beta}) = 0$. Since $\beta\cup\bar{\beta} = 1$ and $(\alpha\bar{\gamma})1 = \alpha\bar{\gamma}$ we have $\alpha\bar{\gamma} = 0$, the syllogism's conclusion.

It can also be shown that all valid syllogisms of the second kind have the form

$$\alpha\beta \neq 0,\ \beta\bar{\gamma} = 0\ \therefore\ \alpha\gamma \neq 0.$$

To establish the validity of the form we first observe that since $\alpha 0 = 0$, if $\alpha\beta \neq 0$ then $\alpha \neq 0$ and $\beta \neq 0$. Since $\alpha 0 = 0$, and $\beta\bar{\gamma} = 0$ as a premiss, $\alpha(\beta\bar{\gamma}) = 0$. By association we have $(\alpha\beta)\bar{\gamma}$ $= 0$. Now $\alpha\beta = (\alpha\beta)1$ and $\gamma\cup\bar{\gamma} = 1$, hence $\alpha\beta = (\alpha\beta)(\gamma\cup\bar{\gamma})$, and by distribution, $\alpha\beta = (\alpha\beta)\gamma\cup(\alpha\beta)\bar{\gamma}$. But $(\alpha\beta)\gamma\cup 0 = (\alpha\beta)\gamma$, and we have already shown that $(\alpha\beta)\bar{\gamma} = 0$, hence $\alpha\beta = (\alpha\beta)\gamma$. Since $\alpha\beta \neq 0$ is a premiss, we know that $(\alpha\beta)\gamma \neq 0$. By association and commutation we obtain $(\alpha\gamma)\beta \neq 0$ from which it follows that $\alpha\gamma \neq 0$, which is the syllogism's conclusion. Hence the algebra of classes is adequate not only to validate immediate inferences involving categorical propositions, but is capable of validating categorical syllogisms also.

The symbol '$\subset$' for *class inclusion* is often used in working with the algebra of classes. The expression '$\alpha \subset \beta$' asserts that all members of α, if any, are also members of β, and is used as an alternative symbolization of the A proposition: *All α is β*. It can be defined in terms of the symbols already introduced in various ways: either as $\alpha\bar{\beta} = 0$ or as $\alpha\beta = \alpha$ or as $\alpha\cup\beta = \beta$ or as $\bar{\alpha}\cup\beta$ $= 1$, all of which are obviously equivalent. The relation $\subset$ is reflexive and transitive (cf. pages 142–143) and has the (transposition) property that if $\alpha \subset \beta$ then $\bar{\beta} \subset \bar{\alpha}$. The latter is an immediate consequence of double negation and transposition when '$\alpha \subset \beta$' is rewritten as '$\alpha\bar{\beta} = 0$' and '$\bar{\beta} \subset \bar{\alpha}$' is rewritten as '$\bar{\beta}\bar{\bar{\alpha}} = 0$'. Its reflexiveness is obvious when '$\alpha \subset \alpha$' is rewritten as '$\alpha\bar{\alpha} = 0$', and its transitivity has already been established in our algebraic proof of validity for categorical syllogisms containing only universal propositions.

The algebra of classes can be set up as a formal deductive system. Such a system is called a Boolean Algebra, and a vast number of alternative postulate sets for Boolean Algebra have been proposed. One of them can be set forth as follows.

Special undefined primitive symbols:

$$\mathbf{C}, \cap, \cup, -, \alpha, \beta, \gamma, \ldots$$

AXIOMS:

Ax. 1. If α and β are in $\mathbf{C}$ then $\alpha\cup\beta$ is in $\mathbf{C}$.

Ax. 2. If α and β are in $\mathbf{C}$ then $\alpha\cap\beta$ is in $\mathbf{C}$.

Ax. 3. There is an entity 0 in $\mathbf{C}$ such that $\alpha\cup0 = \alpha$ for any α in $\mathbf{C}$.

Ax. 4. There is an entity 1 in $\mathbf{C}$ such that $\alpha\cap1 = \alpha$ for any α in $\mathbf{C}$.

Ax. 5. If α and β are in $\mathbf{C}$ then $\alpha\cup\beta = \beta\cup\alpha$.

Ax. 6. If α and β are in $\mathbf{C}$ then $\alpha\cap\beta = \beta\cap\alpha$.

Ax. 7. If α, β, γ are in $\mathbf{C}$ then $\alpha\cup(\beta\cap\gamma) = (\alpha\cup\beta)\cap(\alpha\cup\gamma)$.

Ax. 8. If α, β, γ are in $\mathbf{C}$ then $\alpha\cap(\beta\cup\gamma) = (\alpha\cap\beta)\cup(\alpha\cap\gamma)$.

Ax. 9. If there are unique entities 0 and 1 satisfying Axioms 3 and 4 then for every α in $\mathbf{C}$ there is an $-\alpha$ in $\mathbf{C}$ such that

$$\alpha\cup-\alpha = 1 \qquad \text{and} \qquad \alpha\cap-\alpha = 0.$$

Ax. 10. There is an α in $\mathbf{C}$ and a β in $\mathbf{C}$ such that $\alpha \neq \beta$.

The present system* is a formal deductive system rather than a logistic system (cf. Chapter Six). On its intended interpretation, of course, $\mathbf{C}$ is the collection of all classes, 0 and 1 are the null and universal classes, respectively, and the symbols $\cup$, $\cap$, and $-$

* From E. V. Huntington's 'Sets of Independent Postulates for the Algebra of Logic', *Transactions of the American Mathematical Society*, vol. 5 (1904), p. 288.

represent class addition, multiplication, and complementation, respectively.

The reader who is interested in deducing some theorems from these axioms will find the following fairly easy to derive:

Th. 1. There is at most one entity 0 in $\mathbf{C}$ such that $\alpha \cup 0 = \alpha$.
Th. 2. There is at most one entity 1 in $\mathbf{C}$ such that $\alpha \cap 1 = \alpha$.
Th. 3. $\alpha \cup \alpha = \alpha$.
Th. 4. $\alpha \cap \alpha = \alpha$.
Th. 5. $\alpha \cup 1 = 1$.
Th. 6. $\alpha \cap 0 = 0$.
Th. 7. $0 \neq 1$.
Th. 8. If $\alpha = -\beta$ then $\beta = -\alpha$.
Th. 9. $\alpha = --\alpha$.
Th. 10. If $\alpha \cap \beta \neq 0$ then $\alpha \neq 0$.
Th. 11. $\alpha = (\alpha \cap \beta) \cup (\alpha \cap -\beta)$.
Th. 12. $\alpha \cup (\beta \cup \gamma) = (\alpha \cup \beta) \cup \gamma$.
Th. 13. $\alpha \cap (\beta \cap \gamma) = (\alpha \cap \beta) \cap \gamma$.
Th. 14. $0 = -1$.
Th. 15. $\alpha \cup (\alpha \cap \beta) = \alpha$.
Th. 16. $\alpha \neq -\alpha$.
Th. 17. $-(\alpha \cap \beta) = -\alpha \cup -\beta$.
Th. 18. $-(\alpha \cup \beta) = -\alpha \cap -\beta$.
Th. 19. If $\alpha \cap -\beta = 0$ and $\beta \cap -\gamma = 0$, then $\alpha \cap -\gamma = 0$.
Th. 20. If $\alpha \cap \beta \neq 0$ and $\beta \cap -\gamma = 0$, then $\alpha \cap \gamma \neq 0$.

The methods of proof proceed largely by the substitution of equals for equals. For example, Th. 1 is proved by considering any entities 0_1 and 0_2 in $\mathbf{C}$ such that $\alpha \cup 0_1 = \alpha$ and $\alpha \cup 0_2 = \alpha$. Since α is any member of $\mathbf{C}$, we have both $0_1 \cup 0_2 = 0_1$ and $0_2 \cup 0_1 = 0_2$. Since $0_1 \cup 0_2 = 0_2 \cup 0_1$ by Ax. 5, we obtain by substitution first $0_1 \cup 0_2 = 0_2$ and then $0_1 = 0_2$, which establishes the theorem.

The whole of the algebra of classes can be derived within a first-order function calculus. To every property corresponds the class of all individuals which exemplify that property. The expression '$\hat{x}(Fx)$' is commonly used to symbolize the class of all individuals having the property F. More generally, where $\Phi\mu$ is any propositional function containing no free variables other than μ,

$\hat{\mu}(\Phi\mu)$ is the class of all individuals which satisfy that propositional function. The various symbols for classes used in the class algebra can be defined as follows, where α, β, γ, . . . are the classes $\hat{x}(Ax)$, $\hat{x}(Bx)$, $\hat{x}(Cx)$, . . . :

$$\bar{\alpha} = \text{df } \hat{x}(\sim Ax)$$
$$\alpha \cap \beta = \text{df } \hat{x}(Ax \cdot Bx)$$
$$\alpha \cup \beta = \text{df } \hat{x}(Ax \text{ v } Bx)$$
$$0 = \text{df } \hat{x}(Ax \cdot \sim Ax)$$
$$1 = \text{df } \hat{x}(Ax \text{ v } \sim Ax)$$

Class inclusion, equality, and inequality may be defined as follows:

$$\alpha \subset \beta = \text{df } (x)(Ax \supset Bx)$$
$$\alpha = \beta = \text{df } (x)(Ax \equiv Bx)$$
$$\alpha \neq \beta = \text{df } \sim(x)(Ax \equiv Bx)$$

Using these definitions we can express all of the formulas of Boolean Algebra in the notation of propositional functions and quantifiers. When that is done it is easily shown that all of the axioms and hence all of the theorems of Boolean Algebra become provable theorems of our first-order function calculus.

Since a Boolean Algebra is a formal deductive system in its own right, it is susceptible of various interpretations. One of them, of course, is the algebra of classes. But we can give our Boolean Algebra a propositional rather than a class interpretation. Suppose we interpret '**C**' as the collection of all propositions, and 'α,' 'β,' 'γ,' . . . as symbolizing propositions, and interpret '$\cap$,' '$\cup$', and ' $-$ ' as symbolizing conjunction, (weak) disjunction, and negation. Then if we further interpret the equals sign as symbolizing material equivalence, all axioms and theorems of the Boolean Algebra become logically true propositions of the propositional calculus. Hence we can say that the propositional calculus is *a* Boolean Algebra.

From a somewhat different point of view, we can regard a part of the algebra of classes as an alternative interpretation of the propositional calculus. All formulas of a propositional calculus can be expressed in terms of '$\sim$', '$\cdot$', and 'v', with '$p \supset q$' defined

as '$\sim p$ v q' and '$p \equiv q$' defined as '$p \cdot q$ v $\sim p \cdot \sim q$'. We can interpret the propositional symbols 'p', 'q', 'r', . . . as denoting the
classes α, β, γ, . . . ; and where 'p' denotes α, we shall understand '$\sim p$' to denote $\bar{\alpha}$, the complement of α. Where 'p' and 'q'
denote α and β, then '$p \cdot q$' will be understood to denote the product $\alpha\beta$, and 'p v q' will denote the sum $\alpha \cup \beta$.

On the interpretation sketched in the preceding paragraph
every truth-table tautology of the propositional calculus designates the universal class. This can easily be established as follows.
It was proved in Chapter Seven that all (and only) truth table
tautologies can be derived as theorems by repeated application
of R 1 to the three axioms of R.S. Each of those axioms designates
the universal class: Axiom 1, '$P \supset (P \cdot P)$', which can be expressed
as '$\sim p$ v $(p \cdot p)$', denotes $\bar{\alpha} \cup \alpha\alpha$ or $\bar{\alpha} \cup \alpha$, which is the universal
class 1. Axiom 2, '$(P \cdot Q) \supset P$', expressed as '$\sim(p \cdot q)$ v p', denotes
$\overline{\alpha\beta} \cup \alpha$, which by De Morgan's Theorem is $(\bar{\alpha} \cup \bar{\beta}) \cup \alpha$, which by
commutation and association is equal to $(\alpha \cup \bar{\alpha}) \cup \bar{\beta}$, which is
$1 \cup \bar{\beta}$ and equal to 1. Axiom 3, '$(P \supset Q) \supset [\sim(Q \cdot R) \supset \sim(R \cdot P)]$',
expressed as '$\sim(\sim p$ v $q)$ v $[\sim\sim(q \cdot r)$ v $\sim(r \cdot p)]$', denotes $\overline{\bar{\alpha} \cup \beta} \cup$
$\overline{\overline{\beta\gamma} \cup \gamma\alpha}$, which is equal by De Morgan's Theorem and double
negation to $\alpha\bar{\beta} \cup \beta\gamma \cup \bar{\gamma} \cup \bar{\alpha}$. The latter is equal, by the Law of
Expansion, to $\alpha\bar{\beta}(\gamma \cup \bar{\gamma}) \cup \beta\gamma(\alpha \cup \bar{\alpha}) \cup \bar{\gamma}(\alpha \cup \bar{\alpha})(\beta \cup \bar{\beta}) \cup \bar{\alpha}(\beta \cup \bar{\beta})$
$(\gamma \cup \bar{\gamma})$, which by repeated uses of distribution is equal to
$\alpha\beta\gamma \cup \alpha\beta\bar{\gamma} \cup \beta\gamma\alpha \cup \beta\gamma\bar{\alpha} \cup \bar{\gamma}\alpha\beta \cup \bar{\gamma}\alpha\bar{\beta} \cup \bar{\gamma}\bar{\alpha}\beta \cup \bar{\gamma}\bar{\alpha}\bar{\beta} \cup \bar{\alpha}\beta\gamma \cup \bar{\alpha}\beta\bar{\gamma} \cup$
$\bar{\alpha}\bar{\beta}\gamma \cup \bar{\alpha}\bar{\beta}\bar{\gamma}$. If we now use commutation to rearrange the terms of
the latter expression, and combine equal terms by the principle
that $\alpha \cup \alpha = \alpha$, we obtain $\alpha\beta\gamma \cup \alpha\beta\bar{\gamma} \cup \alpha\bar{\beta}\gamma \cup \alpha\bar{\beta}\bar{\gamma} \cup \bar{\alpha}\beta\gamma \cup \bar{\alpha}\beta\bar{\gamma} \cup$
$\bar{\alpha}\bar{\beta}\gamma \cup \bar{\alpha}\bar{\beta}\bar{\gamma}$, a (disjunctive) Boolean Expansion involving 3 simple
class terms. Since it is the sum of 2^3 distinct products it designates
the universal class.

Next we show that any formula of the propositional calculus
must designate the universal class if it 'follows' by R 1 from two
formulas each of which designates the universal class. R 1 permits us to pass to Q from P and $P \supset Q$ (or $\sim P$ v Q). Now suppose
that 'P' denotes α and that 'Q' denotes β, so that '$\sim P$ v Q'
denotes $\bar{\alpha} \cup \beta$. Under the assumption that $\alpha = 1$ and $\bar{\alpha} \cup \beta = 1$ it

is easily demonstrated that $\beta = 1$. For since $1 \cap 1 = 1$, $\alpha(\bar{\alpha} \cup \beta)$ $= 1$. By distribution, $\alpha\bar{\alpha} \cup \alpha\beta = 1$, and since $\alpha\bar{\alpha} = 0$, it follows that $\alpha\beta = 1$. But $\alpha\beta = 1$ implies both that $\alpha = 1$ *and* that $\beta = 1$, the latter being the desired conclusion.

Therefore every provable theorem of R.S. designates the universal class.

Next we wish to prove that if Π is a class expression such that $\Pi = 1$ is logically true, then Π is designated by a theorem of R.S. We know that $\Pi = 1$ if and only if its Boolean Expansion Σ involves n simple class terms and is the sum of 2^n distinct products. But any Boolean Expansion involving the simple class terms α, β, γ, . . . will be denoted by a disjunctive Boolean normal form formula (cf. pages 36ff.) which involves the statement variables p, q, r, . . . where 'p' denotes α, 'q' denotes β, 'r' denotes γ, etc., and the latter will be the disjunction of as many conjunctions as the former is the sum of products. Hence if Σ is a Boolean Expansion in n simple class terms which is the sum of 2^n products, then it is denoted by the Boolean normal form S which contains n statement variables and is the disjunction of 2^n conjunctions. The latter is therefore a tautology, and hence a provable theorem of R.S. Moreover, the class algebra principles by which Π is expanded into Σ all have their analogues in tautology-preserving transformations in the propositional calculus, so that if $\Pi = \Sigma$ and 'P' denotes Π and 'S' denotes Σ, then if 'S' is a tautology, 'P' is a tautology also, and therefore a theorem of R.S.

It is shown in this way that a class algebra equation of the form $\Pi = 1$ is logically true if and only if the *wff* 'P' which designates Π is a theorem of the propositional calculus. Since every equation of the class algebra is equivalent to an equation of the forms $\Pi = 1$ ($\Gamma = \Lambda$ is equivalent to $\Gamma \subset \Lambda$ and $\Lambda \subset \Gamma$, which are equivalent to $\bar{\Gamma} \cup \Lambda = 1$ and $\bar{\Lambda} \cup \Gamma = 1$, whose combined expression is $(\bar{\Gamma} \cup \Lambda)(\bar{\Lambda} \cup \Gamma) = 1$), it follows that to every logically true equation of the class algebra corresponds a provable theorem of the propositional calculus.

Similarly, logically true inequations of the class algebra correspond to *wffs* of R.S. which are *not* provable as theorems. In the first place, any inequation $\Gamma \neq \Lambda$ is equivalent to an inequation of the form $\Pi \neq 1$, namely $(\overline{\Gamma} \cup \Lambda)(\overline{\Lambda} \cup \Gamma) \neq 1$. And if it is logically true that $\Pi \neq 1$, then it is not logically true that $\Pi = 1$, from which it follows that the *wff* which designates Π is not a provable theorem in R.S. Since we have an effective criterion for distinguishing between theorems and non-theorems of R.S., we have therein an effective criterion for distinguishing between logically true equations and inequations of the class algebra.

The preceding discussion should suffice to indicate the intimacy of the connection between the algebra of classes and the propositional calculus.

The Ramified Theory
of Types

The *simple* theory of types, which was expounded briefly on pages 162–164, suffices to eliminate such logical paradoxes as that of the alleged property *impredicable*. But there is another kind of paradox or contradiction which is not prevented by the simple theory of types. One example of this other kind is the paradox of the liar, which was discussed on pages 188–189. These two kinds of paradoxes were first explicitly distinguished by F. P. Ramsey in 1926.* Since then those of the first kind have been known as 'logical paradoxes', the second kind either as 'epistemo-logical paradoxes' or, more usually, as 'semantical paradoxes'.

A singularly clear example of a semantical paradox is due to Kurt Grelling.† The Grelling paradox can be stated informally as

---

* 'The Foundations of Mathematics' by F. P. Ramsey, in *Proceedings of the London Mathematical Society*, second series, vol. XXV (1926), pp. 338–384. Reprinted in *The Foundations of Mathematics* (London and New York, 1931), pp. 1–61.

† 'Bemerkungen zu den Paradoxien von Russell und Burali-Forti' by K. Grelling and L. Nelson, in *Abhandlung der Fries'schen Schule*, n.s. vol. II (1907–1908), pp. 300–324.

follows. Some words designate properties which are exemplified by the words themselves, e.g., 'English' is an English word, and 'short' is a short word. Other words designate properties which are not exemplified by the words themselves, e.g., 'French' is not a French word, and 'long' is not a long word. We shall use the word 'heterological' to designate the property possessed by words which designate properties *not* exemplified by themselves. Thus the words 'French' and 'long' are both heterological. The contradiction now arises when we ask whether or not the word 'heterological' is heterological. If it is heterological, then it designates a property which it does not exemplify, and since it designates heterological, it is not heterological. But if it is not heterological, then the property which it designates *is* exemplified by itself, so that it *is* heterological. Here is the contradiction made explicit: if it is then it isn't, and if it isn't then it is.

A somewhat more formal derivation of the Grelling paradox, patterned after Ramsey's version of it,[*] is the following. Where 'Des' designates the name relation, so that 's designates ϕ' is symbolized as 's Des ϕ', we begin with the definition

$$\text{Het(s)} = \text{df} \; (\exists \phi) : s \text{Des}\phi \cdot s \text{Des}\psi \equiv_\psi \psi = \phi \cdot \sim \phi(s).†$$

CASE 1.

(1) Het('Het')	$\supset : (\exists \phi) : '\text{Het'}\text{Des}\phi \cdot '\text{Het'}\text{Des}\psi \equiv_\psi \psi$	
	$= \phi \cdot \sim \phi(\text{'Het'})$	
(2)	$\supset : '\text{Het'}\text{Des}\phi \cdot '\text{Het'}\text{Des}\psi \equiv_\psi \psi$	
	$= \phi \cdot \sim \phi(\text{'Het'})$	
(3)	$\supset : '\text{Het'}\text{Des}\phi \cdot '\text{Het'}\text{DesHet} \equiv \text{Het}$	
	$= \phi \cdot \sim \phi(\text{'Het'})$	
(4)	$\supset : '\text{Het'}\text{DesHet} \equiv \text{Het} = \phi \cdot \sim \phi(\text{'Het'})$	
(5)	$\supset : \text{Het} = \phi \cdot \sim \phi(\text{'Het'})$	
(6)	$\supset : \sim \text{Het}(\text{'Het'})$	

CASE 2.

(1) $\sim \text{Het}(\text{'Het'}) \supset : (\phi) \sim ['\text{Het'}\text{Des}\phi \cdot '\text{Het'}\text{Des}\psi \equiv_\psi \psi$
$= \phi \cdot \sim \phi(\text{'Het'})]$

---

[*] *Op. cit.*, p. 358 and pp. 369–372; reprint p. 27 and pp. 42–46.

† Where writing the *psi* as a subscript to the equivalence symbol serves to abbreviate the universal quantification of the equivalence with respect to *psi*, so that 'sDes $\psi \equiv_\psi \psi = \phi$' is an abbreviation for '$(\psi)[\text{sDes}\psi \equiv \psi = \phi]$'.

(2) $\supset$:'Het'DesHet $\supset$ $\sim$['Het'Desψ $\equiv_\psi \psi$
$=$ Het$\cdot\sim$Het('Het')]

(3) $\supset$:'Het'Desψ $\equiv_\psi \psi$ $=$ Het$\cdot$ $\supset$ $\cdot$Het('Het')

(4) $\supset$:'Het'Desψ $\equiv_\psi \psi$ $=$ Het (assuming 'Het'
univocal)

(5) $\supset$:Het('Het')

Hence

$$\text{Het('Het')} \equiv \sim\text{Het('Het')}$$

which is a contradiction.

The derivation of the preceding contradiction did not violate any restrictions imposed by the simple theory of logical types, so the adoption of that theory does not suffice to prevent such contradictions. Contradictions of this second kind can be eliminated, however, by the adoption of a more complicated version of the theory of logical types, known as the 'ramified' (or 'branching') theory of logical types. Now according to the simple theory of logical types, all entities are divided into different logical types, of which the lowest contains all individuals, the next lowest consists of all properties of individuals (designated by functions of individuals), the next, of all properties of properties of individuals (designated by functions of functions of individuals), and so on. There are also hierarchies of relations among individuals and properties, and of properties of relations, but they need not be considered here. Where we use lower case letters to denote individuals and capital letters to designate properties, then we can represent this hierarchy as follows, where the subscript attached to a function indicates its proper level in the hierarchy:

$$\begin{matrix} \cdot & \cdot & \cdot & \cdot \\ \cdot & \cdot & \cdot & \cdot \\ \cdot & \cdot & \cdot & \cdot \end{matrix}$$

type 3: F_3, G_3, H_3, . . .
type 2: F_2, G_2, H_2, . . .
type 1: F_1, G_1, H_1, . . .
type 0: a, b, c, . . . , x, y, z

Only a function of type 1 can significantly be predicated of an individual, and in general, a function of type i can be significantly predicated of a function of type j if and only if $i = j + 1$.

The preceding hierarchy presents a rough 'picture' of the simple theory of logical types. Now the ramified theory proceeds to divide each type above level zero into a further hierarchy. Thus all functions of type 1, which may significantly be predicated of individuals, are divided into different *orders* in the following fashion.

All propositional functions of type 1 which contain either no quantifiers or else quantifiers on individual variables only are said to be *first order* functions. For example, $F_1(x)$ and $(y)[F_1(y) \supset G_1(x)]$ are first order functions of type 1. First order functions will have a left superscript 1 attached to indicate their position in the hierarchy of orders. Thus all first order functions of type 1 may be listed as $^1F_1$, $^1G_1$, $^1H_1$, . . . Next, all propositional functions of type 1 which contain quantifiers on first order functions but no quantifiers on any other functions are *second order* functions. Examples of second order functions of type 1 are $(^1F_1)[^1F_1(x) \equiv {}^1F_1(a)]$ and $(\exists^1G_1)(\exists y)[^1G_1(y) \supset {}^1H_1(x)]$. Second order functions will have a left superscript 2 attached, and all second order functions of type 1 may be listed as $^2F_1$, $^2G_1$, $^2H_1$, . . . In general, an nth order function of type 1 will contain quantifiers on functions of order $n - 1$, but no quantifiers on functions of order m where $m \geq n$.

The ramified theory of logical types can be described compendiously by means of the following two dimensional array:

Order 1	Order 2	Order 3	. . .
. .	.	.	
. .	.	.	
. .	.	.	
type 3: $^1F_3$, $^1G_3$, $^1H_3$, . . . ;	$^2F_3$, $^2G_3$, $^2H_3$, ... ;	$^3F_3$, $^3G_3$, $^3H_3$, ... ;	. . .
type 2: $^1F_2$, $^1G_2$, $^1H_2$, . . . ;	$^2F_2$, $^2G_2$, $^2H_2$, ... ;	$^3F_2$, $^3G_2$, $^3H_2$, ... ;	. . .
type 1: $^1F_1$, $^1G_1$, $^1H_1$, . . . ;	$^2F_1$, $^2G_1$, $^2H_1$, ... ;	$^3F_1$, $^3G_1$, $^3H_1$, ... ;	. . .

Just as the simple hierarchy of types prevents us from speaking about all functions or properties, permitting us to speak only about all functions of individuals, or all functions of functions of individuals, or etc., so the hierarchy of orders prevents us from speaking about all functions or properties of a given type, permitting us to speak only about all first order functions of a given type, or all second order functions of a given type, etc. Thus we cannot, according to the ramified theory of types, say that Bob has all of Al's good qualities, which would ordinarily be symbolized as

$$(F_1)\{[G_2(F_1)\cdot F_1(a)] \supset F_1(b)\}.$$

Instead, we can say that Bob has all of Al's good *first order* qualities, symbolized as

$$({}^1F_1)\{[{}^1G_2({}^1F_1)\cdot{}^1F_1(a)] \supset {}^1F_1(b)\}$$

or that Bob has all of Al's good *second order* qualities, symbolized as

$$({}^2F_1)\{[{}^1G_2({}^2F_1)\cdot{}^2F_1(a)] \supset {}^2F_1(b)\}$$

or that Bob has all of Al's good n^{th} order qualities, for any specified n. It should be noticed that the property of having all of Al's first order properties, symbolized by the function

$$({}^1F_1)[{}^1F_1(a) \supset {}^1F_1(x)]$$

is a *second order* property.

The preceding formulation of the ramified theory of logical types is crude, but it suffices to eliminate the Grelling paradox. In Case 1 the step from (2) to (3) is rejected on the grounds that the function 'Het' is of higher order than the function variable 'ψ' and may not be instantiated in its place. In Case 2 the step from (1) to (2) is likewise rejected on the grounds that the function 'Het' is of higher order than the function variable 'ϕ' and may not be instantiated in its place.

Another feature of the ramified theory of logical types is that it divides *propositions* into a hierarchy of propositions of different orders. Just as any function (of any type) is a first order function if it makes no reference to any totality of functions of that type (i.e., contains no quantifier on any function variable of that type), so any proposition is said to be a *first order proposition* if it makes no reference to any totality of propositions (i.e., contains no quantifier on any propositional variable). In general, a proposition is of order $n + 1$ if it contains a quantifier on a propositional variable of order n but contains no quantifier on any propositional variable of order m where $m \geq n$.* The restriction here is that we can never refer to *all* propositions, but only to all propositions of this or that specified order. Thus we cannot say that 'None of the propositions uttered by Smith tends to incriminate him', which we might partially symbolize as

$$(p) \; [(\text{Smith utters } p) \supset \sim(p \text{ tends to incriminate Smith})]$$

but can say instead either that 'None of the first order propositions uttered by Smith tends to incriminate him', or that 'None of the second order propositions uttered by Smith tends to incriminate him', or etc. We would partially symbolize the second of these alternative propositions as

$$(^2p)[(\text{Smith utters } {}^2p) \supset \sim({}^2p \text{ tends to incriminate Smith})].$$

That proposition contains a quantifier on a propositional variable of order 2, and is therefore a proposition of order 3.

By dividing propositions into different orders and permitting reference only to propositions of some specified order or orders, the ramified theory of logical types effectively prevents the paradox of the liar. Any version of that paradox involves the assertion that *all propositions satisfying a certain condition are false*, where the assertion itself is a proposition which satisfies that condition. (The condition in question might be *being asserted by the speaker*, or *being written in a specified location*, or *being uttered by a Cretan*, or etc.) The paradox is fully explicit when the assertion in question is the *only* proposition which satisfies the specified condition, for in that case if it is true then it is false, and if it is false then it is true. Such a contradiction is prevented by the ramified theory of logical types in the following way. The assertion can refer only to all propositions of a certain order, so that it can assert only for

---

* In *Principia Mathematica*, propositions are also divided into different orders on the basis of differences in the orders of the functions they contain. But we shall ignore that (dubious) subtlety in the present exposition.

some specified n that *all n^{th} order propositions satisfying a certain condition are false*. But no paradox can arise here, because the italicized sentence expresses a proposition of order $n + 1$, and even if it satisfies the specified condition, it is not an nth order proposition and therefore does not assert its own falsehood.

The ramified theory of logical types, including both the hierarchy of types and the hierarchy of orders, was recommended by Russell and Whitehead not only for 'its ability to solve certain contradictions', but also for having 'a certain consonance with common sense which makes it inherently credible'.* They claimed to have deduced the theory from what they called the 'vicious-circle principle', of which one of their formulations was: 'Whatever involves *all* of a collection must not be one of the collection'.† But that principle is not obvious, and their putative deduction is not convincing.‡ The chief merit of the theory of logical types, at least of its ramified version, would seem to be its prevention of the paradoxes.

There are difficulties as well as advantages entailed by the ramified theory of logical types. One of these concerns the notion of identity, which was discussed on pages 148ff. and 161. The usual definition of identity (of individuals) is

$$(x = y) = \mathrm{df}\ (F_1)[F_1(x) \equiv F_1(y)]$$

from which definition all of the usual properties of the identity relation can be deduced. But that definition violates the ramified theory of logical types, since in it reference is made to *all* functions of type 1. Were we to replace it by the definition

$$(x = y) = \mathrm{df}\ (^1F_1)[^1F_1(x) \equiv {}^1F_1(y)]$$

---

* *Principia Mathematica* by A. N. Whitehead and B. Russell, Introduction to the first edition, Chapter II.

† *Ibid.*

‡ In his 'Foundations of Mathematics', F. P. Ramsey remarked on the 'rather sloppy way' in which the type theory was deduced from the 'vicious-circle principle' (p. 356, p. 24 of reprint), and challenged the validity of that principle itself, holding that ' . . . we may refer to a man as the tallest in a group, thus identifying him by means of a totality of which he is himself a member without there being any vicious circle' (p. 368, p. 41 of reprint).

which provides that x and y are identical if they have all of their *first order* properties in common, the possibility arises that x and y might be identical and nevertheless have different *second order* properties. It should be clear that for any n, defining identity as the sharing of all properties of order n would permit identical individuals to differ with respect to properties of order m where $m > n$. If we accept the restrictions of the ramified theory of logical types, then we cannot define the identity relation, and even if we accept it as primitive or undefined, we could not state all the rules for its usage (as enunciated on pages 149–151).

Other disadvantages of the ramified theory of logical types are more technical, and will merely be mentioned. Mathematicians wish to establish their theorems for *all* functions (of numbers), but they cannot do so if they permit themselves to be bound by the hierarchy of orders. Moreover, certain existence theorems in analysis, such as that of the Least Upper Bound, cannot be proved within the restrictions of the ramified theory of types. The Cantorean theory of the infinite, which is basic to nearly all of modern mathematics, cannot be established within the rigid framework of the ramified type theory. And even the principle of mathematical induction must be abandoned in its full generality, for its complete statement is prevented by the ramified theory of logical types.

To relax the excessive restrictions of the hierarchy of orders the 'Axiom of Reducibility' was introduced. That axiom asserts that to any function of any order and any type there corresponds a formally equivalent *first order* function of the same type (two functions are *formally equivalent* when for any admissible argument they are either both true or both false). In the presence of this axiom, the identity relation *can* be satisfactorily defined in terms of first order functions, and all of the disadvantages mentioned in the preceding paragraph disappear. The question naturally arises: does the Axiom of Reducibility relax the restrictions of the ramified theory of logical types sufficiently to permit the reintroduction of the paradoxes? It seems clear that if to a logical system like that of *Principia Mathematica*, which contains both the rami-

fied type theory and the Axiom of Reducibility, *all* of the semantical terms such as 'true', 'false', and 'designates' are added, and
names for all functions are added also, then at least some of the
paradoxes reappear.* On the other hand, if the names of *some*
functions are left out, then even in the presence of the semantical
terms the paradoxes do not seem to be derivable even with the aid
of the Axiom of Reducibility.†

It may not be out of place here to indicate briefly how the
'levels of language' method of avoiding the semantical paradoxes‡
is remarkably similar to the ramified type theory's hierarchy of
orders.§ Confining our remarks to the Grelling paradox, we
note that it does not arise in an object language (like the extended
function calculus, for example) when we assume that there are in
it no symbols which designate symbols. Nor does it arise in the
metalanguage of that object language. Since the metalanguage
contains synonyms for all symbols of the object language and
names for all symbols of the object language, as well as its own
variables and the name relation (which we write as 'Des'),
the symbol 'Het' can be defined in it. By definition:

$$\text{Het}(v)\cdot \;\equiv\; :\cdot (\exists\phi):v\text{Des}\phi\cdot v\text{Des}\psi \;\equiv_\psi\; \psi \;=\; \phi\cdot\sim\phi(v).$$

Yet the Grelling cannot be derived in the metalanguage, because
although there is a symbol for the function Het there is no symbol
for the name of that function. In other words, in the metalanguage, although we could substitute 'Het' for 'ϕ', we cannot substitute ' 'Het' ' for 'v' because ' 'Het' ' is not a symbol of the
metalanguage.

So far there are no complications. The paradox does not arise
in the object language because it contains no names for the sym-

* Cf. the author's article on 'The Inconsistency or Redundancy of *Principia
Mathematica*' in *Philosophy and Phenomenological Research*, vol. XI, No. 2, December,
1950, pp. 190–199.

† Cf. the review of the preceding article by Alonzo Church in *The Journal of
Symbolic Logic*, vol. XVI, No. 2, June, 1951, pp. 154–155.

‡ First suggested by Bertrand Russell in his Introduction to L. Wittgenstein's
Tractatus logico-philosophicus (London and New York, 1922), p. 23.

§ The remainder of this appendix is reprinted by permission from 'The Inconsistency or Redundancy of *Principia Mathematica*', *Philosophy and Phenomenological
Research*, vol. XI. Copyright 1950 by the University of Buffalo.

bols in it; and it does not arise in the metalanguage because there is no name for the function symbol 'Het' in that language. The *threat* of the Grelling only arises in the meta-metalanguage. *If* certain safeguards or refinements of the levels of language theory are ignored, the paradox seems to be derivable. Ignoring those safeguards, we have, by definition, in the meta-metalanguage,

$$\text{Het}(v)\cdot \equiv : \cdot (\exists\phi):v\text{Des}\phi\cdot v\text{Des}\psi \equiv_\psi \psi = \phi\cdot\sim\phi(v).$$

Since the meta-metalanguage *does* contain a name for the function symbol 'Het', we substitute that name, ' 'Het' ', for the variable 'v' and obtain the contradiction as in our first derivation.

The way in which the safeguards of the levels of language theory serve to prevent this contradiction makes it very similar to the theory of orders. The definition of Het in the meta-meta-language which was written above requires the addition of subscripts to resolve its ambiguity. Once these ambiguities are pointed out and resolved, the contradiction vanishes.

In the first place, the meta-metalanguage contains two symbols for the name relation, 'Des$_1$' and 'Des$_2$'.* The first of these is the meta-metalanguage's synonym for the name relation in the metalanguage. The full sentence.

$$v\text{Des}_1\phi$$

asserts that the function symbol denoted by 'v' is a symbol of the object language and designates the function ϕ. The second has no synonym in the metalanguage. The full sentence

$$v\text{Des}_2\phi$$

asserts that the function symbol denoted by 'v' is a symbol of the metalanguage and designates the function ϕ. These are quite different, since we assume in this discussion that although every symbol of the object language has a synonym in the metalanguage, there are no symbols common to the two languages.

---

* As was suggested by Ramsey in a somewhat different context. *Op. cit.*, p. 370, in reprint, p. 43.

And in the second place, the meta-metalanguage contains two symbols 'Het₁' and 'Het₂', between whose meanings there is significant difference. The first of these is the meta-metalanguage's synonym for the function symbol 'Het' of the metalanguage. The full sentence

$$\text{Het}_1(v)$$

asserts that the function symbol denoted by 'v' is a symbol of the object language and has the property of designating in the object language a property which it does not possess. The second has no synonym in the metalanguage. The full sentence

$$\text{Het}_2(v)$$

asserts that the function symbol denoted by 'v' is a symbol of the metalanguage and has the property of designating in the metalanguage a property which it does not possess. Their definitions are different:

$$\text{Het}_1(v) = \text{df} \ (\exists\phi):v\text{Des}_1\phi \cdot v\text{Des}_1\psi \equiv_\psi \psi = \phi \cdot \sim\phi(v)$$

and

$$\text{Het}_2(v) = \text{df} \ (\exists\phi):v\text{Des}_2\phi \cdot v\text{Des}_2\psi \equiv_\psi \psi = \phi \cdot \sim\phi(v).$$

It is clear that we cannot define Het₁ in terms of Des₂ because the values of the arguments of the two functions are terms of different languages, of the object language for Het₁ and of the metalanguage for Des₂. The same consideration suffices to show that Het₂ cannot be defined in terms of Des₁.

No version of the Grelling can be derived from the definition of Het₁, because the only values of its arguments are terms of the object language, and there is no term of the object language analogous to either 'Het₁' or 'Het₂'. The only possibility lies in the direction of deriving a contradiction from the definition of Het₂, and this is thwarted by something remarkably like *Principia's* theory of orders.

In the definition of Het₂ we cannot substitute for 'v' the name of the symbol for that function, because although the function symbol 'Het₂' occurs in the meta-metalanguage, no *name* of that function symbol does. The best we can do is to substitute the meta-metalanguage's name of the function symbol of the meta-language which is synonymous with 'Het$_1$', for which we *do* have a name in the meta-metalanguage (call it ' 'Het' '). Making the substitution, we have

$$\text{Het}_2(\text{'Het'}) \cdot \equiv \; : \cdot (\exists \phi) : \text{'Het'Des}_2 \phi \cdot \text{'Het'Des}_2 \psi \equiv_\psi \psi = \phi \cdot \sim \phi(\text{'Het'}).$$

If we endeavor to deduce a contradiction from this equivalence by an argument parallel to earlier versions, we are unable to do so. There is a choice of function symbol to substitute for the generalized function variable 'ψ', for there are two function symbols in our meta-metalanguage that look promising: 'Het$_1$' and 'Het$_2$'.

If we substitute 'Het$_1$', we obtain

$$\text{Het}_2(\text{'Het'}) \cdot \supset \; : \text{'Het'Des}_2 \phi \cdot \text{'Het'Des}_2 \text{Het}_1 \equiv \text{Het}_1 = \phi \cdot \sim \phi(\text{'Het'}).$$

Since ' 'Het' ' is the meta-metalanguage's name for the function symbol of the metalanguage which is synonymous with 'Het$_1$', we have

$$\text{'Het'Des}_2 \text{Het}_1 \cdot \text{'Het'Des}_2 \text{Het}_1 \equiv \text{Het}_1 = \phi$$

and consequently

$$\text{Het}_2(\text{'Het'}) \supset \sim \text{Het}_1(\text{'Het'}).$$

But this is no part of any contradiction, being antecedently known on independent grounds; for if any term satisfies Het$_2$ it is in the metalanguage and not in the object language, while only terms of the object language satisfy Het$_1$.

On the other hand, if we substitute 'Het$_2$', we obtain

$$\text{Het}_2(\text{'Het'}) \supset \; : \text{'Het'Des}_2 \phi \cdot \text{'Het'Des}_2 \text{Het}_2 \equiv \text{Het}_2 = \phi \cdot \sim \phi(\text{'Het'}).$$

From this, *if* ' 'Het'Des$_2$Het$_2$' were true, we should indeed be able to obtain a contradiction. But ' 'Het'Des$_2$Het$_2$' is *not* true, because the argument ' 'Het' ' denotes a symbol of the metalanguage while the property denoted by the argument 'Het$_2$' is not denoted by any symbol of the metalanguage. In other words,

' 'Het'Des$_2$Het$_2$' is false because 'Het$_2$' is a symbol of the meta-metalanguage which has no synonym in the metalanguage.

This is very like the theory of orders, because the contradiction is evaded by arranging that certain symbols of the meta-metalanguage are defined *over certain ranges*. Thus 'Des$_1$' is defined over a narrower range than 'Des$_2$', and 'Het$_1$' is defined over a narrower range than 'Het$_2$'; Des$_1$ and Het$_1$ being satisfied only by symbols of the object language, Des$_2$ and Het$_2$ being satisfied only by symbols of the metalanguage, which is a wider and more inclusive language. Not only is the levels of language theory remarkably analogous to the theory of orders, but where each metalanguage is conceived as actually containing the object language with which it deals,* it can be identified with the Russellian theory of orders *as applied to symbols* rather than to the functions they denote.

In spite of the indicated similarities, there are fundamental differences between the two. Most significant is that unlike the ramified type theory, the levels of language device for avoiding the paradoxes does not jeopardize the derivation of any parts of classical mathematics, so that no need arises for any analogue to the reducibility axiom.

---

* This conception is recommended by A. Tarski in his 'Semantic Conception of Truth', *Philosophy and Phenomenological Research*, vol. IV (1944), pp. 341–375. Reprinted in H. Feigl and W. Sellars, *Readings in Philosophical Analysis* (New York, 1949), pp. 52–84. Cf. especially p. 350, in reprint, pp. 60–61.

Special Symbols

Index

349